Journeys
in Literature and Nonfiction

8

Book Staff and Contributors

Margaret Thomas   *Supervising Content Specialist*
David Shireman   *Manager, Instructional Design*
Steve Mawyer   *Senior Media Editor*
Tim Mansfield   *Writer*
Susan Raley   *Text Editor*
Tricia Battipede   *Senior Creative Manager*
Jayoung Cho   *Cover Designer*
Caitlin Gildrien   *Print Visual Designer*
Sheila Smith   *Print Visual Designer, Cover Designer*

About K12 Inc.

K12 Inc. (NYSE: LRN) is driving innovation and advancing the quality of education by delivering state-of-the-art, digital learning platforms and technology to students and school districts across the globe. K12's award winning curriculum serves over 2,000 schools and school districts and has delivered millions of courses over the past decade. K12 is a company of educators providing online and blended education solutions to charter schools, public school districts, private schools, and directly to families. The K12 program is offered through more than 70 partner public schools, and through school districts and public and private schools serving students in all 50 states and more than 100 countries. More information can be found at K12.com.

ISBN: 978-1-60153-516-0

Printed by LSC Communications, Crawfordsville, IN, USA, May 2020

Journeys

in Literature and Nonfiction

8

K12 Summit
CURRICULUM

Table of Contents

Lights in the Darkness

Telling Tales

Just the Facts

The Power of Poetry

Persistence and Persuasion

Enduring Truths

Explorations and Explanations

Life Stories

adapted from

Nurse and Spy in the Union Army

by S. Emma E. Edmonds

The next day I went to Lebanon, Kentucky—dressed in one of the rebel prisoner's clothes—and thus disguised, made another trip to rebeldom. My business supposedly was to be buying up butter and eggs, at the farm-houses for the rebel army. I passed through the rebel army lines somewhere, without knowing it. Coming to a little village toward evening, I found it occupied by a strong force of rebel cavalry.

The first house I went to was filled with officers and citizens. I had stumbled upon a wedding party. Captain Logan, a recruiting officer, had been married that afternoon to a brilliant young widow whose husband had been killed in the rebel army a few months before.

I was questioned pretty sharply by the handsome captain about my business in that area. But finding me an innocent, straightforward Kentuckian, he concluded that I was all right. But he also decided that I was old enough to be in the army and bantered me considerably upon my want of patriotism.

I tried to make my escape from that village as soon as possible, but just as I was beginning to congratulate myself upon my escape, who should confront me but Captain Logan.

Said he: "See here, my lad; I think the best thing you can do is to enlist and join a company which is just forming here in the village and will leave in the morning. We are giving a bonus to all who freely enlist and are **conscripting** those who refuse. Which do you propose to do, enlist and get the bounty, or refuse and get nothing?"

I replied, "I think I shall wait a few days before I decide."

"But we can't wait for you to decide," said the captain; "the Yankees may be upon us any moment, for we are not far from their lines, and we will leave here either to-night or in the morning early. You have two hours to decide this question, and until then you will be under guard." In two hours, he came for my decision. I told him that I would wait until I was conscripted.

---

conscripting drafting into military service

"Well," said he, "you will not have long to wait for that. You may consider yourself a soldier of the Confederacy from now on and subject to military discipline."

This seemed to me like pretty serious business, especially as I would be required to take the oath of allegiance to the Confederate Government. However, I did not despair, but trusted in my resourcefulness to escape. I knew that if I refused to be sworn into the confederate army, that in all probability my true character would be discovered. I would have to suffer the penalty of death—and that, too, in the most brutal manner.

I was glad to find that it was a company of cavalry that was being organized, for if I could get on a good horse there would be some hope of my escape.

Music and dancing was kept up all night, and it was after daylight when the captain made his appearance. A few moments more and we were trotting briskly over the country, the captain complimenting me on my horsemanship. He told me how grateful I would be to him when the war was over, and the South had won. Then, I would be proud that I had been one of the soldiers of the Southern confederacy, who had drenched my saber in Yankee blood.

We had traveled about half an hour, when we suddenly came across a patrolling party of the Federals, cavalry in front and infantry in the rear. A contest soon commenced;

we were ordered to advance in line, which we did, until we came within a few yards of the Yankees.

The confederate company advanced, but my horse suddenly became unmanageable. It required a second or two to bring him right again. Before I could catch up with the company and get in line the opposing parties had met in a hand to hand fight.

All were engaged in fighting, and I, by accident, got on the Federal side of the line. None saw me for several minutes, except the Federal officer, who had recognized me. He signed to me to fall in next to him. That brought me face to face with my rebel captain, to whom I owed such a debt of gratitude. Thinking this would be a good time to cancel all obligations to him, I discharged the contents of my pistol in his face.

This act made me the center of attraction. Every rebel wanted to have the pleasure of killing me first, and a simultaneous dash was made toward me and numerous saber strokes aimed at my head. Our men at once rushed between me and the enemy, and warded off the blows with their sabers. They attacked the rebels with such fury that the rebels were driven back several **rods**.

The infantry now came up. They got a position where they had a complete cross-fire on the rebels and poured in volley after volley until nearly half the rebels lay upon the ground. Finding it useless to fight longer at such a

rods units of length, each equal to about 5.5 yards

disadvantage, the rebels turned and fled. They left behind eleven killed, twenty-nine wounded, and seventeen prisoners. The confederate captain was wounded badly but not mortally; his handsome face was very much disfigured.

Our men suffered considerable loss before the infantry came up, but afterward **scarcely** lost a man. I escaped without receiving a scratch, but my horse was badly cut across the neck with a saber, but which did not injure him materially, only for a short time. I rejoiced at having once more escaped from the confederate lines.

I was highly commended by the commanding general for my coolness throughout the whole affair. I was told kindly that I would not be permitted to go out again in that area as a spy. If I did, I would surely meet with some of those who had seen me desert their ranks. Then, I would consequently be hung up in the nearest tree.

Not having any particular desire for such a lofty position, I turned my attention to more quiet and less dangerous duties.

Being forbidden from further explorations in that region outside of our lines, I was appointed to act as detective inside of the lines. There were many spies in our midst who were daily giving information to the enemy and had baffled all attempts at discovery.

I dressed in citizen's clothes and proceeded to Louisville, Kentucky, and there mingled freely with the citizens. I

....

scarcely hardly

visited the different places of public resort and made many confederate acquaintances.

At length I found a merchant who was the most bitter in his criticisms of the Yankees that it has ever been my lot to meet. I thought he would be a pretty good person to assist me in my undertakings. Stepping into his store one morning I inquired if he was in need of a clerk. He replied that he would require help in a few days as one of his clerks was going to leave.

S. Emma E. Edmonds, who hid that she was a woman— first as a traveling salesman and then as a soldier in the U.S. Army

Then he questioned me—Who was I, where did I come from, and what had brought me to that city? Well, I was a foreigner, and wishing to see a little of this great American war, I had come "down South." Now that I was here, finding myself scarce of money, I would like to find some employment. This was literally true. I was a foreigner, and very often scarce of money, and really wished him to employ me.

After I had been at the store for several days, I was asked how I would like to go out to the nearest camp and sell some small articles to the soldiers. I would like it much; so was sent with an assortment of pocket knives, combs, and suspenders. By the middle of the afternoon I had sold out my stock in trade, returned to the store, and gave a good account of myself and of the goods entrusted to my care.

My employer was pleased with my success and seemed interested in me. Each day brought some new proof of his confidence. Things went on this way for two weeks, in which time I had succeeded, by the good merchant's assistance, in finding a clue to three rebel spies then within our lines.

I was often questioned by my employer about my political opinions. But of course I did not know anything about politics—in fact I hardly knew how to apply the terms Federal and Confederate. I often misused them when talking in the store. I was frequently told that I must not call the d—d Yankees, Confederates. Pains were taken to instruct me, and give me insight into the true state of affairs as seen by Southern **secessionists**.

At last I expressed a desire to enter the Confederate service. I asked the merchant how I should manage to get through the Yankee lines if I should decide to take such a step. After a long conversation and much planning, we at last decided that I should go through our lines the next night with a person known to the merchant. The person was considered by our troops a thorough Union man since he had taken the oath of allegiance to the Federal Government. But who in reality, was a rebel spy.

....

secessionists people who supported those states that left the Union in the American Civil War

That afternoon I was sent out again to sell some goods to the soldiers. While I was gone, I took the favorable opportunity of informing the Provost Marshal of my intended escape the following night together with my brother spy.

After telling him that I might not be able to leave the store again with any more definite information without creating suspicion, I explained that he had better send someone to the store so that I might enclose in the parcel the necessary information.

Not long after I returned to the store, a gentleman came in, to whom I was introduced. I was told that this was the person who would conduct me through the lines. He was not announced in his true character, but I understood at once that this gentlemanly person was the spy before referred to. He questioned me pretty sharply, but I being "slow of speech," referred him to the merchant, whose eloquence had convinced me of my duty to the Southern confederacy.

My employer stood beside me and gave him a brief history of our acquaintance and of his confidence in me.

The spy evidently took me for a poor green boy whom the merchant had flattered into the idea of becoming a soldier, but who did not realize the responsibility of my position. I confirmed him in that belief by saying— "Well, I suppose if I don't like soldiering they will let me go home again?"

The Provost Marshal himself came in the store during the day. I had my document ready informing him what time we would start and what direction we were to take.

The night came, and we started about nine o'clock. As we walked along toward the rebel lines the spy seemed to think that I was a true patriot in the rebel cause. He entertained me with a long conversation concerning his exploits in the secret service. He told me of the other two who were still in camp. He said one of them was a peddler, and the other sold photographs of our generals.

We were making our way in the darkness, talking in a low, confidential tone, when suddenly a number of cavalry dashed upon us and took us both prisoners. As soon as we were captured we were searched. Documents found on my companion condemned him as a spy. We were then marched back to Louisville and put under guard. The next morning, he was taken care of, and I was sent to General M.'s headquarters.

The next thing to be done was to find the other two spies. The peddler was found and put under arrest, but the dealer in photographs had made his escape.

I never dared go back to Louisville again, for I had ample reason to believe that my life would pay the penalty if I did. ❖

A Cub Pilot

from Life on the Mississippi
by Mark Twain

You may already know Mark Twain as the author of
The Adventures of Tom Sawyer. *Mark Twain was
born in 1835 as Samuel Langhorne Clemens. In his
autobiographical book,* Life on the Mississippi, *he wrote,*
"When I was a boy, there was but one permanent ambition
among my comrades in our village on the west bank of the
Mississippi River. That was to be a steamboatsman. Other
ambitions faded out, each in its turn; but the ambition to
be a steamboatsman always remained."

*When he was little more than twenty years old,
Clemens achieved his boyhood ambition—he became a*

*riverboat **pilot**. A riverboat pilot steers ships in and out of port, often through dangerous waters. In order to keep the ship from running aground, it's important for the pilot to remain constantly aware of the depth of the water. In Clemens's time, the water's depth was measured by throwing in a line with a lead weight attached—which is why the men who read the line were called "leadsmen." When a leadsman measured a depth of two fathoms—a fathom is six feet—he would cry out, "Mark twain!" (Twain is an old-fashioned word for "two.") That cry gave Clemens the pen name by which we know him best.*

The following selection is from Mark Twain's Life on the Mississippi.

There is one **faculty** which a pilot must **incessantly cultivate** until he has brought it to absolute perfection. Nothing short of perfection will do. That faculty is memory. He cannot stop with merely thinking a thing is so and so; he must know it; for this is one of the "exact" sciences. With what scorn a pilot was looked upon, in the old times,

---

pilot a person employed to steer a ship in and out of port, often through dangerous waters; a "cub pilot" is a pilot in training
faculty ability; skill
incessantly constantly; unceasingly
cultivate to develop; to improve by labor, care, or study

if he ever **ventured** to deal in that feeble phrase, "I think," instead of the **vigorous** one, "I know!"

One cannot easily realize what a tremendous thing it is to know every trivial detail of twelve hundred miles of river and know it with absolute exactness. If you will take the longest street in New York and travel up and down it, **conning** its features patiently until you know every house and window and lamppost and big and little sign by heart, and know them so accurately that you can instantly name the one you are **abreast** of when you are set down at random in that street in the middle of an inky black night, you will then have a **tolerable notion** of the amount and the exactness of a pilot's knowledge who carries the Mississippi River in his head. And then, if you will go on until you know every street crossing, the character, size, and position of the crossing stones, and the varying depth of mud in each of these numberless places, you will have some idea of what the pilot must know in order to keep a Mississippi steamer out of trouble. Next, if you will take half of the signs in that long street, and *change their places* once a month, and still manage to know their new positions accurately on dark nights, and keep up with these

....

ventured attempted; took the chance
vigorous strong; powerful
conning studying; examining closely
abreast beside; alongside
tolerable acceptable; good enough
notion idea; concept; understanding

repeated changes without making any mistakes, you will understand what is required of a pilot's **peerless** memory by the **fickle** Mississippi.

I think a pilot's memory is about the most wonderful thing in the world. To know the Old and New Testaments by heart and be able to recite them **glibly**, forward or backward, or begin at random anywhere in the book and recite both ways and never trip or make a mistake, is no extravagant mass of knowledge, and no marvelous **facility**, compared to a pilot's massed knowledge of the Mississippi and his marvelous facility in the handling of it. I make this comparison deliberately and believe I am not expanding the truth when I do it. Many will think my figure too strong, but pilots will not.

A pilot must have a memory, but there are two higher qualities which he must also have. He must have good and quick judgment and decision, and a cool, calm courage that no peril can shake. Give a man the merest trifle of **pluck** to start with, and by the time he has become a pilot, he cannot be **unmanned** by any danger a steamboat can get into; but one cannot quite say the same for judgment. Judgment is a

peerless unmatched; superior beyond comparison
fickle likely to change without warning; unpredictable
glibly with casual, offhand ease
facility effortless skill; ease in performance
pluck courage; determination
unmanned dispirited; discouraged

matter of brains, and a man must *start* with a good stock of that article, or he will never succeed as a pilot.

The growth of courage in the pilot-house is steady all the time, but it does not reach a high and satisfactory condition until some time after the young pilot has been "standing his own watch" alone and under the staggering weight of all the responsibilities connected with the position. When the apprentice has become pretty thoroughly acquainted with the river, he goes clattering along so fearlessly with his steamboat, night or day, that he presently begins to imagine that it is *his* courage that animates him; but the first time the pilot steps out and leaves him to his own devices, he finds out it was the other man's. He discovers that the article has been left out of his own cargo altogether. The whole river is bristling with dangers in a moment; he is not prepared for them; he does not know how to meet them; all his knowledge **forsakes** him; and within fifteen minutes he is as white as a sheet and scared almost to death. Therefore pilots wisely train these cubs by various strategic tricks to look danger in the face a little more calmly. A favorite way of theirs is to play a friendly **swindle** upon the candidate.

Mr. Bixby, my chief, served me in this fashion once, and for years afterward I used to blush, even in my sleep, when I thought of it. I had become a good **steersman**; so good, indeed, that I had all the work to do on our watch, night and day. Mr. Bixby seldom made a suggestion to me; all he ever did was to take the wheel on particularly bad nights or in particularly bad crossings, land the boat when she needed to be landed, play gentleman of leisure nine-tenths of the watch, and collect the wages. The lower river was about bank-full, and if anybody had questioned my ability to run any crossing between **Cairo** and New Orleans without help or instruction, I should have felt **irreparably** hurt. The idea of being afraid of any crossing

....

forsakes abandons
swindle fraud; trick
steersman one who steers a ship
Cairo a city in Illinois, where the Mississippi River is joined by the Ohio River
irreparably irreversibly; beyond repair

in the lot, in the *daytime*, was a thing too **preposterous** for contemplation. Well, one matchless summer's day I was bowling down the bend above Island 66, **brimful** of self-conceit and carrying my nose as high as a giraffe's, when Mr. Bixby said,

"I am going below awhile. I suppose you know the next crossing?"

This was almost an **affront**. It was about the plainest and simplest crossing in the whole river. One couldn't come to any harm, whether he ran it right or not; and as for depth, there never had been any bottom there. I knew all this, perfectly well.

"Know how to *run* it? Why, I can run it with my eyes shut."

"How much water is there in it?"

"Well, that is an odd question. I couldn't get bottom there with a church steeple."

"You think so, do you?"

The very tone of the question shook my confidence. That was what Mr. Bixby was expecting. He left, without saying anything more. I began to imagine all sorts of things. Mr. Bixby, unknown to me, of course, sent somebody down to the **forecastle** with some mysterious instructions to the

preposterous ridiculously foolish
brimful full to the top
affront an insult
forecastle a section of the upper deck of a ship

leadsmen, another messenger was sent to whisper among the officers, and then Mr. Bixby went into hiding behind a smokestack where he could observe results. Presently the captain stepped out on the hurricane-deck; next the chief mate appeared; then a clerk. Every moment or two a **straggler** was added to my audience, and before I got to the head of the island, I had fifteen or twenty people assembled down there under my nose. I began to wonder what the trouble was. As I started across, the captain glanced aloft at me and said, with a **sham** uneasiness in his voice,

"Where is Mr. Bixby?"

"Gone below, sir."

But that did the business for me. My imagination began to construct dangers out of nothing, and they multiplied faster than I could keep the run of them. All at once I imagined I saw **shoal** water ahead! The wave of coward agony that surged through me then came near dislocating every joint in me. All my confidence in that crossing vanished. I seized the bell-rope; dropped it, ashamed; seized it again; dropped it once more; clutched it tremblingly once again, and pulled it so feebly that I could hardly hear the stroke myself. Captain and mate sang out instantly, and both together:

"Starboard lead there! And quick about it!"

....

straggler one who has fallen behind
sham fake; false; pretended
shoal shallow

This was another shock. I began to climb the wheel like a squirrel, but I would hardly get the boat started to port before I would see new dangers on that side, and away I would spin to the other, only to find perils accumulating to **starboard** and be crazy to get to **port** again. Then came the leadsman's **sepulchral** cry:

"D-e-e-p four!"

Deep four in a bottomless crossing! The terror of it took my breath away. "M-a-r-k three! M-a-r-k three! Quarter-less-three! Half twain!"

This was frightful! I seized the bell-ropes and stopped the engines.

"Quarter twain! Quarter twain! *Mark* twain!"

I was helpless. I did not know what in the world to do. I was quaking from head to foot, and I could have hung my hat on my eyes, they stuck out so far.

"Quarter-*less*-twain! Nine-and-a-*half*!"

We were *drawing* nine! My hands were in a nerveless flutter. I could not ring a bell intelligibly with them. I flew to the speaking-tube and shouted to the engineer,

"Oh, Ben, if you love me, back her! Quick, Ben! Oh, back the immortal soul out of her!"

I heard the door close gently. I looked around, and there stood Mr. Bixby, smiling a bland, sweet smile. Then the

----

starboard when looking forward, the right side of a ship
port when looking forward, the left side of a ship
sepulchral low and hollow in tone; suggestive of a grave or burial

audience on the hurricane-deck sent up a thundergust of humiliating laughter. I saw it all, now, and felt **meaner** than the meanest man in human history. I laid in the lead, set the boat in her marks, came ahead on the engines, and said,

"It was a fine trick to play on an orphan, *wasn't* it? I suppose I'll never hear the last of how I was stupid enough to heave the lead at the head of 66."

"Well, no, you won't, maybe. In fact I hope you won't; for I want you to learn something by that experience. Didn't you know there was no bottom in that crossing?"

"Yes, sir, I did."

"Very well, then. You shouldn't have allowed me or anybody else to shake your confidence in that knowledge. Try to remember that. And another thing: when you get into a dangerous place, don't turn coward. That isn't going to help matters any."

It was a good enough lesson, but learned the hard way. Yet about the hardest part of it was that for months I so often had to hear a phrase which I had conceived a particular distaste for. It was, "Oh, Ben, if you love me, back her!" ❖

. . . .

meaner more unworthy; more shameful; more contemptible

Lincoln School, 418 P Street, Sacramento, CA

excerpt from
Barrio Boy

by Ernesto Galarza

Ernesto Galarza was born in 1905 in the Mexican town of Jalcocotán. The Mexican Revolution of 1910 compelled his family to immigrate to the United States, where they eventually settled in Sacramento, California. Like many other immigrants, they worked on the farms in the area. Encouraged by one of his teachers, Galarza went on to attend college, and in time received a doctoral degree from Columbia University. Galarza became a historian, a professor, and a champion for the rights of farm workers and other laborers. He told the story of his early years in Barrio Boy, first published in 1971. Galarza died in 1984.

....

barrio in the United States, a Spanish-speaking neighborhood in a city or town

My mother and I walked south on Fifth Street one morning to the corner of Q Street and turned right. Half of the block was occupied by the Lincoln School. It was a three-story wooden building, with two wings that gave it the shape of a double-T connected by a central hall. It was a new building, painted yellow, with a shingled roof that was not like the red tile of the school in Mazatlán. I noticed other differences, none of them very reassuring.

We walked up the wide staircase hand in hand and through the door, which closed by itself. A mechanical contraption screwed to the top shut it behind us quietly.

Up to this point the adventure of enrolling me in the school had been carefully rehearsed. Mrs. Dodson had told us how to find it and we had circled it several times on our walks. Friends in the barrio explained that the director was called a principal, and that it was a lady and not a man. They assured us that there was always a person at the school who could speak Spanish.

Exactly as we had been told, there was a sign on the door in both Spanish and English: "Principal." We crossed the hall and entered the office of Miss Nettie Hopley.

Miss Hopley was at a roll-top desk to one side, sitting in a swivel chair that moved on wheels. There was a sofa against the opposite wall, flanked by two windows and a door that opened on a small balcony. Chairs were set around a table and framed pictures hung on the walls of a man with long white hair and another with a sad face and a black beard.

The principal half turned in the swivel chair to look at us over the pinch glasses crossed on the ridge of her nose. To do this she had to duck her head slightly as if she were about to step through a low doorway.

What Miss Hopley said to us we did not know but we saw in her eyes a warm welcome and when she took off her glasses and straightened up she smiled wholeheartedly, like Mrs. Dodson. We were, of course, saying nothing, only catching the friendliness of her voice and the sparkle in her eyes while she said words we did not understand. She signaled us to the table. Almost tiptoeing across the office, I **maneuvered** myself to keep my mother between me and the **gringo** lady. In a matter of seconds I had to decide whether she was a possible friend or a **menace**. We sat down.

Then Miss Hopley did a **formidable** thing. She stood up. Had she been standing when we entered she would have seemed tall. But rising from her chair she soared. And what she carried up and up with her was a **buxom superstructure**, firm shoulders, a straight sharp nose, full

---

maneuvered moved purposefully
gringo slang term for a non-Hispanic person, especially American or English
menace threat
formidable extremely impressive; inspiring awe or wonder
buxom ample; full-figured
superstructure the upper part of a building or structure

cheeks slightly molded by a curved line along the nostrils, thin lips that moved like steel springs, and a high forehead topped by hair gathered in a bun. Miss Hopley was not a giant in body but when she mobilized it to a standing position she seemed a match for giants. I decided I liked her.

She strode to a door in the far corner of the office, opened it and called a name. A boy of about ten years appeared in the doorway. He sat down at one end of the table. He was brown like us, a plump kid with shiny black hair combed straight back, neat, cool, and faintly obnoxious.

Miss Hopley joined us with a large book and some papers in her hand. She, too, sat down and the questions and answers began by way of our interpreter. My name was Ernesto. My mother's name was Henriqueta. My birth certificate was in **San Blas**. Here was my last report card from the **Escuela Municipal Numero 3 para Varones of Mazatlán**, and so forth. Miss Hopley put things down in the book and my mother signed a card.

As long as the questions continued, **Doña** Henriqueta could stay and I was secure. Now that they were over, Miss Hopley saw her to the door, dismissed our interpreter and without further ado took me by the hand and strode down the hall to Miss Ryan's first grade.

....

San Blas a town on the west coast of Mexico
Escuela Municipal Numero 3 para Varones of Mazatlán Municipal School Number 3 for Boys of Mazatlán (a city in western Mexico)
doña in Spanish, a respectful title for a woman

Miss Ryan took me to a seat at the front of the room, into which I shrank—the better to survey her. She was, to skinny, somewhat runty me, of a withering height when she patrolled the class. And when I least expected it, there she was, crouching by my desk, her blond radiant face level with mine, her voice patiently maneuvering me over the awful idiocies of the English language.

During the next few weeks Miss Ryan overcame my fears of tall, energetic teachers as she bent over my desk to help me with a word in the pre-primer. Step by step, she loosened me and my classmates from the safe anchorage of the desks for recitations at the blackboard and consultations at her desk. Frequently she burst into happy announcements

to the whole class. "Ito can read a sentence," and small Japanese Ito, squint-eyed and shy, slowly read aloud while the class listened in wonder: "Come, Skipper, come. Come and run." The Korean, Portuguese, Italian, and Polish first graders had similar moments of glory, no less shining than mine the day I conquered "butterfly," which I had been persistently pronouncing in standard Spanish as boo-ter-flee. "Children," Miss Ryan called for attention. "Ernesto has learned how to pronounce *butterfly*!" And I proved it with a perfect imitation of Miss Ryan. From that celebrated success, I was soon able to match Ito's progress as a sentence reader with "Come, butterfly, come fly with me."

Like Ito and several other first graders who did not know English, I received private lessons from Miss Ryan in the closet, a narrow hall off the classroom with a door at each end. Next to one of these doors Miss Ryan placed a large chair for herself and a small one for me. Keeping an eye on the class through the open door, she read with me about sheep in the meadow and a frightened chicken going to see the king, coaching me out of my **phonetic** ruts in words like *pasture, bow-wow-wow, hay,* and *pretty,* which to my Mexican ear and eye had so many unnecessary sounds and letters. She made me watch her lips and then close my eyes as she repeated words I found hard to read. When we came to know each other better, I tried interrupting to tell Miss

....

phonetic relating to pronunciation and the sounds of speech

Ryan how we said it in Spanish. It didn't work. She only said "oh" and went on with *pasture*, *bow-wow-wow*, and *pretty*. It was as if in that closet we were both discovering together the secrets of the English language and grieving together over the tragedies of Bo-Peep. The main reason I was graduated with honors from the first grade was that I had fallen in love with Miss Ryan. Her radiant, no-nonsense character made us either afraid not to love her or love her so we would not be afraid, I am not sure which. It was not only that we sensed she was with it, but also that she was with us.

Like the first grade, the rest of the Lincoln School was a sampling of the lower part of town where many races made their home. My pals in the second grade were Kazushi, whose parents spoke only Japanese; Matti, a skinny Italian boy; and Manuel, a fat Portuguese who would never get into a fight but wrestled you to the ground and just sat on you. Our assortment of nationalities included Koreans, Yugoslavs, Poles, Irish, and home-grown Americans.

At Lincoln, making us into Americans did not mean scrubbing away what made us originally foreign. The teachers called us as our parents did, or as close as they could pronounce our names in Spanish or Japanese. No one was ever scolded or punished for speaking in his native tongue on the playground. Matti told the class about his mother's down quilt, which she had made in Italy with the fine feathers of a thousand geese. Encarnación acted out how boys learned to fish in the Philippines. I astounded the third grade with the story of my travels on a stagecoach, which nobody else in the class had seen except in the museum at Sutter's Fort. After a visit to the Crocker Art Gallery and its collection of heroic paintings of the golden age of California, someone showed a silk scroll with a Chinese painting. Miss Hopley herself had a way of expressing wonder over these matters before a class, her eyes wide open until they popped slightly. It was easy for me to feel that becoming a proud American, as she said we should, did not mean feeling ashamed of being a Mexican. ❖

excerpt from

I Know Why the Caged Bird Sings

by Maya Angelou

On April 4, 1928, Maya Angelou was born Marguerite Johnson in St. Louis, Missouri. The name "Maya" came from her little brother, Bailey, who called her "mya sister." Angelou is a poet, author, playwright, dancer, performer, film producer and director, and champion of civil rights. In 1992, she was honored by being asked to read an original poem at the inauguration of Bill Clinton as president.

In I Know Why the Caged Bird Sings, *Angelou tells the story of her life up to the age of sixteen. The book is the first in a series of autobiographical works.*

When I was three and Bailey four, we had arrived in the musty little town, wearing tags on our wrists which instructed—"To Whom It May Concern"—that we were Marguerite and Bailey Johnson Jr., from Long Beach, California, **en route** to Stamps, Arkansas, **c/o** Mrs. Annie Henderson.

....

en route on the way
c/o care of

Our parents had decided to put an end to their **calamitous** marriage, and Father shipped us home to his mother. A porter had been charged with our welfare—he got off the train the next day in Arizona—and our tickets were pinned to my brother's inside coat pocket.

I don't remember much of the trip, but after we reached the segregated southern part of the journey, things must have looked up. Negro passengers, who always traveled with loaded lunch boxes, felt sorry for "the poor little motherless darlings" and plied us with cold fried chicken and potato salad.

Years later I discovered that the United States had been crossed thousands of times by frightened Black children traveling alone to their newly **affluent** parents in Northern cities, or back to grandmothers in Southern towns when the urban North **reneged** on its economic promises.

The town reacted to us as its inhabitants had reacted to all things new before our coming. It regarded us a while without curiosity but with caution, and after we were seen to be harmless (and children) it closed in around us, as a real mother embraces a stranger's child. Warmly, but not too familiarly.

We lived with our grandmother and uncle in the rear of the Store (it was always spoken of with a capital *s*), which she had owned some twenty-five years.

....

calamitous disastrous; causing great distress or misery
affluent wealthy
reneged failed to fulfill a promise

Early in the century, Momma (we soon stopped calling
her Grandmother) sold lunches to the sawmen in the
lumberyard (east Stamps) and the seedmen at the cotton
gin (west Stamps). Her crisp meat pies and cool lemonade,
when joined to her miraculous ability to be in two places at
the same time, assured her business success. From being a
mobile lunch counter, she set up a stand between the two
points of **fiscal** interest and supplied the workers' needs for
a few years. Then she had the Store built in the heart of
the Negro area. Over the years it became the **lay** center of

....

fiscal relating to financial matters
lay unrelated to church matters

activities in town. On Saturdays, barbers sat their customers in the shade on the porch of the Store, and **troubadours** on their ceaseless crawlings through the South leaned across its benches and sang their sad songs of **The Brazos** while they played **juice harps** and cigar-box guitars.

The formal name of the Store was the Wm. Johnson General Merchandise Store. Customers could find food staples, a good variety of colored thread, **mash** for hogs, corn for chickens, coal oil for lamps, light bulbs for the wealthy, shoestrings, hair dressing, balloons, and flower seeds. Anything not visible had only to be ordered.

Until we became familiar enough to belong to the Store and it to us, we were locked up in a Fun House of Things where the attendant had gone home for life.

Each year I watched the field across from the Store turn caterpillar green, then gradually frosty white. I knew exactly how long it would be before the big wagons would pull into the front yard and load on the cotton pickers at daybreak to carry them to the remains of slavery's plantations.

During the picking season my grandmother would get out of bed at four o'clock (she never used an alarm clock)

....

troubadours traveling singers
The Brazos region in central Texas near the Brazos River
juice harps musical instruments held between the teeth and plucked to play
mash grain mixture used to feed farm animals

and creak down to her knees and chant in a sleep-filled voice, "Our Father, thank you for letting me see this New Day. Thank you that you didn't allow the bed I lay on last night to be my cooling board, nor my blanket my winding sheet. Guide my feet this day along the straight and narrow, and help me to put a bridle on my tongue. Bless this house, and everybody in it. Thank you, in the name of your Son, Jesus Christ, Amen."

Before she had quite arisen, she called our names and issued orders, and pushed her large feet into homemade slippers and across the bare lye-washed wooden floor to light the coal-oil lamp.

The lamplight in the Store gave a soft make-believe feeling to our world which made me want to whisper and walk about on tiptoe. The odors of onions and oranges and kerosene had been mixing all night and wouldn't be disturbed until the wooded slat was removed from the door and the early morning air forced its way in with the bodies of people who had walked miles to reach the pickup place.

"Sister, I'll have two cans of sardines."

"I'm gonna work so fast today I'm gonna make you look like you standing still."

"Lemme have a hunk uh cheese and some sody crackers."

"Just gimme a coupla them fat peanut paddies." That would be from a picker who was taking his lunch. The greasy brown paper sack was stuck behind the bib of his overalls. He'd use the candy as a snack before the noon sun called the workers to rest.

In those tender mornings the Store was full of laughing, joking, boasting and bragging. One man was going to pick two hundred pounds of cotton, and another three hundred. Even the children were promising to bring home fo' bits and six bits.

The champion picker of the day before was the hero of the dawn. If he **prophesied** that the cotton in today's field was going to be sparse and stick to the **bolls** like glue, every listener would grunt a hearty agreement.

The sound of the empty cotton sacks dragging over the floor and the murmurs of waking people were sliced by the cash register as we rang up the five-cent sales.

If the morning sounds and smells were touched with the supernatural, the late afternoon had all the features of the normal Arkansas life. In the dying sunlight the people dragged, rather than their empty cotton sacks.

Brought back to the Store, the pickers would step out of the backs of trucks and fold down, dirt-disappointed, to the ground. No matter how much they had picked, it wasn't enough. Their wages wouldn't even get them out of debt to my grandmother, not to mention the staggering bill that waited on them at the white **commissary** downtown....

prophesied predicted
bolls seed-bearing pods of cotton plants
commissary a store that sells food, equipment, and supplies

During these years in Stamps, I met and fell in love with William Shakespeare. He was my first white love. Although I enjoyed and respected Kipling, Poe, Butler, Thackeray and Henley, I saved my young and loyal passion for Paul Lawrence Dunbar, Langston Hughes, James Weldon Johnson and W.E.B. Du Bois' "Litany at Atlanta." But it was Shakespeare who said, "When in disgrace with fortune and men's eyes." It was a state with which I felt myself most familiar. I **pacified** myself about his whiteness by saying that after all he had been dead so long it couldn't matter to anyone any more.

Bailey and I decided to memorize a scene from *The Merchant of Venice*, but we realized that Momma would question us about the author and that we'd have to tell her that Shakespeare was white, and it wouldn't matter to her whether he was dead or not. So we chose "The Creation" by James Weldon Johnson instead....

Weighing the half-pounds of flour, excluding the scoop, and depositing them dust-free into the thin paper sacks held a simple kind of adventure for me. I developed an eye for measuring how full a silver-looking ladle of flour, mash, meal, sugar or corn had to be to push the scale indicator over to eight ounces or one pound. When I was absolutely accurate our appreciative customers used to admire: "Sister

pacified soothed; calmed; put at peace
The Merchant of Venice one of Shakepeare's plays

Henderson sure got some smart grandchildrens." If I was off in the Store's favor, the eagle-eyed women would say, "Put some more in that sack, child. Don't you try to make your profit offa me."

Then I would quietly but persistently punish myself. For every bad judgment, the fine was no silver-wrapped Kisses, the sweet chocolate drops that I loved more than anything in the world, except Bailey. And maybe canned pineapples. My obsession with pineapples nearly drove me mad. I dreamt of the days when I would be grown and able to buy a whole carton for myself alone.

Although the syrupy golden rings sat in their **exotic** cans on our shelves year round, we only tasted them during Christmas. Momma used the juice to make almost-black fruit cakes. Then she lined heavy soot-encrusted iron skillets with the pineapple rings for rich upside-down cakes. Bailey and I received one slice each, and I carried mine around for hours, shredding off the fruit until nothing was left except the perfume on my fingers. I'd like to think that my desire for pineapples was so sacred that I wouldn't allow myself to steal a can (which was possible) and eat it alone out in the garden, but I'm certain that I must have weighed the possibility of the scent exposing me and didn't have the nerve to attempt it.

....

exotic of foreign origin; exciting because unusual or strange

Until I was thirteen and left Arkansas for good, the Store was my favorite place to be. Alone and empty in the mornings, it looked like an unopened present from a stranger. Opening the front doors was pulling the ribbon off the unexpected gift. The light would come in softly (we faced north), easing itself over the shelves of mackerel, salmon, tobacco, thread. It fell flat on the big vat of lard and by noontime during the summer the grease had softened to a thick soup. Whenever I walked into the Store in the afternoon, I sensed that it was tired. I alone could hear the slow pulse of its job half done. But just before bedtime, after numerous people had walked in and out, had argued over their bills, or joked about their neighbors, or just dropped in "to give Sister Henderson a 'Hi y'all,'" the promise of magic mornings returned to the Store and spread itself over the family in washed life waves ....

[*Marguerite's mother comes to Stamps, and she takes Marguerite away with her for a visit to St. Louis. At about the age of ten, Marguerite returns to Stamps, withdrawn and silent.*]

For nearly a year, I sopped around the house, the Store, the school and the church, like an old biscuit, dirty and **inedible**. Then I met, or rather got to know, the lady who threw me my first life line.

---

inedible impossible to eat

Mrs. Bertha Flowers was the **aristocrat** of Black Stamps. She had the grace of control to appear warm in the coldest weather, and on the Arkansas summer days it seemed she had a private breeze which swirled around, cooling her. She was thin without the **taut** look of wiry people, and her printed **voile** dresses and flowered hats were as right for her as denim overalls for a farmer. She was our side's answer to the richest white woman in town.

Her skin was a rich black that would have peeled like a plum if snagged, but then no one would have thought of getting close enough to Mrs. Flowers to ruffle her dress, let alone snag her skin. She didn't encourage familiarity. She wore gloves too.

I don't think I ever saw Mrs. Flowers laugh, but she smiled often. A slow widening of her thin black lips to show even, small white teeth, then the slow effortless closing. When she chose to smile on me, I always wanted to thank her. The action was so graceful and inclusively **benign**.

She was one of the few gentlewomen I have ever known, and has remained throughout my life the measure of what a human being can be.

Momma had a strange relationship with her. Most often when she passed on the road in front of the Store, she spoke

....

aristocrat person of high social class or status
taut pulled tight
voile lightweight fabric made from cotton
benign kind; pleasant; gentle

to Momma in that soft yet carrying voice, "Good day, Mrs. Henderson." Momma responded with "How you, Sister Flowers?"

Mrs. Flowers didn't belong to our church, nor was she Momma's familiar. Why on earth did she insist on calling her Sister Flowers? Shame made me want to hide my face. Mrs. Flowers deserved better than to be called Sister. Then, Momma left out the verb. Why not ask, "How are you, Mrs. Flowers?" With the unbalanced passion of the young, I hated her for showing her ignorance to Mrs. Flowers. It didn't occur to me for many years that they were as alike as sisters, separated only by formal education.

Although I was upset, neither of the women was in the least shaken by what I thought an unceremonious greeting. Mrs. Flowers would continue her easy **gait** up the hill to her little bungalow, and Momma kept on shelling peas or doing whatever had brought her to the front porch.

Occasionally, though, Mrs. Flowers would drift off the road and down to the Store and Momma would say to me, "Sister, you go on and play." As I left I would hear the beginning of an intimate conversation. Momma persistently using the wrong verb, or none at all.

"Brother and Sister Wilcox is sho'ly the meanest—" "Is" Momma? "Is"? Oh, please, not "is," Momma, for two or more. But they talked, and from the side of the building

----

gait manner of walking

where I waited for the ground to open up and swallow me, I heard the soft-voiced Mrs. Flowers and the textured voice of my grandmother merging and melting. They were interrupted from time to time by giggles that must have come from Mrs. Flowers (Momma never giggled in her life). Then she was gone ....

One summer afternoon, sweet-milk fresh in my memory, she stopped at the Store to buy **provisions**. Another Negro woman of her health and age would have been expected to carry the paper sacks home in one hand, but Momma said, "Sister Flowers, I'll send Bailey up to your house with these things."

She smiled that slow dragging smile, "Thank you, Mrs. Henderson. I'd prefer Marguerite, though." My name was beautiful when she said it. "I've been meaning to talk to her, anyway." They gave each other age-group looks.

Momma said, "Well, that's all right then. Sister, go and change your dress. You going to Sister Flowers'."

The **chifforobe** was a maze. What on earth did one put on to go to Mrs. Flowers' house? I knew I shouldn't put on a Sunday dress. It might be sacrilegious. Certainly not a house dress, since I was already wearing a fresh one. I chose a school dress, naturally. It was formal without

....

provisions supplies
chifforobe a piece of furniture often with drawers on one side and space for hanging clothes on the other

suggesting that going to Mrs. Flowers' house was equivalent to attending church.

I trusted myself back into the Store.

"Now, don't you look nice." I had chosen the right thing, for once.

"Mrs. Henderson, you make most of the children's clothes, don't you?"

"Yes, ma'am. Sure do. Store-bought clothes ain't hardly worth the thread it take to stitch them."

"I'll say you do a lovely job, though, so neat. That dress looks professional."

Momma was enjoying the seldom-received compliments. Since everyone we knew (except Mrs. Flowers, of course) could sew competently, praise was rarely handed out for the commonly practiced craft.

"I try, with the help of the Lord, Sister Flowers, to finish the inside just like I does the outside. Come here, Sister."

I had buttoned up the collar and tied the belt, apron-like, in back. Momma told me to turn around. With one hand she pulled the strings and the belt fell free at both sides of my waist. Then her large hands were at my neck, opening the button loops. I was terrified. What was happening?

"Take it off, Sister." She had her hands on the hem of the dress.

"I don't need to see the inside, Mrs. Henderson, I can tell … " But the dress was over my head and my arms were stuck in the sleeves. Momma said, "That'll do. See here, Sister Flowers, I French-seams around the armholes." Through the cloth film, I saw the shadow approach. "That makes it last longer. Children these days would bust out of sheet-metal clothes. They so rough."

"That is a very good job, Mrs. Henderson. You should be proud. You can put your dress back on, Marguerite."

"No ma'am. Pride is a sin. And 'cording to the Good Book, it goeth before a fall."

"That's right. So the Bible says. It's a good thing to keep in mind."

I wouldn't look at either of them. Momma hadn't thought that taking off my dress in front of Mrs. Flowers would kill me stone dead. If I had refused, she would have thought I was trying to be "womanish" and might have remembered St. Louis. Mrs. Flowers had known that I would be embarrassed and that was even worse. I picked up the groceries and went out to wait in the hot sunshine. It would be fitting if I got a sunstroke and died before they came outside. Just dropped dead on the slanting porch.

There was a little path beside the rocky road, and Mrs. Flowers walked in front swinging her arms and picking her way over the stones.

She said, without turning her head, to me, "I hear you're doing very good school work, Marguerite, but that it's all written. The teachers report that they have trouble getting you to talk in class." We passed the triangular farm on our left and the path widened to allow us to walk together. I hung back in the separate unasked and unanswerable questions.

"Come and walk along with me, Marguerite." I couldn't have refused even if I wanted to. She pronounced my name so nicely. Or more correctly, she spoke each word with such clarity that I was certain a foreigner who didn't understand English could have understood her.

"Now no one is going to make you talk—possibly no one can. But bear in mind, language is man's way of communicating with his fellow man and it is language alone which separates him from the lower animals." That was a totally new idea to me, and I would need time to think about it.

"Your grandmother says you read a lot. Every chance you get. That's good, but not good enough. Words mean more than what is set down on paper. It takes the human voice to infuse them with the shades of deeper meaning."

I memorized the part about the human voice infusing words. It seemed so valid and poetic.

She said she was going to give me some books and that I not only must read them, I must read them aloud. She suggested that I try to make a sentence sound in as many different ways as possible.

"I'll accept no excuse if you return a book to me that has been badly handled." My imagination **boggled** at the

....

boggled hesitated in fear, doubt, or amazement

punishment I would deserve if in fact I did abuse a book of Mrs. Flowers'. Death would be too kind and brief.

The odors in the house surprised me. Somehow I had never connected Mrs. Flowers with food or eating or any other common experience of common people. There must have been an outhouse, too, but my mind never recorded it.

The sweet scent of vanilla had met us as she opened the door.

"I made tea cookies this morning. You see, I had planned to invite you for cookies and lemonade so we could have this little chat. The lemonade is in the icebox."

It followed that Mrs. Flowers would have ice on an ordinary day, when most families in our town bought ice late on Saturdays only a few times during the summer to be used in the wooden ice-cream freezers.

She took the bags from me and disappeared through the kitchen door. I looked around the room that I had never in my wildest fantasies imagined I would see. Browned photographs leered or threatened from the walls and the white, freshly done curtains pushed against themselves and against the wind. I wanted to gobble up the room entire and take it to Bailey, who would help me analyze and enjoy it.

"Have a seat, Marguerite. Over there by the table." She carried a platter covered with a tea towel. Although she warned that she hadn't tried her hand at baking sweets for some time, I was certain that like everything else about her the cookies would be perfect.

They were flat round wafers, slightly browned on the edges and butter-yellow in the center. With the cold lemonade they were sufficient for childhood's lifelong diet. Remembering my manners, I took nice little lady-like bites off the edges. She said she had made them expressly for me and that she had a few in the kitchen that I could take home to my brother. So I jammed one whole cake in my mouth and the rough crumbs scratched the insides of my jaws, and if I hadn't had to swallow, it would have been a dream come true.

As I ate she began the first of what we later called "my lessons in living." She said that I must always be intolerant of ignorance but understanding of illiteracy. That some people, unable to go to school, were more educated and even more intelligent than college professors. She encouraged me to listen carefully to what country people called mother wit. That in those homely sayings was couched the collective wisdom of generations.

When I finished the cookies she brushed off the table and brought a thick, small book from the bookcase. I had read *A Tale of Two Cities* and found it up to my standards as a romantic novel. She opened the first page and I heard poetry for the first time in my life.

A Tale of Two Cities a historical novel by the English novelist Charles Dickens, published in 1859, and set in the time of the French Revolution

"It was the best of times and the worst of times…" Her voice slid in and curved down through and over the words. She was nearly singing. I wanted to look at the pages. Were they the same that I had read? Or were there notes, music, lined on the pages, as in a hymn book? Her sounds began **cascading** gently. I knew from listening to a thousand preachers that she was nearing the end of her reading, and I hadn't really heard, heard to understand, a single word.

"How do you like that?"

It occurred to me that she expected a response. The sweet vanilla flavor was still on my tongue and her reading was a wonder in my ears. I had to speak.

I said, "Yes, ma'am." It was the least I could do, but it was the most also.

"There's one more thing. Take this book of poems and memorize one for me. Next time you pay me a visit, I want you to recite."

I have tried often to search behind the sophistication of years for the enchantment I so easily found in those gifts. The essence escapes but its **aura** remains. To be allowed, no, invited, into the private lives of strangers, and to share their joys and fears, was a chance to exchange the Southern bitter **wormwood** for a cup of **mead** with **Beowulf** or a hot

---

cascading pouring down like a waterfall
aura an invisible breath, glow, or presence
wormwood a bitter-tasting plant; anything harsh or bitter
mead a wine made from fermented honey and water
Beowulf the hero of an epic poem dating from about the eighth century

cup of tea and milk with **Oliver Twist**. When I said aloud, **"It is a far, far better thing** that I do, than I have ever done ..." tears of love filled my eyes at my selflessness.

On that first day, I ran down the hill and into the road (few cars ever came along it) and had the good sense to stop running before I reached the Store.

I was liked, and what a difference it made. I was respected not as Mrs. Henderson's grandchild or Bailey's sister but for just being Marguerite Johnson.

Childhood's logic never asks to be proved (all conclusions are absolute). I didn't question why Mrs. Flowers had singled me out for attention, nor did it occur to me that Momma might have asked her to give me a little talking to. All I cared about was that she had made tea cookies for *me* and read to *me* from her favorite book. It was enough to prove that she liked me. ❖

Oliver Twist the main character in *Oliver Twist*, a novel by Charles Dickens, published in 1837–38
"It is a far, far better thing..." a famous quotation from the ending of *A Tale of Two Cities*

Frederick Douglass

excerpts from

Narrative of the Life of Frederick Douglass

by Frederick Douglass

Chapter I

I was born in Tuckahoe, near Hillsborough, and about twelve miles from Easton, in Talbot county, Maryland. I have no accurate knowledge of my age, never having seen any authentic record containing it. By far the larger part of the slaves know as little of their ages as horses know of theirs, and it is the wish of most masters within my knowledge to keep their slaves thus ignorant. I do not remember to have ever met a slave who could tell of his birthday. They seldom come nearer to it than planting-time, harvest-time, cherry-time, spring-time, or fall-time. A want of information concerning my own was a source of unhappiness to me even during childhood. The white children could tell their ages. I could not tell why I ought to be deprived of the same privilege. I was not allowed to make any inquiries of my master concerning it. He deemed all such inquiries on the part of a slave improper and impertinent, and evidence of a restless spirit. The nearest estimate I can give makes me now between twenty-seven and twenty-eight years of age. I come to this, from hearing my master say, some time during 1835, I was about seventeen years old.

My mother was named Harriet Bailey. She was the daughter of Isaac and Betsey Bailey, both colored, and quite dark. My mother was of a darker complexion than either my grandmother or grandfather.

My father was a white man. He was admitted to be such by all I ever heard speak of my parentage. The opinion was also whispered that my master was my father; but of the correctness of this opinion, I know nothing; the means of knowing was withheld from me. My mother and I were separated when I was but an infant—before I knew her as my mother. It is a common custom, in the part of Maryland from which I ran away, to part children from their mothers at a very early age. Frequently, before the child has reached its twelfth month, its mother is taken from it, and hired out on some farm a considerable distance off, and the child is placed under the care of an old woman, too old for field labor. For what this separation is done, I do not know, unless it be to hinder the development of the child's affection toward its mother, and to blunt and destroy the natural affection of the mother for the child. This is the inevitable result.

I never saw my mother, to know her as such, more than four or five times in my life; and each of these times was very short in duration, and at night. She was hired by a Mr. Stewart, who lived about twelve miles from my home.

She made her journeys to see me in the night, travelling the whole distance on foot, after the performance of her day's work. She was a field hand, and a whipping is the penalty of not being in the field at sunrise, unless a slave has special permission from his or her master to the contrary—a permission which they seldom get, and one that gives to him that gives it the proud name of being a kind master. I do not recollect of ever seeing my mother by the light of day. She was with me in the night. She would lie down with me, and get me to sleep, but long before I waked she was gone. Very little communication ever took place between us. Death soon ended what little we could have while she lived, and with it her hardships and suffering. She died when I was about seven years old, on one of my master's farms, near Lee's Mill. I was not allowed to be present during her illness, at her death, or burial. She was gone long before I knew any thing about it. Never having enjoyed, to any considerable extent, her soothing presence, her tender and watchful care, I received the tidings of her death with much the same emotions I should have probably felt at the death of a stranger.

Called thus suddenly away, she left me without the slightest intimation of who my father was. The whisper that my master was my father, may or may not be true; and, true or false, it is of but little consequence to my purpose whilst the fact remains, in all its glaring **odiousness**, that

odiousness hatefulness

slaveholders have ordained, and by law established, that the children of slave women shall in all cases follow the condition of their mothers; and this is done too obviously to administer to their own lusts, and make a gratification of their wicked desires profitable as well as pleasurable; for by this cunning arrangement, the slaveholder, in cases not a few, sustains to his slaves the double relation of master and father.

I know of such cases; and it is worthy of remark that such slaves invariably suffer greater hardships, and have more to contend with, than others. They are, in the first place, a constant offence to their mistress. She is ever disposed to find fault with them; they can seldom do any thing to please her; she is never better pleased than when she sees them under the lash, especially when she suspects her husband of showing to his mulatto children favors which he withholds from his black slaves. The master is frequently compelled to sell this class of his slaves, out of deference to the feelings of his white wife; and, cruel as the deed may strike any one to be, for a man to sell his own children to human flesh-mongers, it is often the dictate of humanity for him to do so; for, unless he does this, he must not only whip them himself, but must stand by and see one white son tie up his brother, of but few shades darker complexion than himself, and ply the gory lash to his naked back; and if he lisp one word of disapproval, it is set down to his parental partiality, and only makes a bad matter worse, both for himself and the slave whom he would protect and defend.

Every year brings with it multitudes of this class of slaves. It was doubtless in consequence of a knowledge of this fact, that one great statesman of the south predicted the downfall of slavery by the inevitable laws of population. Whether this prophecy is ever fulfilled or not, it is nevertheless plain that a very different-looking class of people are springing up at the south, and are now held in slavery, from those originally brought to this country from Africa; and if their increase do no other good, it will do away the force of the argument, that God cursed Ham, and therefore American slavery is right. If the lineal descendants of Ham are alone to be scripturally enslaved, it is certain that slavery at the south must soon become unscriptural; for thousands are ushered into the world, annually, who, like myself, owe their existence to white fathers, and those fathers most frequently their own masters.

I have had two masters. My first master's name was Anthony. I do not remember his first name. He was generally called Captain Anthony—a title which, I presume, he acquired by sailing a craft on the Chesapeake Bay. He was not considered a rich slaveholder. He owned two or three farms, and about thirty slaves. His farms and slaves were under the care of an **overseer**. The overseer's name was Plummer. Mr. Plummer was a miserable

---

overseer someone who manages laborers (slaves)

drunkard, a profane swearer, and a savage monster. He always went armed with a cowskin and a heavy **cudgel**. I have known him to cut and slash the women's heads so horribly, that even master would be enraged at his cruelty, and would threaten to whip him if he did not mind himself. Master, however, was not a humane slaveholder. It required extraordinary barbarity on the part of an overseer to affect him. He was a cruel man, hardened by a long life of slaveholding. He would at times seem to take great pleasure in whipping a slave. I have often been awakened at the dawn of day by the most heart-rending shrieks of an own aunt of mine, whom he used to tie up to a joist, and whip upon her naked back till she was literally covered with blood. No words, no tears, no prayers, from his gory victim, seemed to move his iron heart from its bloody purpose. The louder she screamed, the harder he whipped; and where the blood ran fastest, there he whipped longest. He would whip her to make her scream, and whip her to make her hush; and not until overcome by fatigue, would he cease to swing the blood-clotted cowskin. I remember the first time I ever witnessed this horrible exhibition. I was quite a child, but I well remember it. I never shall forget it whilst I remember any thing. It was the first of a long series of such outrages, of which I was doomed to be a witness and a participant. It struck me with awful force. It was the blood-stained gate, the entrance to the hell of slavery,

cudgel a club

through which I was about to pass. It was a most terrible spectacle. I wish I could commit to paper the feelings with which I beheld it.

This occurrence took place very soon after I went to live with my old master, and under the following circumstances. Aunt Hester went out one night,—where or for what I do not know,—and happened to be absent when my master desired her presence. He had ordered her not to go out evenings, and warned her that she must never let him catch her in company with a young man, who was paying attention to her belonging to Colonel Lloyd. The young man's name was Ned Roberts, generally called Lloyd's Ned. Why master was so careful of her, may be safely left to conjecture. She was a woman of noble form, and of graceful proportions, having very few equals, and fewer superiors, in personal appearance, among the colored or white women of our neighborhood.

Aunt Hester had not only disobeyed his orders in going out, but had been found in company with Lloyd's Ned; which circumstance, I found, from what he said while whipping her, was the chief offence. Had he been a man of pure morals himself, he might have been thought interested in protecting the innocence of my aunt; but those who knew him will not suspect him of any such virtue. Before he commenced whipping Aunt Hester, he took her into the kitchen, and stripped her from neck to waist, leaving her neck, shoulders, and back, entirely naked. He then told her to cross her hands, calling her at the same time a d——d b——h. After crossing her hands, he tied them with a strong rope, and led her to a stool under a large hook in the joist, put in for the purpose. He made her get upon the stool, and tied her hands to the hook. She now stood fair for his infernal purpose. Her arms were stretched up at their full length, so that she stood upon the ends of her toes. He then said to her, "Now, you d——d b——h, I'll learn you how to disobey my orders!" and after rolling up his sleeves, he commenced to lay on the heavy cowskin, and soon the warm, red blood (amid heart-rending shrieks from her, and horrid oaths from him) came dripping to the floor. I was so terrified and horror-stricken at the sight, that I hid myself in a closet, and dared not venture out till long after the bloody transaction was over. I expected it would be my turn next. It was all new to me. I had never seen any thing like it before. I had always lived with my grandmother on the outskirts of the plantation, where she was put to raise the children of the younger women. I had therefore been, until now, out of the way of the bloody scenes that often occurred on the plantation.

Chapter II

My master's family consisted of two sons, Andrew and Richard; one daughter, Lucretia, and her husband, Captain Thomas Auld. They lived in one house, upon the home plantation of Colonel Edward Lloyd. My master was Colonel Lloyd's clerk and superintendent. He was what might be called the overseer of the overseers. I spent two years of childhood on this plantation in my old master's family. It was here that I witnessed the bloody transaction recorded in the first chapter; and as I received my first impressions of slavery on this plantation, I will give some description of it, and of slavery as it there existed. The plantation is about twelve miles north of Easton, in Talbot county, and is situated on the border of Miles River. The principal products raised upon it were tobacco, corn, and wheat. These were raised in great abundance; so that, with the products of this and the other farms belonging to him, he was able to keep in almost constant employment a large **sloop**, in carrying them to market at Baltimore. This sloop was named Sally Lloyd, in honor of one of the colonel's daughters. My master's son-in-law, Captain Auld, was master of the vessel; she was otherwise manned by the colonel's own slaves. Their names were Peter, Isaac, Rich, and Jake. These were esteemed very highly by the other slaves, and looked upon as the privileged ones of

sloop a large sailing boat with one mast

the plantation; for it was no small affair, in the eyes of the slaves, to be allowed to see Baltimore.

Colonel Lloyd kept from three to four hundred slaves on his home plantation, and owned a large number more on the neighboring farms belonging to him. The names of the farms nearest to the home plantation were Wye Town and New Design. "Wye Town" was under the overseership of a man named Noah Willis. New Design was under the overseership of a Mr. Townsend. The overseers of these, and all the rest of the farms, numbering over twenty, received advice and direction from the managers of the home plantation. This was the great business place. It was the seat of government for the whole twenty farms. All disputes among the overseers were settled here. If a slave was convicted of any high misdemeanor, became unmanageable, or evinced a determination to run away, he was brought immediately here, severely whipped, put on board the sloop, carried to Baltimore, and sold to Austin Woolfolk, or some other slave-trader, as a warning to the slaves remaining.

Here, too, the slaves of all the other farms received their monthly allowance of food, and their yearly clothing. The men and women slaves received, as their monthly allowance of food, eight pounds of pork, or its equivalent in fish, and one bushel of corn meal. Their yearly clothing consisted of two coarse linen shirts, one pair of linen trousers, like the shirts, one jacket, one pair of trousers for winter, made of coarse negro cloth, one pair of stockings, and one pair of shoes; the whole of which could not have cost more than seven dollars. The allowance of the slave children was given to their mothers, or the old women having the care of them. The children unable to work in the field had neither shoes, stockings, jackets, nor trousers, given to them; their clothing consisted of two coarse linen shirts per year. When these failed them, they went naked until the next allowance-day. Children from seven to ten years old, of both sexes, almost naked, might be seen at all seasons of the year.

There were no beds given the slaves, unless one coarse blanket be considered such, and none but the men and women had these. This, however, is not considered a very great **privation**. They find less difficulty from the want of beds, than from the want of time to sleep; for when their day's work in the field is done, the most of them having their washing, mending, and cooking to do, and having few or none of the ordinary facilities for doing either of these, very many of their sleeping hours are consumed in preparing for the field the coming day; and when this is done, old and young, male and female, married and single, drop down side by side, on one common bed,—the cold, damp floor,—each covering himself or herself with their miserable blankets; and here they sleep till they are summoned to the field by the driver's horn. At the sound

privation lack of necessities

of this, all must rise, and be off to the field. There must be no halting; every one must be at his or her post; and woe betides them who hear not this morning summons to the field; for if they are not awakened by the sense of hearing, they are by the sense of feeling: no age nor sex finds any favor. Mr. Severe, the overseer, used to stand by the door of the quarter, armed with a large hickory stick and heavy cowskin, ready to whip any one who was so unfortunate as not to hear, or, from any other cause, was prevented from being ready to start for the field at the sound of the horn.

Mr. Severe was rightly named: he was a cruel man. I have seen him whip a woman, causing the blood to run half an hour at the time; and this, too, in the midst of her crying children, pleading for their mother's release. He seemed to take pleasure in manifesting his **fiendish** barbarity. Added to his cruelty, he was a profane swearer. It was enough to chill the blood and stiffen the hair of an ordinary man to hear him talk. Scarce a sentence escaped him but that was commenced or concluded by some horrid oath. The field was the place to witness his cruelty and profanity. His presence made it both the field of blood and of blasphemy. From the rising till the going down of the sun, he was cursing, raving, cutting, and slashing among the slaves of the field, in the most frightful manner. His career was short. He died very soon after I went to Colonel Lloyd's; and he died as he lived, uttering,

fiendish cruel or wicked

with his dying groans, bitter curses and horrid oaths. His death was regarded by the slaves as the result of a merciful providence.

Mr. Severe's place was filled by a Mr. Hopkins. He was a very different man. He was less cruel, less profane, and made less noise, than Mr. Severe. His course was characterized by no extraordinary demonstrations of cruelty. He whipped, but seemed to take no pleasure in it. He was called by the slaves a good overseer.

The home plantation of Colonel Lloyd wore the appearance of a country village. All the mechanical operations for all the farms were performed here. The shoemaking and mending, the blacksmithing, **cartwrighting**, **coopering**, weaving, and grain-grinding, were all performed by the slaves on the home plantation. The whole place wore a business-like aspect very unlike the neighboring farms. The number of houses, too, conspired to give it advantage over the neighboring farms. It was called by the slaves the *Great House Farm*. Few privileges were esteemed higher, by the slaves of the out-farms, than that of being selected to do errands at the Great House Farm. It was associated in their minds with greatness. A representative could not be prouder of his election to a seat in the American Congress, than a slave on one of the out-farms would be of his election to do errands at the

....
cartwrighting the making of carts
coopering the making of barrels

Great House Farm. They regarded it as evidence of great confidence reposed in them by their overseers; and it was on this account, as well as a constant desire to be out of the field from under the driver's lash, that they esteemed it a high privilege, one worth careful living for. He was called the smartest and most trusty fellow, who had this honor conferred upon him the most frequently. The competitors for this office sought as diligently to please their overseers, as the office-seekers in the political parties seek to please and deceive the people. The same traits of character might be seen in Colonel Lloyd's slaves, as are seen in the slaves of the political parties.

The slaves selected to go to the Great House Farm, for the monthly allowance for themselves and their fellow-slaves, were peculiarly enthusiastic. While on their way, they would make the dense old woods, for miles around, reverberate with their wild songs, revealing at once the highest joy and the deepest sadness. They would compose and sing as they went along, consulting neither time nor tune. The thought that came up, came out—if not in the word, in the sound;—and as frequently in the one as in the other. They would sometimes sing the most pathetic sentiment in the most **rapturous** tone, and the most rapturous sentiment in the most pathetic tone. Into all of their songs they would manage to weave something of the Great House Farm. Especially would they do this, when

rapturous ecstatic; joyful

leaving home. They would then sing most exultingly the following words:

"I am going away to the Great House Farm!
O, yea! O, yea! O!"

This they would sing, as a chorus, to words which to many would seem unmeaning jargon, but which, nevertheless, were full of meaning to themselves. I have sometimes thought that the mere hearing of reading of whole volumes of philosophy on the subject could do.

I did not, when a slave, understand the deep meaning of those rude and apparently incoherent songs. I was myself within the circle; so that I neither saw nor heard as those without might see and hear. They told a tale of woe which was then altogether beyond my feeble comprehension; they were tones loud, long, and deep; they breathed the prayer and complaint of souls boiling over with the bitterest anguish. Every tone was a testimony against slavery, and a prayer to God for deliverance from chains. The hearing of those wild notes always depressed my spirit, and filled me with **ineffable** sadness. I have frequently found myself in tears while hearing them. The mere recurrence to those songs, even now, afflicts me; and while I am writing these lines, an expression of feeling has already found its way down my cheek. To those songs I trace my first glimmering conception of the dehumanizing

ineffable unspeakable

character of slavery. I can never get rid of that conception. Those songs still follow me, to deepen my hatred of slavery, and quicken my sympathies for my brethren in bonds. If any one wishes to be impressed with the soul-killing effects of slavery, let him go to Colonel Lloyd's plantation, and, on allowance-day, place himself in the deep pine woods, and there let him, in silence, analyze the sounds that shall pass through the chambers of his soul,—and if he is not thus impressed, it will only be because "there is no flesh in his **obdurate** heart."

I have often been utterly astonished, since I came to the north, to find persons who could speak of the singing, among slaves, as evidence of their contentment and happiness. It is impossible to conceive of a greater mistake. Slaves sing most when they are most unhappy. The songs of the slave represent the sorrows of his heart; and he is relieved by them, only as an aching heart is relieved by its tears. At least, such is my experience. I have often sung to drown my sorrow, but seldom to express my happiness. Crying for joy, and singing for joy, were alike uncommon to me while in the jaws of slavery. The singing of a man cast away upon a desolate island might be as appropriately considered as evidence of contentment and happiness, as the singing of a slave; the songs of the one and of the other are prompted by the same emotion.

....

obdurate hardened; unfeeling

Chapter VI

My new mistress proved to be all she appeared when I first met her at the door,—a woman of the kindest heart and finest feelings. She had never had a slave under her control previously to myself, and prior to her marriage she had been dependent upon her own industry for a living. She was by trade a weaver; and by constant application to her business, she had been in a good degree preserved from the blighting and dehumanizing effects of slavery. I was utterly astonished at her goodness. I scarcely knew how to behave towards her. She was entirely unlike any other white woman I had ever seen. I could not approach her as I was accustomed to approach other white ladies. My early instruction was all out of place. The crouching servility, usually so acceptable a quality in a slave, did not answer when manifested toward her. Her favor was not gained by it; she seemed to be disturbed by it. She did not deem it impudent or unmannerly for a slave to look her in the face. The meanest slave was put fully at ease in her presence, and none left without feeling better for having seen her. Her face was made of heavenly smiles, and her voice of tranquil music.

But, alas! this kind heart had but a short time to remain such. The fatal poison of irresponsible power was already in her hands, and soon commenced its **infernal** work.

....

infernal evil; awful

That cheerful eye, under the influence of slavery, soon became red with rage; that voice, made all of sweet accord, changed to one of harsh and horrid discord; and that angelic face gave place to that of a demon.

Very soon after I went to live with Mr. and Mrs. Auld, she very kindly commenced to teach me the A, B, C. After I had learned this, she assisted me in learning to spell words of three or four letters. Just at this point of my progress, Mr. Auld found out what was going on, and at once forbade Mrs. Auld to instruct me further, telling her, among other things, that it was unlawful, as well as unsafe, to teach a slave to read. To use his own words, further, he said, "If you give a nigger an inch, he will take an ell. A nigger should know nothing but to obey his master—to do as he is told to do. Learning would *spoil* the best nigger in the world. Now," said he, "if you teach that nigger (speaking of myself) how to read, there would be no keeping him. It would forever unfit him to be a slave. He would at once become unmanageable, and of no value to his master. As to himself, it could do him no good, but a great deal of harm. It would make him discontented and unhappy." These words sank deep into my heart, stirred up sentiments within that lay slumbering, and called into existence an entirely new train of thought. It was a new and special revelation, explaining dark and mysterious things, with which my youthful understanding had struggled, but struggled in vain. I now understood what had been to me a most perplexing difficulty—to wit, the white man's power to enslave the black man. It was a grand achievement, and I prized it highly. From that moment, I understood the pathway from slavery to freedom. It was just what I wanted, and I got it at a time when I the least expected it. Whilst I was saddened by the thought of losing the aid of my kind mistress, I was gladdened by the invaluable instruction which, by the merest accident, I had gained from my master. Though conscious of the difficulty of learning without a teacher, I set out with high hope, and a fixed purpose, at whatever cost of trouble, to learn how to read. The very decided manner with which he spoke, and strove to impress his wife with the evil consequences of giving me instruction, served to convince me that he was deeply sensible of the truths he was uttering. It gave me the best assurance that I might rely with the utmost confidence on the results which, he said, would flow from teaching me to read. What he most dreaded, that I most desired. What he most loved, that I most hated. That which to him was a great evil, to be carefully shunned, was to me a great good, to be diligently sought; and the argument which he so warmly urged, against my learning to read, only served to inspire me with a desire and determination to learn. In learning to read, I owe almost as much to the bitter opposition of my master, as to the kindly aid of my mistress. I acknowledge the benefit of both.

I had resided but a short time in Baltimore before I observed a marked difference, in the treatment of slaves, from that which I had witnessed in the country. A city slave is almost a freeman, compared with a slave on the plantation. He is much better fed and clothed, and enjoys privileges altogether unknown to the slave on the plantation. There is a **vestige** of decency, a sense of shame, that does much to curb and check those outbreaks of atrocious cruelty so commonly enacted upon the plantation. He is a desperate slaveholder, who will shock the humanity of his non-slaveholding neighbors with the cries of his **lacerated** slave. Few are willing to incur the **odium** attaching to the reputation of being a cruel master; and above all things, they would not be known as not giving a slave enough to eat. Every city slaveholder is anxious to have it known of him, that he feeds his slaves well; and it is due to them to say, that most of them do give their slaves enough to eat. There are, however, some painful exceptions to this rule. Directly opposite to us, on Philpot Street, lived Mr. Thomas Hamilton. He owned two slaves. Their names were Henrietta and Mary. Henrietta was about twenty-two years of age, Mary was about fourteen; and of all the mangled and emaciated creatures I ever looked upon, these two were the most so. His heart

---

vestige trace; remnant
lacerated cut up
odium disgrace

must be harder than stone, that could look upon these unmoved. The head, neck, and shoulders of Mary were literally cut to pieces. I have frequently felt her head, and found it nearly covered with festering sores, caused by the lash of her cruel mistress. I do not know that her master ever whipped her, but I have been an eyewitness to the cruelty of Mrs. Hamilton. I used to be in Mr. Hamilton's house nearly every day. Mrs. Hamilton used to sit in a large chair in the middle of the room, with a heavy cowskin always by her side, and scarce an hour passed during the day but was marked by the blood of one of these slaves. The girls seldom passed her without her saying, "Move faster, you *black gip!*" at the same time giving them a blow with the cowskin over the head or shoulders, often drawing the blood. She would then say, "Take that, you *black yip!*" continuing, "If you don't move faster, I'll move you!" Added to the cruel lashings to which these slaves were subjected, they were kept nearly half-starved. They seldom knew what it was to eat a full meal. I have seen Mary contending with the pigs for the **offal** thrown into the street. So much was Mary kicked and cut to pieces, that she was oftener called *"pecked"* than by her name.

....

offal animal waste

Chapter VII

I lived in Master Hugh's family about seven years. During this time, I succeeded in learning to read and write. In accomplishing this, I was compelled to resort to various stratagems. I had no regular teacher. My mistress, who had kindly commenced to instruct me, had, in compliance with the advice and direction of her husband, not only ceased to instruct, but had set her face against my being instructed by any one else. It is due, however, to my mistress to say of her, that she did not adopt this course of treatment immediately. She at first lacked the depravity indispensable to shutting me up in mental darkness. It was at least necessary for her to have some training in the exercise of irresponsible power, to make her equal to the task of treating me as though I were a brute.

My mistress was, as I have said, a kind and tender-hearted woman; and in the simplicity of her soul she commenced, when I first went to live with her, to treat me as she supposed one human being ought to treat another. In entering upon the duties of a slaveholder, she did not seem to perceive that I sustained to her the relation of a mere chattel, and that for her to treat me as a human being was not only wrong, but dangerously so. Slavery proved as injurious to her as it did to me. When I went there, she was a pious, warm, and tender-hearted woman. There was no sorrow or suffering for which she had not a tear. She had bread for the hungry, clothes for the naked, and comfort for every mourner that came within her reach. Slavery soon proved its ability to divest her of these heavenly qualities. Under its influence, the tender heart became stone, and the lamblike disposition gave way to one of tiger-like fierceness. The first step in her downward course was in her ceasing to instruct me. She now commenced to practise her husband's **precepts**. She finally became even more violent in her opposition than her husband himself. She was not satisfied with simply doing as well as he had commanded; she seemed anxious to do better. Nothing seemed to make her more angry than to see me with a newspaper. She seemed to think that here lay the danger. I have had her rush at me with a face made all up of fury, and snatch from me a newspaper, in a manner that fully revealed her apprehension. She was an apt woman; and a little experience soon demonstrated, to her satisfaction, that education and slavery were incompatible with each other.

From this time I was most narrowly watched. If I was in a separate room any considerable length of time, I was sure to be suspected of having a book, and was at once called to give an account of myself. All this, however, was too late. The first step had been taken. Mistress, in teaching me the alphabet, had given me the *inch*, and no precaution could prevent me from taking the *ell*.

precepts laws or rules

The plan which I adopted, and the one by which I was most successful, was that of making friends of all the little white boys whom I met in the street. As many of these as I could, I converted into teachers. With their kindly aid, obtained at different times and in different places, I finally succeeded in learning to read. When I was sent of errands, I always took my book with me, and by going one part of my errand quickly, I found time to get a lesson before my return. I used also to carry bread with me, enough of which was always in the house, and to which I was always welcome; for I was much better off in this regard than many of the poor white children in our neighborhood. This bread I used to bestow upon the hungry little urchins, who, in return, would give me that more valuable bread of knowledge. I am strongly tempted to give the names of two or three of those little boys, as a testimonial of the gratitude and affection I bear them; but prudence forbids;—not that it would injure me, but it might embarrass them; for it is almost an unpardonable offence to teach slaves to read in this Christian country. It is enough to say of the dear little fellows, that they lived on Philpot Street, very near Durgin and Bailey's ship-yard. I used to talk this matter of slavery over with them. I would sometimes say to them, I wished I could be as free as they would be when they got to be men. "You will be free as soon as you are twenty-one, *but I am a slave for life!* Have not I as good a right to be free as you have?" These words used to trouble them; they would express for me the liveliest sympathy, and console me with the hope that something would occur by which I might be free.

I was now about twelve years old, and the thought of being *a slave for life* began to bear heavily upon my heart. Just about this time, I got hold of a book entitled "The Columbian Orator." Every opportunity I got, I used to read this book. Among much of other interesting matter, I found in it a dialogue between a master and his slave. The slave was represented as having run away from his master three times. The dialogue represented the conversation which took place between them, when the slave was retaken the third time. In this dialogue, the whole argument in behalf of slavery was brought forward by the master, all of which was disposed of by the slave. The slave was made to say some very smart as well as impressive things in reply to his master—things which had the desired though unexpected effect; for the conversation resulted in the voluntary emancipation of the slave on the part of the master.

In the same book, I met with one of Sheridan's mighty speeches on and in behalf of Catholic emancipation. These were choice documents to me. I read them over and over again with **unabated** interest. They gave tongue to interesting thoughts of my own soul, which had frequently flashed through my mind, and died away for

....

unabated with full force

want of utterance. The moral which I gained from the dialogue was the power of truth over the conscience of even a slaveholder. What I got from Sheridan was a bold **denunciation** of slavery, and a powerful **vindication** of human rights. The reading of these documents enabled me to utter my thoughts, and to meet the arguments brought forward to sustain slavery; but while they relieved me of one difficulty, they brought on another even more painful than the one of which I was relieved. The more I read, the more I was led to abhor and detest my enslavers. I could regard them in no other light than a band of successful robbers, who had left their homes, and gone to Africa, and stolen us from our homes, and in a strange land reduced us to slavery. I loathed them as being the meanest as well as the most wicked of men. As I read and contemplated the subject, behold! that very discontentment which Master Hugh had predicted would follow my learning to read had already come, to torment and sting my soul to unutterable anguish. As I writhed under it, I would at times feel that learning to read had been a curse rather than a blessing. It had given me a view of my wretched condition, without the remedy. It opened my eyes to the horrible pit, but to no ladder upon which to get out. In moments of agony, I envied my fellow-slaves for their stupidity. I have often wished myself a beast. I preferred the condition of the

denunciation a public accusation
vindication the justification of a claim

meanest reptile to my own. Any thing, no matter what, to get rid of thinking! It was this everlasting thinking of my condition that tormented me. There was no getting rid of it. It was pressed upon me by every object within sight or hearing, animate or inanimate. The silver trump of freedom had roused my soul to eternal wakefulness. Freedom now appeared, to disappear no more forever. It was heard in every sound, and seen in every thing. It was ever present to torment me with a sense of my wretched condition. I saw nothing without seeing it, I heard nothing without hearing it, and felt nothing without feeling it. It looked from every star, it smiled in every calm, breathed in every wind, and moved in every storm.

I often found myself regretting my own existence, and wishing myself dead; and but for the hope of being free, I have no doubt but that I should have killed myself, or done something for which I should have been killed. While in this state of mind, I was eager to hear any one speak of slavery. I was a ready listener. Every little while, I could hear something about the abolitionists. It was some time before I found what the word meant. It was always used in such connections as to make it an interesting word to me. If a slave ran away and succeeded in getting clear, or if a slave killed his master, set fire to a barn, or did any thing very wrong in the mind of a slaveholder, it was spoken of as the fruit of *abolition*. Hearing the word in this connection very often, I set about learning what it meant. The dictionary afforded me little or no help. I found it was "the act of abolishing;" but then I did not know what was to be abolished. Here I was perplexed. I did not dare to ask any one about its meaning, for I was satisfied that it was something they wanted me to know very little about. After a patient waiting, I got one of our city papers, containing an account of the number of petitions from the north, praying for the abolition of slavery in the District of Columbia, and of the slave trade between the States. From this time I understood the words *abolition* and *abolitionist*, and always drew near when that word was spoken, expecting to hear something of importance to myself and fellow-slaves. The light broke in upon me by degrees. I went one day down on the wharf of Mr. Waters; and seeing two Irishmen unloading a scow of stone, I went, unasked, and helped them. When we had finished, one of them came to me and asked me if I were a slave. I told him I was. He asked, "Are ye a slave for life?" I told him that I was. The good Irishman seemed to be deeply affected by the statement. He said to the other that it was a pity so fine a little fellow as myself should be a slave for life. He said it was a shame to hold me. They both advised me to run away to the north; that I should find friends there, and that I should be free. I pretended not to be interested in what they said, and treated them as if I did not understand them; for I feared they might be **treacherous**. White men

....

treacherous dangerous

have been known to encourage slaves to escape, and then, to get the reward, catch them and return them to their masters. I was afraid that these seemingly good men might use me so; but I nevertheless remembered their advice, and from that time I resolved to run away. I looked forward to a time at which it would be safe for me to escape. I was too young to think of doing so immediately; besides, I wished to learn how to write, as I might have occasion to write my own pass. I consoled myself with the hope that I should one day find a good chance. Meanwhile, I would learn to write.

The idea as to how I might learn to write was suggested to me by being in Durgin and Bailey's ship-yard, and frequently seeing the ship carpenters, after **hewing**, and getting a piece of timber ready for use, write on the timber the name of that part of the ship for which it was intended. When a piece of timber was intended for the larboard side, it would be marked thus—"L." When a piece was for the starboard side, it would be marked thus—"S." A piece for the larboard side forward, would be marked thus—"L. F." When a piece was for starboard side forward, it would be marked thus—"S. F." For larboard aft, it would be marked thus—"L. A." For starboard aft, it would be marked thus—"S. A." I soon learned the names of these letters, and for what they were intended when placed upon a piece of timber in the ship-yard. I immediately commenced copying them, and in a short time was able to make the four letters

hewing cutting

named. After that, when I met with any boy who I knew could write, I would tell him I could write as well as he. The next word would be, "I don't believe you. Let me see you try it." I would then make the letters which I had been so fortunate as to learn, and ask him to beat that. In this way I got a good many lessons in writing, which it is quite possible I should never have gotten in any other way. During this time, my copy-book was the board fence, brick wall, and pavement; my pen and ink was a lump of chalk. With these, I learned mainly how to write. I then commenced and continued copying the Italics in Webster's Spelling Book, until I could make them all without looking on the book. By this time, my little Master Thomas had gone to school, and learned how to write, and had written over a number of copy-books. These had been brought home, and shown to some of our near neighbors, and then laid aside. My mistress used to go to class meeting at the Wilk Street meetinghouse every Monday afternoon, and leave me to take care of the house. When left thus, I used to spend the time in writing in the spaces left in Master Thomas's copy-book, copying what he had written. I continued to do this until I could write a hand very similar to that of Master Thomas. Thus, after a long, tedious effort for years, I finally succeeded in learning how to write.

Chapter X

I had left Master Thomas's house, and went to live with Mr. Covey, on the 1st of January, 1833. I was now, for the first time in my life, a field hand. In my new employment, I found myself even more awkward than a country boy appeared to be in a large city. I had been at my new home but one week before Mr. Covey gave me a very severe whipping, cutting my back, causing the blood to run, and raising ridges on my flesh as large as my little finger. The details of this affair are as follows: Mr. Covey sent me, very early in the morning of one of our coldest days in the month of January, to the woods, to get a load of wood. He gave me a team of unbroken oxen. He told me which was the in-hand ox, and which the off-hand one. He then tied the end of a large rope around the horns of the in-hand ox, and gave me the other end of it, and told me, if the oxen started to run, that I must hold on upon the rope. I had never driven oxen before, and of course I was very awkward. I, however, succeeded in getting to the edge of the woods with little difficulty; but I had got a very few rods into the woods, when the oxen took fright, and started full tilt, carrying the cart against trees, and over stumps, in the most frightful manner. I expected every moment that my brains would be dashed out against the trees. After running thus for a considerable distance, they finally upset the cart, dashing it with great force against a tree, and threw themselves into a dense thicket. How I escaped death, I do not know. There I was, entirely alone, in a thick wood, in a place new to me. My cart was upset and shattered, my oxen were entangled among the young trees, and there was none to help me. After a long spell of effort, I succeeded in getting my cart righted, my oxen disentangled, and again yoked to the cart. I now proceeded with my team to the place where I had, the day before, been chopping wood, and loaded my cart pretty heavily, thinking in this way to tame my oxen. I then proceeded on my way home. I had now consumed one half of the day. I got out of the woods safely, and now felt out of danger. I stopped my oxen to open the woods gate; and just as I did so, before I could get hold of my ox-rope, the oxen again started, rushed through the gate, catching it between the wheel and the body of the cart, tearing it to pieces, and coming within a few inches of crushing me against the gate-post. Thus twice, in one short day, I escaped death by the merest chance. On my return, I told Mr. Covey what had happened, and how it happened. He ordered me to return to the woods again immediately. I did so, and he followed on after me. Just as I got into the woods, he came up and told me to stop my cart, and that he would teach me how to **trifle** away my time, and break gates. He then went to a large gum-tree, and with his axe cut three large switches, and, after trimming them up

trifle waste

neatly with his pocketknife, he ordered me to take off my clothes. I made him no answer, but stood with my clothes on. He repeated his order. I still made him no answer, nor did I move to strip myself. Upon this he rushed at me with the fierceness of a tiger, tore off my clothes, and lashed me till he had worn out his switches, cutting me so savagely as to leave the marks visible for a long time after. This whipping was the first of a number just like it, and for similar offences.

I lived with Mr. Covey one year. During the first six months, of that year, scarce a week passed without his whipping me. I was seldom free from a sore back. My awkwardness was almost always his excuse for whipping me. We were worked fully up to the point of endurance. Long before day we were up, our horses fed, and by the first approach of day we were off to the field with our hoes and ploughing teams. Mr. Covey gave us enough to eat, but scarce time to eat it. We were often less than five minutes taking our meals. We were often in the field from the first approach of day till its last lingering ray had left us; and at saving-fodder time, midnight often caught us in the field binding blades.

Covey would be out with us. The way he used to stand it, was this. He would spend the most of his afternoons in bed. He would then come out fresh in the evening, ready to urge us on with his words, example, and frequently with the whip. Mr. Covey was one of the few slaveholders who could and did work with his hands. He was a hard-working man. He knew by himself just what a man or a boy could do. There was no deceiving him. His work went on in his absence almost as well as in his presence; and he had the faculty of making us feel that he was ever present with us. This he did by surprising us. He seldom approached the spot where we were at work openly, if he could do it secretly. He always aimed at taking us by surprise. Such was his cunning, that we used to call him, among ourselves, "the snake." When we were at work in the cornfield, he would sometimes crawl on his hands and knees to avoid detection, and all at once he would rise nearly in our midst, and scream out, "Ha, ha! Come, come! Dash on, dash on!" This being his mode of attack, it was never safe to stop a single minute. His comings were like a thief in the night. He appeared to us as being ever at hand. He was under every tree, behind every stump, in every bush, and at every window, on the plantation. He would sometimes mount his horse, as if bound to St. Michael's, a distance of seven miles, and in half an hour afterwards you would see him coiled up in the corner of the wood-fence, watching every motion of the slaves. He would, for this purpose, leave his horse tied up in the woods. Again, he would sometimes walk up to us, and give us orders as though he was upon the point of starting on a long journey, turn his back upon us, and make as though he was going to the house to get ready; and, before he would get half way thither, he would turn short and crawl into a fence-corner, or behind some tree, and there watch us till the going down of the sun.

Mr. Covey's *forte* consisted in his power to deceive. His life was devoted to planning and perpetrating the grossest deceptions. Every thing he possessed in the shape of learning or religion, he made conform to his disposition to deceive. He seemed to think himself equal to deceiving the Almighty. He would make a short prayer in the morning, and a long prayer at night; and, strange as it may seem, few men would at times appear more devotional than he. The exercises of his family devotions were always commenced with singing; and, as he was a very poor singer himself, the duty of raising the hymn generally came upon me. He would read his hymn, and nod at me to commence. I would at times do so; at others, I would not. My non-compliance would almost always produce much confusion. To show himself independent of me, he would start and stagger through with his hymn in the most **discordant** manner. In this state of mind, he prayed with more than ordinary spirit. Poor man! such was his disposition, and success at deceiving, I do verily believe that he sometimes deceived himself into the solemn belief, that he was a sincere worshipper of the most high God; and this, too, at a time when he may be said to have been guilty of

....

forte strength; specialty
discordant off-key; harsh-sounding

compelling his woman slave to commit the sin of adultery. The facts in the case are these: Mr. Covey was a poor man; he was just commencing in life; he was only able to buy one slave; and, shocking as is the fact, he bought her, as he said, for *a breeder*. This woman was named Caroline. Mr. Covey bought her from Mr. Thomas Lowe, about six miles from St. Michael's. She was a large, able-bodied woman, about twenty years old. She had already given birth to one child, which proved her to be just what he wanted. After buying her, he hired a married man of Mr. Samuel Harrison, to live with him one year; and him he used to fasten up with her every night! The result was, that, at the end of the year, the miserable woman gave birth to twins. At this result Mr. Covey seemed to be highly pleased, both with the man and the wretched woman. Such was his joy, and that of his wife, that nothing they could do for Caroline during her confinement was too good, or too hard, to be done. The children were regarded as being quite an addition to his wealth.

If at any one time of my life more than another, I was made to drink the bitterest **dregs** of slavery, that time was during the first six months of my stay with Mr. Covey. We were worked in all weathers. It was never too hot or too cold; it could never rain, blow, hail, or snow, too hard for us to work in the field. Work, work, work, was scarcely more the order of the day than of the night. The longest

....
dregs the less-pleasant residue at the bottom of a drink

days were too short for him, and the shortest nights too long for him. I was somewhat unmanageable when I first went there, but a few months of this discipline tamed me. Mr. Covey succeeded in breaking me. I was broken in body, soul, and spirit. My natural elasticity was crushed, my intellect languished, the disposition to read departed, the cheerful spark that lingered about my eye died; the dark night of slavery closed in upon me; and behold a man transformed into a brute!

Sunday was my only leisure time. I spent this in a sort of beast-like stupor, between sleep and wake, under some large tree. At times I would rise up, a flash of energetic freedom would dart through my soul, accompanied with a faint beam of hope, that flickered for a moment, and then vanished. I sank down again, mourning over my wretched condition. I was sometimes prompted to take my life, and that of Covey, but was prevented by a combination of hope and fear. My sufferings on this plantation seem now like a dream rather than a stern reality.

Our house stood within a few rods of the Chesapeake Bay, whose broad bosom was ever white with sails from every quarter of the habitable globe. Those beautiful vessels, robed in purest white, so delightful to the eye of freemen, were to me so many shrouded ghosts, to terrify and torment me with thoughts of my wretched condition. I have often, in the deep stillness of a summer's Sabbath, stood all alone upon the lofty banks of that noble bay, and traced, with saddened heart and tearful eye, the countless number of sails moving off to the mighty ocean. The sight of these always affected me powerfully. My thoughts would compel utterance; and there, with no audience but the Almighty, I would pour out my soul's complaint, in my rude way, with an **apostrophe** to the moving multitude of ships:—

"You are loosed from your **moorings**, and are free; I am fast in my chains, and am a slave! You move merrily before the gentle gale, and I sadly before the bloody whip! You are freedom's swift-winged angels, that fly round the world; I am confined in bands of iron! O that I were free! O, that I were on one of your gallant decks, and under your protecting wing! Alas! betwixt me and you, the **turbid** waters roll. Go on, go on. O that I could also go! Could I but swim! If I could fly! O, why was I born a man, of whom to make a brute! The glad ship is gone; she hides in the dim distance. I am left in the hottest hell of unending slavery. O God, save me! God, deliver me! Let me be free! Is there any God? Why am I a slave? I will run away. I will not stand it. Get caught, or get clear, I'll try it. I had as well die with ague as the fever. I have only one life to lose. I had as well be killed running as die standing. Only think of it; one hundred miles straight north, and I am free! Try it? Yes! God helping me, I will. It cannot be that I shall live and

....

apostrophe an aside that addresses an abstract object
moorings places where boats or ships are tied up
turbid dark; full of turmoil

die a slave. I will take to the water. This very bay shall yet bear me into freedom. The steamboats steered in a northeast course from North Point. I will do the same; and when I get to the head of the bay, I will turn my canoe adrift, and walk straight through Delaware into Pennsylvania. When I get there, I shall not be required to have a pass; I can travel without being disturbed. Let but the first opportunity offer, and, come what will, I am off. Meanwhile, I will try to bear up under the yoke. I am not the only slave in the world. Why should I fret? I can bear as much as any of them. Besides, I am but a boy, and all boys are bound to some one. It may be that my misery in slavery will only increase my happiness when I get free. There is a better day coming."

Thus I used to think, and thus I used to speak to myself; **goaded** almost to madness at one moment, and at the next reconciling myself to my wretched lot.

I have already intimated that my condition was much worse, during the first six months of my stay at Mr. Covey's, than in the last six. The circumstances leading to the change in Mr. Covey's course toward me form an epoch in my humble history. You have seen how a man was made a slave; you shall see how a slave was made a man. On one of the hottest days of the month of August, 1833, Bill Smith, William Hughes, a slave named Eli, and myself,

---

goaded prodded or prompted

were engaged in fanning wheat. Hughes was clearing the fanned wheat from before the fan. Eli was turning, Smith was feeding, and I was carrying wheat to the fan. The work was simple, requiring strength rather than intellect; yet, to one entirely unused to such work, it came very hard. About three o'clock of that day, I broke down; my strength failed me; I was seized with a violent aching of the head, attended with extreme dizziness; I trembled in every limb. Finding what was coming, I nerved myself up, feeling it would never do to stop work. I stood as long as I could stagger to the hopper with grain. When I could stand no longer, I fell, and felt as if held down by an immense weight. The fan of course stopped; every one had his own work to do; and no one could do the work of the other, and have his own go on at the same time.

Mr. Covey was at the house, about one hundred yards from the treading-yard where we were fanning. On hearing the fan stop, he left immediately, and came to the spot where we were. He hastily inquired what the matter was. Bill answered that I was sick, and there was no one to bring wheat to the fan. I had by this time crawled away under the side of the post and rail-fence by which the yard was enclosed, hoping to find relief by getting out of the sun. He then asked where I was. He was told by one of the hands. He came to the spot, and, after looking at me awhile, asked me what was the matter. I told him as well as I could, for I scarce had strength to speak. He then gave me a savage kick in the side, and told me to get up. I tried to do so, but fell back in the attempt. He gave me another kick, and again told me to rise. I again tried, and succeeded in gaining my feet; but, stooping to get the tub with which I was feeding the fan, I again staggered and fell. While down in this situation, Mr. Covey took up the hickory slat with which Hughes had been striking off the half-bushel measure, and with it gave me a heavy blow upon the head, making a large wound, and the blood ran freely; and with this again told me to get up. I made no effort to comply, having now made up my mind to let him do his worst. In a short time after receiving this blow, my head grew better. Mr. Covey had now left me to my fate. At this moment I resolved, for the first time, to go to my master, enter a complaint, and ask his protection. In order to do this, I must that afternoon walk seven miles; and this, under the circumstances, was truly a severe undertaking. I was exceedingly feeble; made so as much by the kicks and blows which I received, as by the severe fit of sickness to which I had been subjected. I, however, watched my chance, while Covey was looking in an opposite direction, and started for St. Michael's. I succeeded in getting a considerable distance on my way to the woods, when Covey discovered me, and called after me to come back, threatening what he would do if I did not come. I disregarded both his calls and his threats, and made my way to the woods as fast as my feeble state would allow;

and thinking I might be overhauled by him if I kept the road, I walked through the woods, keeping far enough from the road to avoid detection, and near enough to prevent losing my way. I had not gone far before my little strength again failed me. I could go no farther. I fell down, and lay for a considerable time. The blood was yet oozing from the wound on my head. For a time I thought I should bleed to death; and think now that I should have done so, but that the blood so matted my hair as to stop the wound. After lying there about three quarters of an hour, I nerved myself up again, and started on my way, through bogs and briers, barefooted and bareheaded, tearing my feet sometimes at nearly every step; and after a journey of about seven miles, occupying some five hours to perform it, I arrived at master's store. I then presented an appearance enough to affect any but a heart of iron. From the crown of my head to my feet, I was covered with blood. My hair was all clotted with dust and blood; my shirt was stiff with blood. I suppose I looked like a man who had escaped a den of wild beasts, and barely escaped them. In this state I appeared before my master, humbly entreating him to **interpose** his authority for my protection. I told him all the circumstances as well as I could, and it seemed, as I spoke, at times to affect him. He would then walk the floor, and seek to justify Covey by saying he expected I deserved it. He

---

interpose to intervene

asked me what I wanted. I told him, to let me get a new home; that as sure as I lived with Mr. Covey again, I should live with but to die with him; that Covey would surely kill me; he was in a fair way for it. Master Thomas ridiculed the idea that there was any danger of Mr. Covey's killing me, and said that he knew Mr. Covey; that he was a good man, and that he could not think of taking me from him; that, should he do so, he would lose the whole year's wages; that I belonged to Mr. Covey for one year, and that I must go back to him, come what might; and that I must not trouble him with any more stories, or that he would himself *get hold of me*. After threatening me thus, he gave me a very large dose of salts, telling me that I might remain in St. Michael's that night, (it being quite late,) but that I must be off back to Mr. Covey's early in the morning; and that if I did not, he would *get hold of me*, which meant that he would whip me. I remained all night, and, according to his orders, I started off to Covey's in the morning, (Saturday morning,) wearied in body and broken in spirit. I got no supper that night, or breakfast that morning. I reached Covey's about nine o'clock; and just as I was getting over the fence that divided Mrs. Kemp's fields from ours, out ran Covey with his cowskin, to give me another whipping. Before he could reach me, I succeeded in getting to the cornfield; and as the corn was very high, it afforded me the means of hiding. He seemed very angry, and searched for me a long time. My behavior was altogether unaccountable.

He finally gave up the chase, thinking, I suppose, that I must come home for something to eat; he would give himself no further trouble in looking for me. I spent that day mostly in the woods, having the alternative before me,—to go home and be whipped to death, or stay in the woods and be starved to death. That night, I fell in with Sandy Jenkins, a slave with whom I was somewhat acquainted. Sandy had a free wife who lived about four miles from Mr. Covey's; and it being Saturday, he was on his way to see her. I told him my circumstances, and he very kindly invited me to go home with him. I went home with him, and talked this whole matter over, and got his advice as to what course it was best for me to pursue. I found Sandy an old adviser. He told me, with great solemnity, I must go back to Covey; but that before I went, I must go with him into another part of the woods, where there was a certain *root*, which, if I would take some of it with me, carrying it *always on my right side*, would render it impossible for Mr. Covey, or any other white man, to whip me. He said he had carried it for years; and since he had done so, he had never received a blow, and never expected to while he carried it. I at first rejected the idea, that the simple carrying of a root in my pocket would have any such effect as he had said, and was not disposed to take it; but Sandy impressed the necessity with much earnestness, telling me it could do no harm, if it did no good. To please him, I at length took the root, and, according to his direction, carried it upon my right side. This was Sunday morning. I immediately started for home; and upon entering the yard gate, out came Mr. Covey on his way to meeting. He spoke to me very kindly, bade me drive the pigs from a lot near by, and passed on towards the church. Now, this singular conduct of Mr. Covey really made me begin to think that there was something in the *root* which Sandy had given me; and had it been on any other day than Sunday, I could have attributed the conduct to no other cause than the influence of that root; and as it was, I was half inclined to think the *root* to be something more than I at first had taken it to be. All went well till Monday morning. On this morning, the virtue of the *root* was fully tested. Long before daylight, I was called to go and rub, curry, and feed, the horses. I obeyed, and was glad to obey. But whilst thus engaged, whilst in the act of throwing down some blades from the loft, Mr. Covey entered the stable with a long rope; and just as I was half out of the loft, he caught hold of my legs, and was about tying me. As soon as I found what he was up to, I gave a sudden spring, and as I did so, he holding to my legs, I was brought sprawling on the stable floor. Mr. Covey seemed now to think he had me, and could do what he pleased; but at this moment— from whence came the spirit I don't know—I resolved to fight; and, suiting my action to the resolution, I seized Covey hard by the throat; and as I did so, I rose. He held on to me, and I to him. My resistance was so entirely unexpected that Covey seemed taken all aback. He trembled like a leaf. This gave me assurance, and I held him uneasy, causing the blood to run where I touched him with the ends of my fingers. Mr. Covey soon called out to Hughes for help. Hughes came, and, while Covey held me, attempted to tie my right hand. While he was in the act of doing so, I watched my chance, and gave him a heavy kick close under the ribs. This kick fairly sickened Hughes, so that he left me in the hands of Mr. Covey. This kick had the effect of not only weakening Hughes, but Covey also. When he saw Hughes bending over with pain, his courage **quailed**. He asked me if I meant to persist in my resistance. I told him I did, come what might; that he had used me like a brute for six months, and that I was determined to be used so no longer. With that, he strove to drag me to a stick that was lying just out of the stable door. He meant to knock me down. But just as he was leaning over to get the stick, I seized him with both hands by his collar, and brought him by a sudden snatch to the ground. By this time, Bill came. Covey called upon him for assistance. Bill wanted to know what he could do. Covey said, "Take hold of him, take hold of him!" Bill said his master hired him out to work, and not to help to whip me; so he left Covey and myself to fight our own battle out. We were at it for nearly two hours. Covey at length let me go, puffing and blowing at a great rate, saying that if I had not resisted, he

....

quailed cowered

would not have whipped me half so much. The truth was, that he had not whipped me at all. I considered him as getting entirely the worst end of the bargain; for he had drawn no blood from me, but I had from him. The whole six months afterwards, that I spent with Mr. Covey, he never laid the weight of his finger upon me in anger. He would occasionally say, he didn't want to get hold of me again. "No," thought I, "you need not; for you will come off worse than you did before."

This battle with Mr. Covey was the turning-point in my career as a slave. It rekindled the few expiring embers of freedom, and revived within me a sense of my own manhood. It recalled the departed self-confidence, and inspired me again with a determination to be free. The gratification afforded by the triumph was a full compensation for whatever else might follow, even death itself. He only can understand the deep satisfaction which I experienced, who has himself repelled by force the bloody arm of slavery. I felt as I never felt before. It was a glorious resurrection, from the tomb of slavery, to the heaven of freedom. My long-crushed spirit rose, cowardice departed, bold defiance took its place; and I now resolved that, however long I might remain a slave in form, the day had passed forever when I could be a slave in fact. I did not hesitate to let it be known of me, that the white man who expected to succeed in whipping, must also succeed in killing me.

From this time I was never again what might be called fairly whipped, though I remained a slave four years afterwards. I had several fights, but was never whipped.

It was for a long time a matter of surprise to me why Mr. Covey did not immediately have me taken by the constable to the whipping-post, and there regularly whipped for the crime of raising my hand against a white man in defence of myself. And the only explanation I can now think of does not entirely satisfy me; but such as it is, I will give it. Mr. Covey enjoyed the most unbounded reputation for being a first-rate overseer and negro-breaker. It was of considerable importance to him. That reputation was at stake; and had he sent me—a boy about sixteen years old—to the public whipping-post, his reputation would have been lost; so, to save his reputation, he suffered me to go unpunished.

My term of actual service to Mr. Edward Covey ended on Christmas day, 1833. The days between Christmas and New Year's day are allowed as holidays; and, accordingly, we were not required to perform any labor, more than to feed and take care of the stock. This time we regarded as our own, by the grace of our masters; and we therefore used or abused it nearly as we pleased. Those of us who had families at a distance, were generally allowed to spend the whole six days in their society. This time, however, was spent in various ways. The staid, sober, thinking and industrious ones of our number would employ themselves in making corn-brooms, mats, horse-collars, and baskets; and another class of us would spend the time in hunting opossums, hares, and coons. But by far the larger part engaged in such sports and merriments as playing ball, wrestling, running foot-races, fiddling, dancing, and drinking whisky; and this latter mode of spending the time was by far the most agreeable to the feelings of our masters. A slave who would work during the holidays was considered by our masters as scarcely deserving them. He was regarded as one who rejected the favor of his master. It was deemed a disgrace not to get drunk at Christmas; and he was regarded as lazy indeed, who had not provided himself with the necessary means, during the year, to get whisky enough to last him through Christmas.

From what I know of the effect of these holidays upon the slave, I believe them to be among the most effective means in the hands of the slaveholder in keeping down the spirit of insurrection. Were the slaveholders at once to abandon this practice, I have not the slightest doubt it would lead to an immediate insurrection among the slaves. These holidays serve as conductors, or safety-valves, to carry off the rebellious spirit of enslaved humanity. But for these, the slave would be forced up to the wildest desperation; and woe betide the slaveholder, the day he ventures to remove or hinder the operation of those conductors! I warn him that, in such an event, a spirit will go forth in their midst, more to be dreaded than the most appalling earthquake.

The holidays are part and parcel of the gross fraud, wrong, and inhumanity of slavery. They are professedly a custom established by the benevolence of the slaveholders; but I undertake to say, it is the result of selfishness, and one of the grossest frauds committed upon the down-trodden slave. They do not give the slaves this time because they would not like to have their work during its continuance, but because they know it would be unsafe to deprive them of it. This will be seen by the fact, that the slaveholders like to have their slaves spend those days just in such a manner as to make them as glad of their ending as of their beginning. Their object seems to be, to disgust their slaves with freedom, by plunging them into the lowest depths of dissipation. For instance, the slaveholders not only like to see the slave drink of his own accord, but will adopt various plans to make him drunk. One plan is, to make bets on their slaves, as to who can drink the most whisky without getting drunk; and in this way they succeed in getting whole multitudes to drink to excess. Thus, when the slave asks for virtuous freedom, the cunning slaveholder, knowing his ignorance, cheats him with a dose of vicious dissipation, artfully labelled with the name of liberty. The most of us used to drink it down, and the result was just what might be supposed; many of us were led to think that there was little to choose between liberty and slavery. We felt, and very properly too, that we had almost as well be slaves to man as to rum. So, when the holidays ended, we staggered up from the filth of our wallowing, took a long breath, and marched to the field,—feeling, upon the whole, rather glad to go, from what our master had deceived us into a belief was freedom, back to the arms of slavery.

I have said that this mode of treatment is a part of the whole system of fraud and inhumanity of slavery. It is so. The mode here adopted to disgust the slave with freedom, by allowing him to see only the abuse of it, is carried out in other things. For instance, a slave loves molasses; he steals some. His master, in many cases, goes off to town, and buys a large quantity; he returns, takes his whip, and commands the slave to eat the molasses, until the poor fellow is made sick at the very mention of it. The same mode is sometimes adopted to make the slaves refrain from asking for more food than their regular allowance. A slave runs through his allowance, and applies for more. His master is enraged at him; but, not willing to send him off without food, gives him more than is necessary, and compels him to eat it within a given time. Then, if he complains that he cannot eat it, he is said to be satisfied neither full nor fasting, and is whipped for being hard to please! I have an abundance of such illustrations of the same principle, drawn from my own observation, but think the cases I have cited sufficient. The practice is a very common one.

On the first of January, 1834, I left Mr. Covey, and went to live with Mr. William Freeland, who lived about three miles from St. Michael's. I soon found Mr. Freeland a very different man from Mr. Covey. Though not rich, he was what would be called an educated southern gentleman. Mr. Covey, as I have shown, was a well-trained negro-breaker and slave-driver. The former (slaveholder though he was) seemed to possess some regard for honor, some reverence for justice, and some respect for humanity. The latter seemed totally insensible to all such sentiments. Mr. Freeland had many of the faults peculiar to slaveholders, such as being very passionate and fretful; but I must do him the justice to say, that he was exceedingly free from those degrading vices to which Mr. Covey was constantly addicted. The one was open and frank, and we always knew where to find him. The other was a most artful deceiver, and could be understood only by such as were skilful enough to detect his cunningly-devised frauds. Another advantage I gained in my new master was, he made no pretensions to, or profession of, religion; and this, in my opinion, was truly a great advantage. I assert most unhesitatingly, that the religion of the south is a mere covering for the most horrid crimes,—a justifier of the most appalling barbarity,—a sanctifier of the most hateful frauds,—and a dark shelter under, which the darkest, foulest, grossest, and most infernal deeds of slaveholders find the strongest protection. Were I to be again reduced to the chains of slavery, next to that enslavement, I should regard being the slave of a religious master the greatest calamity that could befall me. For of all slaveholders with whom I have ever met, religious slaveholders are the worst. I have ever found them the meanest and basest, the most cruel and cowardly, of all others. It was my unhappy lot not only to belong to a religious slaveholder, but to live in a community of such religionists. Very near Mr. Freeland lived the Rev. Daniel Weeden, and in the same neighborhood lived the Rev. Rigby Hopkins. These were members and ministers in the Reformed Methodist Church. Mr. Weeden owned, among others, a woman slave, whose name I have forgotten. This woman's back, for weeks, was kept literally raw, made so by the lash of this merciless, *religious* wretch. He used to hire hands. His maxim was, Behave well or behave ill, it is the duty of a master occasionally to whip a slave, to remind him of his master's authority. Such was his theory, and such his practice.

Mr. Hopkins was even worse than Mr. Weeden. His chief boast was his ability to manage slaves. The peculiar feature of his government was that of whipping slaves in advance of deserving it. He always managed to have one or more of his slaves to whip every Monday morning. He did this to alarm their fears, and strike terror into those who escaped. His plan was to whip for the smallest offences, to prevent the commission of large ones. Mr. Hopkins could always find some excuse for whipping a slave. It would astonish one, unaccustomed to a slaveholding life, to see with what wonderful ease a slaveholder can find things, of which to make occasion to whip a slave. A mere look, word, or motion,—a mistake, accident, or want of power,—are all matters for which a slave may be whipped at any time. Does a slave look dissatisfied? It is said, he has the devil in him, and it must be whipped out. Does he speak loudly when spoken to by his master? Then he is getting high-minded, and should be taken down a button-hole lower. Does he forget to pull off his hat at the approach of a white person? Then he is wanting in reverence, and should be whipped for it. Does he ever venture to vindicate his conduct, when **censured** for it? Then he is guilty of **impudence**,—one of the greatest crimes of which a slave can be guilty. Does he ever venture to suggest a different mode of doing things from that pointed out by his master? He is indeed presumptuous, and getting above himself; and nothing less than a flogging will do for him. Does for it a slave must always be whipped. Mr. Hopkins could always find something of this sort to justify the use of the lash, and he seldom failed to embrace such opportunities. There was not a man in the whole county, with whom the slaves who had the getting their own home, would not prefer to live, rather than with this Rev. Mr. Hopkins. And yet there was

censured rebuked; punished
impudence disrespect

not a man any where round, who made higher professions of religion, or was more active in revivals,—more attentive to the class, love-feast, prayer and preaching meetings, or more devotional in his family,—that prayed earlier, later, louder, and longer,—than this same reverend slave-driver, Rigby Hopkins.

But to return to Mr. Freeland, and to my experience while in his employment. He, like Mr. Covey, gave us enough to eat; but, unlike Mr. Covey, he also gave us sufficient time to take our meals. He worked us hard, but always between sunrise and sunset. He required a good deal of work to be done, but gave us good tools with which to work. His farm was large, but he employed hands enough to work it, and with ease, compared with many of his neighbors. My treatment, while in his employment, was heavenly, compared with what I experienced at the hands of Mr. Edward Covey.

Mr. Freeland was himself the owner of but two slaves. Their names were Henry Harris and John Harris. The rest of his hands he hired. These consisted of myself, Sandy Jenkins,* and Handy Caldwell.

Henry and John were quite intelligent, and in a very little while after I went there, I succeeded in creating in

---

* This is the same man who gave me the roots to prevent my being whipped by Mr. Covey. He was "a clever soul." We used frequently to talk about the fight with Covey, and as often as we did so, he would claim my success as the result of the roots which he gave me. This superstition is very common among the more ignorant slaves. A slave seldom dies but that his death is attributed to trickery.

them a strong desire to learn how to read. This desire soon sprang up in the others also. They very soon mustered up some old spelling-books, and nothing would do but that I must keep a Sabbath school. I agreed to do so, and accordingly devoted my Sundays to teaching these my loved fellow-slaves how to read. Neither of them knew his letters when I went there. Some of the slaves of the neighboring farms found what was going on, and also **availed** themselves of this little opportunity to learn to read. It was understood, among all who came, that there must be as little display about it as possible. It was necessary to keep our religious masters at St. Michael's unacquainted with the fact, that, instead of spending the Sabbath in wrestling, boxing, and drinking whisky, we were trying to learn how to read the will of God; for they had much rather see us engaged in those degrading sports, than to see us behaving like intellectual, moral, and accountable beings. My blood boils as I think of the bloody manner in which Messrs. Wright Fairbanks and Garrison West, both class-leaders, in connection with many others, rushed in upon us with sticks and stones, and broke up our virtuous little Sabbath school, at St. Michael's—all calling themselves Christians! humble followers of the Lord Jesus Christ! But I am again digressing.

I held my Sabbath school at the house of a free colored man, whose name I deem it imprudent to mention; for

availed used or helped

should it be known, it might embarrass him greatly, though
the crime of holding the school was committed ten years
ago. I had at one time over forty scholars, and those of
the right sort, ardently desiring to learn. They were of all
ages, though mostly men and women. I look back to those
Sundays with an amount of pleasure not to be expressed.
They were great days to my soul. The work of instructing
my dear fellow-slaves was the sweetest engagement with
which I was ever blessed. We loved each other, and to leave
them at the close of the Sabbath was a severe cross indeed.
When I think that these precious souls are to-day shut up in
the prison-house of slavery, my feelings overcome me, and
I am almost ready to ask, "Does a righteous God govern
the universe? and for what does he hold the thunders in
his right hand, if not to smite the oppressor, and deliver the
spoiled out of the hand of the spoiler?" These dear souls
came not to Sabbath school because it was popular to do
so, nor did I teach them because it was reputable to be thus
engaged. Every moment they spent in that school, they
were liable to be taken up, and given thirty-nine lashes.
They came because they wished to learn. Their minds had
been starved by their cruel masters. They had been shut
up in mental darkness. I taught them, because it was the
delight of my soul to be doing something that looked like
bettering the condition of my race. I kept up my school
nearly the whole year I lived with Mr. Freeland; and, beside
my Sabbath school, I devoted three evenings in the week,

during the winter, to teaching the slaves at home. And I have the happiness to know, that several of those who came to Sabbath school learned how to read; and that one, at least, is now free through my agency.

The year passed off smoothly. It seemed only about half as long as the year which preceded it. I went through it without receiving a single blow. I will give Mr. Freeland the credit of being the best master I ever had, *till I became my own master.* For the ease with which I passed the year, I was, however, somewhat indebted to the society of my fellow-slaves. They were noble souls; they not only possessed loving hearts, but brave ones. We were linked and interlinked with each other. I loved them with a love stronger than any thing I have experienced since. It is sometimes said that we slaves do not love and confide in each other. In answer to this assertion, I can say, I never loved any or confided in any people more than my fellow-slaves, and especially those with whom I lived at Mr. Freeland's. I believe we would have died for each other. We never undertook to do any thing, of any importance, without a mutual consultation. We never moved separately. We were one; and as much so by our tempers and dispositions, as by the mutual hardships to which we were necessarily subjected by our condition as slaves.

At the close of the year 1834, Mr. Freeland again hired me of my master, for the year 1835. But, by this time, I began to want to live *upon free land* as well as *with Freeland*;

and I was no longer content, therefore, to live with him or any other slaveholder. I began, with the commencement of the year, to prepare myself for a final struggle, which should decide my fate one way or the other. My tendency was upward. I was fast approaching manhood, and year after year had passed, and I was still a slave. These thoughts roused me—I must do something. I therefore resolved that 1835 should not pass without witnessing an attempt, on my part, to secure my liberty. But I was not willing to cherish this determination alone. My fellow-slaves were dear to me. I was anxious to have them participate with me in this, my lifegiving determination. I therefore, though with great prudence, commenced early to ascertain their views and feelings in regard to their condition, and to imbue their minds with thoughts of freedom. I bent myself to devising ways and means for our escape, and meanwhile strove, on all fitting occasions, to impress them with the gross fraud and inhumanity of slavery. I went first to Henry, next to John, then to the others. I found, in them all, warm hearts and noble spirits. They were ready to hear, and ready to act when a feasible plan should be proposed. This was what I wanted. I talked to them of our want of manhood, if we submitted to our enslavement without at least one noble effort to be free. We met often, and consulted frequently, and told our hopes and fears, recounted the difficulties, real and imagined, which we should be called on to meet. At times we were almost disposed to give up, and try to content ourselves with our wretched lot; at others, we were firm and unbending in our determination to go. Whenever we suggested any plan, there was shrinking—the odds were fearful. Our path was beset with the greatest obstacles; and if we succeeded in gaining the end of it, our right to be free was yet questionable—we were yet liable to be returned to bondage. We could see no spot, this side of the ocean, where we could be free. We knew nothing about Canada. Our knowledge of the north did not extend farther than New York; and to go there, and be forever harassed with the frightful liability of being returned to slavery—with the certainty of being treated tenfold worse than before—the thought was truly a horrible one, and one which it was not easy to overcome. The case sometimes stood thus: At every gate through which we were to pass, we saw a watchman— at every ferry a guard—on every bridge a sentinel—and in every wood a patrol. We were hemmed in upon every side. Here were the difficulties, real or imagined—the good to be sought, and the evil to be shunned. On the one hand, there stood slavery, a stern reality, glaring frightfully upon us,— its robes already crimsoned with the blood of millions, and even now feasting itself greedily upon our own flesh. On the other hand, away back in the dim distance, under the flickering light of the north star, behind some craggy hill or snow-covered mountain, stood a doubtful freedom—half frozen—beckoning us to come and share its hospitality. This in itself was sometimes enough to stagger us; but when we permitted ourselves to survey the road, we were frequently appalled. Upon either side we saw grim death, assuming the most horrid shapes. Now it was starvation, causing us to eat our own flesh;—now we were contending with the waves, and were drowned;—now we were overtaken, and torn to pieces by the fangs of the terrible bloodhound. We were stung by scorpions, chased by wild beasts, bitten by snakes, and finally, after having nearly reached the desired spot,—after swimming rivers, encountering wild beasts, sleeping in the woods, suffering hunger and nakedness,— we were overtaken by our pursuers, and, in our resistance, we were shot dead upon the spot! I say, this picture sometimes appalled us, and made us

> "rather bear those ills we had,
> Than fly to others, that we knew not of."

In coming to a fixed determination to run away, we did more than Patrick Henry, when he resolved upon liberty or death. With us it was a doubtful liberty at most, and almost certain death if we failed. For my part, I should prefer death to hopeless bondage.

Sandy, one of our number, gave up the notion, but still encouraged us. Our company then consisted of Henry Harris, John Harris, Henry Bailey, Charles Roberts, and myself. Henry Bailey was my uncle, and belonged to my master. Charles married my aunt: he belonged to my master's father-in-law, Mr. William Hamilton.

The plan we finally concluded upon was, to get a large canoe belonging to Mr. Hamilton, and upon the Saturday night previous to Easter holidays, paddle directly up the Chesapeake Bay. On our arrival at the head of the bay, a distance of seventy or eighty miles from where we lived, it was our purpose to turn our canoe adrift, and follow the guidance of the north star till we got beyond the limits of Maryland. Our reason for taking the water route was, that we were less liable to be suspected as runaways; we hoped to be regarded as fishermen; whereas, if we should take the land route, we should be subjected to interruptions of almost every kind. Any one having a white face, and being so disposed, could stop us, and subject us to examination.

The week before our intended start, I wrote several protections, one for each of us. As well as I can remember, they were in the following words, to wit:—

This is to certify that I, the undersigned, have given the bearer, my servant, full liberty to go to Baltimore, and spend the Easter holidays. Written with mine own hand, &c., 1835.

WILLIAM HAMILTON,
Near St. Michael's, in Talbot county, Maryland.

We were not going to Baltimore; but, in going up the bay, we went toward Baltimore, and these protections were only intended to protect us while on the bay.

As the time drew near for our departure, our anxiety became more and more intense. It was truly a matter of life and death with us. The strength of our determination was about to be fully tested. At this time, I was very active in explaining every difficulty, removing every doubt, dispelling every fear, and inspiring all with the firmness indispensable to success in our undertaking; assuring them that half was gained the instant we made the move; we had talked long enough; we were now ready to move; if not now, we never should be; and if we did not intend to move now, we had as well fold our arms, sit down, and acknowledge ourselves fit only to be slaves. This, none of us were prepared to acknowledge. Every man stood firm; and at our last meeting, we pledged ourselves afresh, in the most solemn manner, that, at the time appointed, we would certainly start in pursuit of freedom. This was in the middle of the week, at the end of which we were to be off. We went, as usual, to our several fields of labor, but with bosoms highly agitated with thoughts of our truly hazardous undertaking. We tried to conceal our feelings as much as possible; and I think we succeeded very well.

After a painful waiting, the Saturday morning, whose night was to witness our departure, came. I hailed it with joy, bring what of sadness it might. Friday night was a sleepless one for me. I probably felt more anxious than the rest, because I was, by common consent, at the head of the whole affair. The responsibility of success or failure lay heavily upon me. The glory of the one, and the confusion of the other, were alike mine. The first two hours of that morning were such as I never experienced before, and hope never to again. Early in the morning, we went, as usual, to the field. We were spreading manure; and all at once, while thus engaged, I was overwhelmed with an indescribable feeling, in the fulness of which I turned to Sandy, who was near by, and said, "We are betrayed!" "Well," said he, "that thought has this moment struck me." We said no more. I was never more certain of any thing.

The horn was blown as usual, and we went up from the field to the house for breakfast. I went for the form, more than for want of any thing to eat that morning. Just as I got to the house, in looking out at the lane gate, I saw four white men, with two colored men. The white men were on horseback, and the colored ones were walking behind, as if tied. I watched them a few moments till they got up to our lane gate. Here they halted, and tied the colored men to the gate-post. I was not yet certain as to what the matter was. In a few moments, in rode Mr. Hamilton, with a speed **betokening** great excitement. He came to the door, and inquired if Master William was in. He was told he was at the barn. Mr. Hamilton, without dismounting,

----

betokening indicating or showing

rode up to the barn with extraordinary speed. In a few moments, he and Mr. Freeland returned to the house. By this time, the three constables rode up, and in great haste dismounted, tied their horses, and met Master William and Mr. Hamilton returning from the barn; and after talking awhile, they all walked up to the kitchen door. There was no one in the kitchen but myself and John. Henry and Sandy were up at the barn. Mr. Freeland put his head in at the door, and called me by name, saying, there were some gentlemen at the door who wished to see me. I stepped to the door, and inquired what they wanted. They at once seized me, and, without giving me any satisfaction, tied me—lashing my hands closely together. I insisted upon knowing what the matter was. They at length said, that they had learned I had been in a "scrape," and that I was to be examined before my master; and if their information proved false, I should not be hurt.

In a few moments, they succeeded in tying John. They then turned to Henry, who had by this time returned, and commanded him to cross his hands. "I won't!" said Henry, in a firm tone, indicating his readiness to meet the consequences of his refusal. "Won't you?" said Tom Graham, the constable. "No, I won't!" said Henry, in a still stronger tone. With this, two of the constables pulled out their shining pistols, and swore, by their Creator, that they would make him cross his hands or kill him. Each cocked his pistol, and, with fingers on the trigger, walked up to

Henry, saying, at the same time, if he did not cross his hands, they would blow his damned heart out. "Shoot me, shoot me!" said Henry; "you can't kill me but once. Shoot, shoot,—and be damned! *I won't be tied!*" This he said in a tone of loud defiance; and at the same time, with a motion as quick as lightning, he with one single stroke dashed the pistols from the hand of each constable. As he did this, all hands fell upon him, and, after beating him some time, they finally overpowered him, and got him tied.

During the scuffle, I managed, I know not how, to get my pass out, and, without being discovered, put it into the fire. We were all now tied; and just as we were to leave for Easton jail, Betsy Freeland, mother of William Freeland, came to the door with her hands full of biscuits, and divided them between Henry and John. She then delivered herself of a speech, to the following effect:—addressing herself to me, she said, *"You devil! You yellow devil!* it was you that put it into the heads of Henry and John to run away. But for you, you long-legged mulatto devil! Henry nor John would never have thought of such a thing." I made no reply, and was immediately hurried off towards St. Michael's. Just a moment previous to the scuffle with Henry, Mr. Hamilton suggested the propriety of making a search for the protections which he had understood Frederick had written for himself and the rest. But, just at the moment he was about carrying his proposal into effect, his aid was needed in helping to tie Henry; and the excitement attending the scuffle caused them either to forget, or to deem it unsafe, under the circumstances, to search. So we were not yet convicted of the intention to run away.

When we got about half way to St. Michael's, while the constables having us in charge were looking ahead, Henry inquired of me what he should do with his pass. I told him to eat it with his biscuit, and own nothing; and we passed the word around, "*Own nothing;*" and "*Own nothing!*" said we all. Our confidence in each other was unshaken. We were resolved to succeed or fail together, after the calamity had befallen us as much as before. We were now prepared for any thing. We were to be dragged that morning fifteen miles behind horses, and then to be placed in the Easton jail. When we reached St. Michael's, we underwent a sort of examination. We all denied that we ever intended to run away. We did this more to bring out the evidence against us, than from any hope of getting clear of being sold; for, as I have said, we were ready for that. The fact was, we cared but little where we went, so we went together. Our greatest concern was about separation. We dreaded that more than any thing this side of death. We found the evidence against us to be the testimony of one person; our master would not tell who it was; but we came to a unanimous decision among ourselves as to who their informant was. We were sent off to the jail at Easton. When we got there, we were delivered up to the sheriff, Mr. Joseph Graham, and by him placed in jail. Henry, John, and myself, were placed in one room together—Charles, and Henry Bailey, in another. Their object in separating us was to hinder **concert**.

We had been in jail scarcely twenty minutes, when a swarm of slave traders, and agents for slave traders, flocked into jail to look at us, and to ascertain if we were for sale. Such a set of beings I never saw before! I felt myself surrounded by so many fiends from **perdition**. A band of pirates never looked more like their father, the devil. They laughed and grinned over us, saying, "Ah, my boys! we have got you, haven't we?" And after taunting us in various ways, they one by one went into an examination of us, with intent to ascertain our value. They would impudently ask us if we would not like to have them for our masters. We would make them no answer, and leave them to find out as best they could. Then they would curse and swear at us, telling us that they could take the devil out of us in a very little while, if we were only in their hands.

While in jail, we found ourselves in much more comfortable quarters than we expected when we went there. We did not get much to eat, nor that which was very good; but we had a good clean room, from the windows of which we could see what was going on in the street, which was very much better than though we had been placed in one of the dark, damp cells. Upon the whole, we got along very well, so far as the jail and its keeper were concerned.

concert working together; unity
perdition damnation; hell

Immediately after the holidays were over, contrary to all our expectations, Mr. Hamilton and Mr. Freeland came up to Easton, and took Charles, the two Henrys, and John, out of jail, and carried them home, leaving me alone. I regarded this separation as a final one. It caused me more pain than any thing else in the whole transaction. I was ready for any thing rather than separation. I supposed that they had consulted together, and had decided that, as I was the whole cause of the intention of the others to run away, it was hard to make the innocent suffer with the guilty; and that they had, therefore, concluded to take the others home, and sell me, as a warning to the others that remained. It is due to the noble Henry to say, he seemed almost as reluctant at leaving the prison as at leaving home to come to the prison. But we knew we should, in all probability, be separated, if we were sold; and since he was in their hands, he concluded to go peaceably home.

I was now left to my fate. I was all alone, and within the walls of a stone prison. But a few days before, and I was full of hope. I expected to have been safe in a land of freedom; but now I was covered with gloom, sunk down to the utmost despair. I thought the possibility of freedom was gone. I was kept in this way about one week, at the end of which, Captain Auld, my master, to my surprise and utter astonishment, came up, and took me out, with the intention of sending me, with a gentleman of his acquaintance, into Alabama. But, from some cause or other, he did not send me to Alabama, but concluded to send me back to Baltimore, to live again with his brother Hugh, and to learn a trade.

Thus, after an absence of three years and one month, I was once more permitted to return to my old home at Baltimore. My master sent me away, because there existed against me a very great prejudice in the community, and he feared I might be killed.

In a few weeks after I went to Baltimore, Master Hugh hired me to Mr. William Gardner, an extensive shipbuilder, on Fell's Point. I was put there to learn how to **calk**. It, however, proved a very unfavorable place for the accomplishment of this object. Mr. Gardner was engaged that spring in building two large man-of-war **brigs**, professedly for the Mexican government. The vessels were to be launched in the July of that year, and in failure thereof, Mr. Gardner was to lose a considerable sum; so that when I entered, all was hurry. There was no time to learn any thing. Every man had to do that which he knew how to do. In entering the shipyard, my orders from Mr. Gardner were, to do whatever the carpenters commanded me to do. This was placing me at the beck and call of about seventy-five men. I was to regard all these as masters. Their word was to be my law. My situation was a most trying one. At times I needed a dozen pair of hands. I was

calk to make watertight
brigs ships

called a dozen ways in the space of a single minute. Three or four voices would strike my ear at the same moment. It was—"Fred., come help me to cant this timber here."—"Fred., come carry this timber yonder."—"Fred., bring that roller here."—"Fred., go get a fresh can of water."—"Fred., come help saw off the end of this timber."—"Fred., go quick, and get the crowbar."—"Fred., hold on the end of this fall."—"Fred., go to the blacksmith's shop, and get a new punch."—"Hurra, Fred! run and bring me a cold chisel."—"I say, Fred., bear a hand, and get up a fire as quick as lightning under that steam-box."—"Halloo, nigger! come, turn this grindstone."—"Come, come! move, move! and *bowse* this timber forward."—"I say, darky, blast your eyes, why don't you heat up some pitch?"—"Halloo! halloo! halloo!" (Three voices at the same time.) "Come here!—Go there!—Hold on where you are! Damn you, if you move, I'll knock your brains out!"

This was my school for eight months; and I might have remained there longer, but for a most horrid fight I had with four of the white apprentices, in which my left eye was nearly knocked out, and I was horribly mangled in other respects. The facts in the case were these: Until a very little while after I went there, white and black ship-carpenters worked side by side, and no one seemed to see any **impropriety** in it. All hands seemed to be very well satisfied. Many of the black carpenters were freemen.

----

impropriety being unsuitable or inappropriate

Things seemed to be going on very well. All at once, the white carpenters knocked off, and said they would not work with free colored workmen. Their reason for this, as alleged, was, that if free colored carpenters were encouraged, they would soon take the trade into their own hands, and poor white men would be thrown out of employment. They therefore felt called upon at once to put a stop to it. And, taking advantage of Mr. Gardner's necessities, they broke off, swearing they would work no longer, unless he would discharge his black carpenters. Now, though this did not extend to me in form, it did reach me in fact. My fellow-apprentices very soon began to feel it degrading to them to work with me. They began to put on airs, and talk about the "niggers" taking the country, saying we all ought to be killed; and, being encouraged by the journeymen, they commenced making my condition as hard as they could, by **hectoring** me around, and sometimes striking me. I, of course, kept the vow I made after the fight with Mr. Covey, and struck back again, regardless of consequences; and while I kept them from combining, I succeeded very well; for I could whip the whole of them, taking them separately. They, however, at length combined, and came upon me, armed with sticks, stones, and heavy handspikes. One came in front with a half brick. There was one at each side of me, and one behind me. While I was attending to

hectoring harassing or bullying

those in front, and on either side, the one behind ran up with the handspike, and struck me a heavy blow upon the head. It stunned me. I fell, and with this they all ran upon me, and fell to beating me with their fists. I let them lay on for a while, gathering strength. In an instant, I gave a sudden surge, and rose to my hands and knees. Just as I did that, one of their number gave me, with his heavy boot, a powerful kick in the left eye. My eyeball seemed to have burst. When they saw my eye closed, and badly swollen, they left me. With this I seized the handspike, and for a time pursued them. But here the carpenters interfered, and I thought I might as well give it up. It was impossible to stand my hand against so many. All this took place in sight of not less than fifty white ship-carpenters, and not one interposed a friendly word; but some cried, "Kill the damned nigger! Kill him! kill him! He struck a white person." I found my only chance for life was in flight. I succeeded in getting away without an additional blow, and barely so; for to strike a white man is death by Lynch law,—and that was the law in Mr. Gardner's ship-yard; nor is there much of any other out of Mr. Gardner's ship-yard.

I went directly home, and told the story of my wrongs to Master Hugh; and I am happy to say of him, irreligious as he was, his conduct was heavenly, compared with that of his brother Thomas under similar circumstances. He listened attentively to my narration of the circumstances leading to the savage outrage, and gave many proofs of his strong indignation at it. The heart of my once overkind mistress was again melted into pity. My puffed-out eye and blood-covered face moved her to tears. She took a chair by me, washed the blood from my face, and, with a mother's tenderness, bound up my head, covering the wounded eye with a lean piece of fresh beef. It was almost compensation for my suffering to witness, once more, a manifestation of kindness from this, my once affectionate old mistress. Master Hugh was very much enraged. He gave expression to his feelings by pouring out curses upon the heads of those who did the deed. As soon as I got a little the better of my bruises, he took me with him to Esquire Watson's, on Bond Street, to see what could be done about the matter. Mr. Watson inquired who saw the assault committed. Master Hugh told him it was done in Mr. Gardner's ship-yard at midday, where there were a large company of men at work. "As to that," he said, "the deed was done, and there was no question as to who did it." His answer was, he could do nothing in the case, unless some white man would come forward and testify. He could issue no warrant on my word. If I had been killed in the presence of a thousand colored people, their testimony combined would have been insufficient to have arrested one of the murderers. Master Hugh, for once, was compelled to say this state of things was too bad. Of course, it was impossible to get any white man to volunteer his testimony in my behalf, and against the white young men. Even those who may have sympathized with me were not prepared to do this. It required a degree of courage unknown to them to do so; for just at that time, the slightest manifestation of humanity toward a colored person was denounced as abolitionism, and that name subjected its bearer to frightful liabilities. The watchwords of the bloody-minded in that region, and in those days, were, "Damn the abolitionists!" and "Damn the niggers!" There was nothing done, and probably nothing would have been done if I had been killed. Such was, and such remains, the state of things in the Christian city of Baltimore.

Master Hugh, finding he could get no redress, refused to let me go back again to Mr. Gardner. He kept me himself, and his wife dressed my wound till I was again restored to health. He then took me into the ship-yard of which he was foreman, in the employment of Mr. Walter Price. There I was immediately set to calking, and very soon learned the art of using my mallet and irons. In the course of one year from the time I left Mr. Gardner's, I was able to command the highest wages given to the most experienced calkers. I was now of some importance to my master. I was bringing him from six to seven dollars per week. I sometimes brought him nine dollars per week: my wages were a dollar and a half a day. After learning how to calk, I sought my own employment, made my own contracts, and collected the money which I earned. My pathway became much more smooth than before; my condition was now much more comfortable. When I could get no calking to do, I did nothing. During these leisure times, those old notions about freedom would steal over me again. When in Mr. Gardner's employment, I was kept in such a perpetual whirl of excitement, I could think of nothing, scarcely, but my life; and in thinking of my life, I almost forgot my liberty. I have observed this in my experience of slavery,— that whenever my condition was improved, instead of its increasing my contentment, it only increased my desire to be free, and set me to thinking of plans to gain my freedom. I have found that, to make a contented slave, it is necessary to make a thoughtless one. It is necessary to darken his moral and mental vision, and, as far as possible, to annihilate the power of reason. He must be able to detect no inconsistencies in slavery; he must be made to feel that slavery is right; and he can be brought to that only when he ceases to be a man.

I was now getting, as I have said, one dollar and fifty cents per day. I contracted for it; I earned it; it was paid to me; it was rightfully my own; yet, upon each returning Saturday night, I was compelled to deliver every cent of that money to Master Hugh. And why? Not because he earned it,—not because he had any hand in earning it,— not because I owed it to him,—nor because he possessed the slightest shadow of a right to it; but solely because he had the power to compel me to give it up. The right of the grim-visaged pirate upon the high seas is exactly the same.

Chapter XI

I now come to that part of my life during which I planned, and finally succeeded in making, my escape from slavery. But before narrating any of the peculiar circumstances, I deem it proper to make known my intention not to state all the facts connected with the transaction. My reasons for pursuing this course may be understood from the following: First, were I to give a minute statement of all the facts, it is not only possible, but quite probable, that others would thereby be involved in the most embarrassing difficulties. Secondly, such a statement would most undoubtedly induce greater vigilance on the part of slaveholders than has existed heretofore among them; which would, of course, be the means of guarding a door whereby some dear brother bondman might escape his galling chains. I deeply regret the necessity that impels me to suppress any thing of importance connected with my experience in slavery. It would afford me great pleasure indeed, as well as materially add to the interest of my narrative, were I at liberty to gratify a curiosity, which I know exists in the minds of many, by an accurate statement of all the facts pertaining to my most fortunate escape. But I must deprive myself of this pleasure, and the curious of the gratification which such a statement would afford. I would allow myself to suffer under the greatest **imputations** which evil-minded

....

imputations charges or accusations

men might suggest, rather than **exculpate** myself, and thereby run the hazard of closing the slightest avenue by which a brother slave might clear himself of the chains and **fetters** of slavery.

I have never approved of the very public manner in which some of our western friends have conducted what they call the *underground railroad*, but which I think, by their open declarations, has been made most emphatically the *upper-ground railroad*. I honor those good men and women for their noble daring, and applaud them for willingly subjecting themselves to bloody persecution, by openly avowing their participation in the escape of slaves. I, however, can see very little good resulting from such a course, either to themselves or the slaves escaping; while, upon the other hand, I see and feel assured that those open declarations are a positive evil to the slaves remaining, who are seeking to escape. They do nothing towards enlightening the slave, whilst they do much towards enlightening the master. They stimulate him to greater watchfulness, and enhance his power to capture his slave. We owe something to the slave south of the line as well as to those north of it; and in aiding the latter on their way to freedom, we should be careful to do nothing which would be likely to hinder the former from escaping from slavery. I

exculpate to clear of fault or blame
fetters shackles used to chain the hands and feet

would keep the merciless slaveholder profoundly ignorant of the means of flight adopted by the slave. I would leave him to imagine himself surrounded by **myriads** of invisible tormentors, ever ready to snatch from his infernal grasp his trembling prey. Let him be left to feel his way in the dark; let darkness commensurate with his crime hover over him; and let him feel that at every step he takes, in pursuit of the flying bondman, he is running the frightful risk of having his hot brains dashed out by an invisible agency. Let us render the tyrant no aid; let us not hold the light by which he can trace the footprints of our flying brother. But enough of this. I will now proceed to the statement of those facts, connected with my escape, for which I am alone responsible, and for which no one can be made to suffer but myself.

In the early part of the year 1838, I became quite restless. I could see no reason why I should, at the end of each week, pour the reward of my toil into the purse of my master. When I carried to him my weekly wages, he would, after counting the money, look me in the face with a robber-like fierceness, and ask, "Is this all?" He was satisfied with nothing less than the last cent. He would, however, when I made him six dollars, sometimes give me six cents, to encourage me. It had the opposite effect. I regarded it as a sort of admission of my right to the

....

myriads very large numbers

whole. The fact that he gave me any part of my wages was proof, to my mind, that he believed me entitled to the whole of them. I always felt worse for having received any thing; for I feared that the giving me a few cents would ease his conscience, and make him feel himself to be a pretty honorable sort of robber. My discontent grew upon me. I was ever on the look-out for means of escape; and, finding no direct means, I determined to try to hire my time, with a view of getting money with which to make my escape. In the spring of 1838, when Master Thomas came to Baltimore to purchase his spring goods, I got an opportunity, and applied to him to allow me to hire my time. He unhesitatingly refused my request, and told me this was another stratagem by which to escape. He told me I could go nowhere but that he could get me; and that, in the event of my running away, he should spare no pains in his efforts to catch me. He exhorted me to content myself, and be obedient. He told me, if I would be happy, I must lay out no plans for the future. He said, if I behaved myself properly, he would take care of me. Indeed, he advised me to complete thoughtlessness of the future, and taught me to depend solely upon him for happiness. He seemed to see fully the pressing necessity of setting aside my intellectual nature, in order to contentment in slavery. But in spite of him, and even in spite of myself, I continued to think, and to think about the injustice of my enslavement, and the means of escape.

About two months after this, I applied to Master Hugh for the privilege of hiring my time. He was not acquainted with the fact that I had applied to Master Thomas, and had been refused. He too, at first, seemed disposed to refuse; but, after some reflection, he granted me the privilege, and proposed the following terms: I was to be allowed all my time, make all contracts with those for whom I worked, and find my own employment; and, in return for this liberty, I was to pay him three dollars at the end of each week; find myself in calking tools, and in board and clothing. My board was two dollars and a half per week. This, with the wear and tear of clothing and calking tools, made my regular expenses about six dollars per week. This amount I was compelled to make up, or relinquish the privilege of hiring my time. Rain or shine, work or no work, at the end of each week the money must be forthcoming, or I must give up my privilege. This arrangement, it will be perceived, was decidedly in my master's favor. It relieved him of all need of looking after me. His money was sure. He received all the benefits of slaveholding without its evils; while I endured all the evils of a slave, and suffered all the care and anxiety of a freeman. I found it a hard bargain. But, hard as it was, I thought it better than the old mode of getting along. It was a step towards freedom to be allowed to bear the responsibilities of a freeman, and I was determined to hold on upon it. I bent myself to the work of making money. I was ready to work at night as well as day, and by the most untiring perseverance and industry, I made enough to meet my expenses, and lay up a little money every week. I went on thus from May till August. Master Hugh then refused to allow me to hire my time longer. The ground for his refusal was a failure on my part, one Saturday night, to pay him for my week's time. This failure was occasioned by my attending a camp meeting about ten miles from Baltimore. During the week, I had entered into an engagement with a number of young friends to start from Baltimore to the camp ground early Saturday evening; and being detained by my employer, I was unable to get down to Master Hugh's without disappointing the company. I knew that Master Hugh was in no special need of the money that night. I therefore decided to go to camp meeting, and upon my return pay him the three dollars. I staid at the camp meeting one day longer than I intended when I left. But as soon as I returned, I called upon him to pay him what he considered his due. I found him very angry; he could scarce restrain his wrath. He said he had a great mind to give me a severe whipping. He wished to know how I dared go out of the city without asking his permission. I told him I hired my time and while I paid him the price which he asked for it, I did not know that I was bound to ask him when and where I should go. This reply troubled him; and, after reflecting a few moments, he turned to me, and said I should hire my time no longer; that the next thing he should know of, I would be running away. Upon the same plea, he told me to bring my tools and clothing home forthwith. I did so; but instead of seeking work, as I had been accustomed to do previously to hiring my time, I spent the whole week without the performance of a single stroke of work. I did this in retaliation. Saturday night, he called upon me as usual for my week's wages. I told him I had no wages; I had done no work that week. Here we were upon the point of coming to blows. He raved, and swore his determination to get hold of me. I did not allow myself a single word; but was resolved, if he laid the weight of his hand upon me, it should be blow for blow. He did not strike me, but told me that he would find me in constant employment in future. I thought the matter over during the next day, Sunday, and finally resolved upon the third day of September, as the day upon which I would make a second attempt to secure my freedom. I now had three weeks during which to prepare for my journey. Early on Monday morning, before Master Hugh had time to make any engagement for me, I went out and got employment of Mr. Butler, at his ship-yard near the drawbridge, upon what is called the City Block, thus making it unnecessary for him to seek employment for me. At the end of the week, I brought him between eight and nine dollars. He seemed very well pleased, and asked why I did not do the same the week before. He little knew what my plans were. My object in working steadily was to remove any suspicion he might entertain of my intent to run away;

and in this I succeeded admirably. I suppose he thought I was never better satisfied with my condition than at the very time during which I was planning my escape. The second week passed, and again I carried him my full wages; and so well pleased was he, that he gave me twenty-five cents, (quite a large sum for a slaveholder to give a slave,) and bade me to make a good use of it. I told him I would.

Things went on without very smoothly indeed, but within there was trouble. It is impossible for me to describe my feelings as the time of my contemplated start drew near. I had a number of warmhearted friends in Baltimore,— friends that I loved almost as I did my life,—and the thought of being separated from them forever was painful beyond expression. It is my opinion that thousands would escape from slavery, who now remain, but for the strong cords of affection that bind them to their friends. The thought of leaving my friends was decidedly the most painful thought with which I had to contend. The love of them was my tender point, and shook my decision more than all things else. Besides the pain of separation, the dread and apprehension of a failure exceeded what I had experienced at my first attempt. The appalling defeat I then sustained returned to torment me. I felt assured that, if I failed in this attempt, my case would be a hopeless one—it would seal my fate as a slave forever. I could not hope to get off with any thing less than the severest punishment, and being placed beyond the means of escape. It required no very vivid imagination to depict the most frightful scenes through which I should have to pass, in case I failed. The wretchedness of slavery, and the blessedness of freedom, were perpetually before me. It was life and death with me. But I remained firm, and, according to my resolution, on the third day of September, 1838, I left my chains, and succeeded in reaching New York without the slightest interruption of any kind. How I did so,—what means I adopted,—what direction I travelled, and by what mode of conveyance,—I must leave unexplained, for the reasons before mentioned.

I have been frequently asked how I felt when I found myself in a free State. I have never been able to answer the question with any satisfaction to myself. It was a moment of the highest excitement I ever experienced. I suppose I felt as one may imagine the unarmed mariner to feel when he is rescued by a friendly man-of-war from the pursuit of a pirate. In writing to a dear friend, immediately after my arrival at New York, I said I felt like one who had escaped a den of hungry lions. This state of mind, however, very soon subsided; and I was again seized with a feeling of great insecurity and loneliness. I was yet liable to be taken back, and subjected to all the tortures of slavery. This in itself was enough to damp the ardor of my enthusiasm. But the loneliness overcame me. There I was in the midst

---

conveyance means of travel

of thousands, and yet a perfect stranger; without home and without friends, in the midst of thousands of my own brethren—children of a common Father, and yet I dared not to unfold to any one of them my sad condition. I was afraid to speak to any one for fear of speaking to the wrong one, and thereby falling into the hands of money-loving kidnappers, whose business it was to lie in wait for the panting fugitive, as the ferocious beasts of the forest lie in wait for their prey. The motto which I adopted when I started from slavery was this—"Trust no man!" I saw in every white man an enemy, and in almost every colored man cause for distrust. It was a most painful situation; and, to understand it, one must needs experience it, or imagine himself in similar circumstances. Let him be a fugitive slave in a strange land—a land given up to be the hunting-ground for slaveholders—whose inhabitants are legalized kidnappers—where he is every moment subjected to the terrible liability of being seized upon by his fellowmen, as the hideous crocodile seizes upon his prey!—I say, let him place himself in my situation—without home or friends—without money or credit—wanting shelter, and no one to give it—wanting bread, and no money to buy it,—and at the same time let him feel that he is pursued by merciless men-hunters, and in total darkness as to what to do, where to go, or where to stay,—perfectly helpless both as to the means of defence and means of escape,—in the midst of plenty, yet suffering the terrible gnawings of

hunger,—in the midst of houses, yet having no home,—
among fellow-men, yet feeling as if in the midst of wild
beasts, whose greediness to swallow up the trembling
and half-famished fugitive is only equalled by that with
which the monsters of the deep swallow up the helpless
fish upon which they subsist,—I say, let him be placed in
this most trying situation,—the situation in which I was
placed,—then, and not till then, will he fully appreciate the
hardships of, and know how to sympathize with, the toil-
worn and whip-scarred fugitive slave.

Thank Heaven, I remained but a short time in this
distressed situation. I was relieved from it by the humane
hand of *Mr. David Ruggles*, whose vigilance, kindness,
and perseverance, I shall never forget. I am glad of an
opportunity to express, as far as words can, the love and
gratitude I bear him. Mr. Ruggles is now afflicted with
blindness, and is himself in need of the same kind offices
which he was once so forward in the performance of
toward others. I had been in New York but a few days, when
Mr. Ruggles sought me out, and very kindly took me to his
boarding-house at the corner of Church and Lespenard
Streets. Mr. Ruggles was then very deeply engaged in the
memorable *Darg* case, as well as attending to a number
of other fugitive slaves, devising ways and means for their
successful escape; and, though watched and hemmed in on
almost every side, he seemed to be more than a match for
his enemies.

Very soon after I went to Mr. Ruggles, he wished to know of me where I wanted to go; as he deemed it unsafe for me to remain in New York. I told him I was a calker, and should like to go where I could get work. I thought of going to Canada; but he decided against it, and in favor of my going to New Bedford, thinking I should be able to get work there at my trade. At this time, Anna,* my intended wife, came on; for I wrote to her immediately after my arrival at New York, (notwithstanding my homeless, houseless, and helpless condition,) informing her of my successful flight, and wishing her to come on forthwith. In a few days after her arrival, Mr. Ruggles called in the Rev. J. W. C. Pennington, who, in the presence of Mr. Ruggles, Mrs. Michaels, and two or three others, performed the marriage ceremony, and gave us a certificate, of which the following is an exact copy:—

This may certify, that I joined together in holy matrimony Frederick Johnson** and Anna Murray, as man and wife, in the presence of Mr. David Ruggles and Mrs. Michaels.

JAMES W. C. PENNINGTON
New York, Sept. 15, 1838

----

* She was free.
** I had changed my name from Frederick *Bailey* to that of *Johnson*.

Upon receiving this certificate, and a five-dollar bill from Mr. Ruggles, I shouldered one part of our baggage, and Anna took up the other, and we set out forthwith to take passage on board of the steamboat John W. Richmond for Newport, on our way to New Bedford. Mr. Ruggles gave me a letter to a Mr. Shaw in Newport, and told me, in case my money did not serve me to New Bedford, to stop in Newport and obtain further assistance; but upon our arrival at Newport, we were so anxious to get to a place of safety, that, notwithstanding we lacked the necessary money to pay our fare, we decided to take seats in the stage, and promise to pay when we got to New Bedford. We were encouraged to do this by two excellent gentlemen, residents of New Bedford, whose names I afterward ascertained to be Joseph Ricketson and William C. Taber. They seemed at once to understand our circumstances, and gave us such assurance of their friendliness as put us fully at ease in their presence.

It was good indeed to meet with such friends, at such a time. Upon reaching New Bedford, we were directed to the house of Mr. Nathan Johnson, by whom we were kindly received, and hospitably provided for. Both Mr. and Mrs. Johnson took a deep and lively interest in our welfare. They proved themselves quite worthy of the name of abolitionists. When the stage-driver found us unable to pay our fare, he held on upon our baggage as security for the debt. I had but to mention the fact to Mr. Johnson, and he forthwith advanced the money.

We now began to feel a degree of safety, and to prepare ourselves for the duties and responsibilities of a life of freedom. On the morning after our arrival at New Bedford, while at the breakfast-table, the question arose as to what name I should be called by. The name given me by my mother was, "Frederick Augustus Washington Bailey." I, however, had dispensed with the two middle names long before I left Maryland so that I was generally known by the name of "Frederick Bailey." I started from Baltimore bearing the name of "Stanley." When I got to New York, I again changed my name to "Frederick Johnson," and thought that would be the last change. But when I got to New Bedford, I found it necessary again to change my name. The reason of this necessity was, that there were so many Johnsons in New Bedford, it was already quite difficult to distinguish between them. I gave Mr. Johnson the privilege of choosing me a name, but told him he must not take from me the name of "Frederick." I must hold on to that, to preserve a sense of my identity. Mr. Johnson had just been reading the "Lady of the Lake," and at once suggested that my name be "Douglass." From that time until now I have been called "Frederick Douglass;" and as I am more widely known by that name than by either of the others, I shall continue to use it as my own.

I was quite disappointed at the general appearance of things in New Bedford. The impression which I had received respecting the character and condition of the people of the north, I found to be singularly erroneous. I had very strangely supposed, while in slavery, that few of the comforts, and scarcely any of the luxuries, of life were enjoyed at the north, compared with what were enjoyed by the slaveholders of the south. I probably came to this conclusion from the fact that northern people owned no slaves. I supposed that they were about upon a level with the non-slaveholding population of the south. I knew *they* were exceedingly poor, and I had been accustomed to regard their poverty as the necessary consequence of their being non-slaveholders. I had somehow imbibed the opinion that, in the absence of slaves, there could be no wealth, and very little refinement. And upon coming to the north, I expected to meet with a rough, hard-handed, and uncultivated population, living in the most Spartan-like simplicity, knowing nothing of the ease, luxury, pomp, and grandeur of southern slaveholders. Such being my conjectures, any one acquainted with the appearance of New Bedford may very readily infer how **palpably** I must have seen my mistake.

In the afternoon of the day when I reached New Bedford, I visited the wharves, to take a view of the

---

palpably capable of being touched

shipping. Here I found myself surrounded with the strongest proofs of wealth. Lying at the wharves, and riding in the stream, I saw many ships of the finest model, in the best order, and of the largest size. Upon the right and left, I was walled in by granite warehouses of the widest dimensions, stowed to their utmost capacity with the necessaries and comforts of life. Added to this, almost every body seemed to be at work, but noiselessly so, compared with what I had been accustomed to in Baltimore. There were no loud songs heard from those engaged in loading and unloading ships. I heard no deep oaths or horrid curses on the laborer. I saw no whipping of men; but all seemed to go smoothly on. Every man appeared to understand his work, and went at it with a sober, yet cheerful earnestness, which betokened the deep interest which he felt in what he was doing, as well as a sense of his own dignity as a man. To me this looked exceedingly strange. From the wharves I strolled around and over the town, gazing with wonder and admiration at the splendid churches, beautiful dwellings, and finely-cultivated gardens; **evincing** an amount of wealth, comfort, taste, and refinement, such as I had never seen in any part of slaveholding Maryland.

Every thing looked clean, new, and beautiful. I saw few or no dilapidated houses, with poverty-stricken inmates; no half-naked children and barefooted women, such as I

....

evincing showing

had been accustomed to see in Hillsborough, Easton, St. Michael's, and Baltimore. The people looked more able, stronger, healthier, and happier, than those of Maryland. I was for once made glad by a view of extreme wealth, without being saddened by seeing extreme poverty. But the most astonishing as well as the most interesting thing to me was the condition of the colored people, a great many of whom, like myself, had escaped thither as a refuge from the hunters of men. I found many, who had not been seven years out of their chains, living in finer houses, and evidently enjoying more of the comforts of life, than the average of slaveholders in Maryland. I will venture to assert, that my friend Mr. Nathan Johnson (of whom I can say with a grateful heart, "I was hungry, and he gave me meat; I was thirsty, and he gave me drink; I was a stranger, and he took me in") lived in a neater house; dined at a better table; took, paid for, and read, more newspapers; better understood the moral, religious, and political character of the nation,—than nine tenths of the slaveholders in Talbot county Maryland. Yet Mr. Johnson was a working man. His hands were hardened by toil, and not his alone, but those also of Mrs. Johnson. I found the colored people much more spirited than I had supposed they would be. I found among them a determination to protect each other from the blood-thirsty kidnapper, at all hazards. Soon after my arrival, I was told of a circumstance which illustrated their spirit. A colored man and a fugitive slave were on unfriendly terms. The former was heard to threaten the latter with informing his master of his whereabouts. Straightway a meeting was called among the colored people, under the stereotyped notice, "Business of importance!" The betrayer was invited to attend. The people came at the appointed hour, and organized the meeting by appointing a very religious old gentleman as president, who, I believe, made a prayer, after which he addressed the meeting as follows: *"Friends, we have got him here, and I would recommend that you young men just take him outside the door, and kill him!"* With this, a number of them bolted at him; but they were intercepted by some more timid than themselves, and the betrayer escaped their vengeance, and has not been seen in New Bedford since. I believe there have been no more such threats, and should there be hereafter, I doubt not that death would be the consequence.

I found employment, the third day after my arrival, in stowing a sloop with a load of oil. It was new, dirty, and hard work for me; but I went at it with a glad heart and a willing hand. I was now my own master. It was a happy moment, the rapture of which can be understood only by those who have been slaves. It was the first work, the reward of which was to be entirely my own. There was no Master Hugh standing ready, the moment I earned the money, to rob me of it. I worked that day with a pleasure I had never before experienced. I was at work for myself and newly-married wife. It was to me the starting-point of a new existence. When I got through with that job, I went in pursuit of a job of calking; but such was the strength of prejudice against color, among the white calkers, that they refused to work with me, and of course I could get no employment.*

Finding my trade of no immediate benefit, I threw off my calking **habiliments**, and prepared myself to do any kind of work I could get to do. Mr. Johnson kindly let me have his wood-horse and saw, and I very soon found myself a plenty of work. There was no work too hard—none too dirty. I was ready to saw wood, shovel coal, carry wood, sweep the chimney, or roll oil casks,—all of which I did for nearly three years in New Bedford, before I became known to the anti-slavery world.

In about four months after I went to New Bedford, there came a young man to me, and inquired if I did not wish to take the "Liberator." I told him I did; but, just having made my escape from slavery, I remarked that I was unable to pay for it then. I, however, finally became a subscriber to it. The paper came, and I read it from week to week with such feelings as it would be quite idle for me to attempt to describe. The paper became my meat and my drink.

....

* I am told that colored persons can now get employment at calking in New Bedford—a result of anti-slavery effort.

habiliments clothing

My soul was set all on fire. Its sympathy for my brethren in bonds— its scathing denunciations of slaveholders—its faithful exposures of slavery—and its powerful attacks upon the upholders of the institution—sent a thrill of joy through my soul, such as I had never felt before!

I had not long been a reader of the "Liberator," before I got a pretty correct idea of the principles, measures and spirit of the anti-slavery reform. I took right hold of the cause. I could do but little; but what I could, I did with a joyful heart, and never felt happier than when in an anti-slavery meeting. I seldom had much to say at the meetings, because what I wanted to say was said so much better by others. But, while attending an anti-slavery convention at Nantucket, on the 11th of August, 1841, I felt strongly moved to speak, and was at the same time much urged to do so by Mr. William C. Coffin, a gentleman who had heard me speak in the colored people's meeting at New Bedford. It was a severe cross, and I took it up reluctantly. The truth was, I felt myself a slave, and the idea of speaking to white people weighed me down. I spoke but a few moments, when I felt a degree of freedom, and said what I desired with considerable ease. From that time until now, I have been engaged in pleading the cause of my brethren— with what success, and with what devotion, I leave those acquainted with my labors to decide. ❖

excerpt from

Captain Canot, or Twenty Years of an African Slaver

by Theodore Canot,
edited from his journals by Brantz Mayer

Chapter X

I was a close watcher of Mongo John whenever he engaged in the purchase of slaves. As each negro was brought before him, Ormond examined the subject, without regard to sex, from head to foot. A careful **manipulation** of the chief muscles, joints, arm-pits and groins was made, to assure soundness. The mouth, too, was inspected, and if a tooth was missing, it was noted as a defect liable to deduction. Eyes, voice, lungs, fingers and toes were not forgotten; so that when the negro passed from the Mongo's hands without **censure**, he might have been readily adopted as a good "life" by an insurance company.

Upon one occasion, to my great astonishment, I saw a **stout** and apparently powerful man discarded by Ormond as utterly worthless. His full muscles and sleek skin, to my

manipulation use of the hands to check
censure strong disapproval
stout sturdy, with a thick body

unpractised eye, **denoted** the height of robust health. Still, I was told that he had been medicated for the market with **bloating** drugs, and sweated with powder and lemon-juice to impart a gloss to his skin. Ormond remarked that these jockey-tricks are as common in Africa as among horse-dealers in Christian lands; and desiring me to feel the negro's pulse, I immediately detected disease or excessive excitement. In a few days I found the poor wretch, abandoned by his owner, a paralyzed wreck in the hut of a villager at Bangalang.

When a slave becomes useless to his master in the interior, or exhibits signs of failing **constitution**, he is soon disposed of to a peddler or broker. These men call to their aid a quack, familiar with drugs, who, for a small compensation, undertakes to refit an impaired body for the temptation of **green-horns**. Sometimes the cheat is successfully effected; but experienced slavers detect it readily by the yellow eye, swollen tongue, and feverish skin.

Chapter XI

At the appointed day, La Fortuna sailed with 220 human beings packed in her hold. Three months afterwards, I received advices that she safely landed 217 in the bay of

denoted indicated
bloating causing swelling
constitution physical health or makeup
green-horns people with no knowledge or experience

Matanzas, and that their sale yielded a clear profit on the voyage of forty-one thousand four hundred and thirty-eight dollars.

As I am now fairly embarked in a trade which absorbed so many of my most **vigorous** years, I suppose the reader will not be loth to learn a little of my experience in the **alleged** "cruelties" of this commerce; and the first question, in all likelihood, that rises to his lips, is a solicitation to be apprised of the embarkation and treatment of slaves on the dreaded voyage.

An African factor of fair repute is ever careful to select his human cargo with **consummate prudence**, so as not only to supply his employers with athletic laborers, but to avoid any taint of disease that may affect the slaves in their transit to Cuba or the American main. Two days before embarkation, the head of every male and female is neatly shaved; and, if the cargo belongs to several owners, each man's brand is impressed on the body of his respective negro. This operation is performed with pieces of silver wire, or small irons fashioned into the merchant's initials, heated just hot enough to blister without burning the skin. When the entire cargo is the venture of but one proprietor, the branding is always **dispensed with**.

....

vigorous strong; energetic
alleged accused, but without proof or legal conviction
consummate prudence extreme care
dispensed with not done

On the appointed day, the *barracoon* or slave-pen is made joyous by the abundant "feed" which signalizes the negro's last hours in his native country. The feast over, they are taken alongside the vessel in canoes; and as they touch the deck, they are entirely stripped, so that women as well as men go out of Africa as they came into it—*naked*. This precaution, it will be understood, is **indispensable**; for perfect nudity, during the whole voyage, is the only means of securing cleanliness and health. In this state, they are immediately ordered below, the men to the hold and the women to the cabin, while boys and girls are, day and night, kept on deck, where their sole protection from the elements is a sail in fair weather, and a *tarpaulin* in foul.

At meal time they are distributed in messes of ten.

This over, a bucket of salt water is served to each mess, by way of "finger glasses" for the **ablution** of hands, after which a *kidd*,—either of rice, farina, yams, or beans,— according to the tribal habit of the negroes, is placed before the squad. In order to prevent greediness or inequality in the appropriation of nourishment, the process is performed by signals from a monitor, whose motions indicate when the darkies shall dip and when they shall swallow.

It is the duty of a guard to report immediately whenever a slave refuses to eat, in order that his **abstinence** may

....

indispensable cannot be done without
ablution washing
abstinence doing without food or drink

be traced to stubbornness or disease. Negroes have sometimes been found in slavers who attempted voluntary starvation; so that, when the watch reports the patient to be "shamming," his appetite is stimulated by the medical antidote of a "**cat**." If the slave, however, is truly ill, he is forthwith ticketed for the sick list by a bead or button around his neck, and dispatched to an infirmary in the forecastle.

These meals occur twice daily,—at ten in the morning and four in the afternoon,—and are terminated by another ablution. Thrice in each twenty-four hours they are served with half a pint of water. Pipes and tobacco are circulated economically among both sexes; but, as each negro cannot be allowed the luxury of a separate bowl, boys are sent round with an adequate supply, allowing a few whiffs to each individual. On regular days,—probably three times a week,—their mouths are carefully rinsed with vinegar, while, nearly every morning, a dram is given as an antidote to scurvy.

Although it is found necessary to keep the sexes apart, they are allowed to converse freely during day while on deck. **Corporal punishment** is never inflicted save by order of an officer, and, even then, not until the culprit understands exactly why it is done. Once a week, the ship's barber scrapes their chins without assistance from

....

cat slang for a whip made of knotted cored attached to a handle
corporal punishment physical punishment

soap; and, on the same day, their nails are closely pared, to insure security from harm in those nightly battles that occur, when the slave contests with his neighbor every inch of plank to which he is glued. During afternoons of **serene** weather, men, women, girls, and boys are allowed to unite in African melodies, which they always enhance by an extemporaneous *tom-tom* on the bottom of a tub or tin kettle.

These hints will apprise the reader that the greatest care, compatible with safety, is taken of a negro's health and cleanliness on the voyage. In every well-conducted slaver, the captain, officers, and crew, are alert and vigilant to preserve the cargo. It is their personal interest, as well as the interest of humanity to do so. The boatswain is **incessant** in his patrol of purification, and disinfecting substances are plenteously distributed. The upper deck is washed and swabbed daily; the slave deck is scraped and holy-stoned; and, at nine o'clock each morning, the captain inspects every part of his craft; so that no vessel, except a man-of-war, can compare with a slaver in systematic order, purity, and neatness. I am not aware that the ship-fever, which sometimes decimates the **emigrants** from Europe, has ever prevailed in these African traders.

....

serene calm
incessant endless; never ceasing
emigrants people leaving one country to go to another

At sundown, the process of stowing the slaves for the night is begun. The second mate and boatswain descend into the hold, whip in hand, and range the slaves in their regular places; those on the right side of the vessel facing forward, and lying in each other's lap, while those on the left are similarly stowed with their faces towards the stern. In this way each negro lies on his right side, which is considered preferable for the action of the heart. In allotting places, particular attention is paid to size, the taller being selected for the greatest breadth of the vessel, while the shorter and younger are lodged near the bows. When the cargo is large and the lower deck crammed, the **supernumeraries** are disposed of on deck, which is securely covered with boards to shield them from moisture. The *strict* discipline of nightly stowage is, of course, of the greatest importance in slavers, else every negro would accommodate himself as if he were a passenger.

In order to insure perfect silence and regularity during night, a slave is chosen as constable from every ten, and furnished with a "cat" to enforce commands during his appointed watch. In **remuneration** for his services, which, it may be believed, are admirably performed whenever the whip is required, he is adorned with an old shirt or tarry trowsers. Now and then, billets of wood are distributed among the sleepers, but this luxury is never granted until

supernumeraries people exceeding the regular number
remuneration payment

the good temper of the negroes is ascertained, for slaves have often been tempted to mutiny by the power of arming themselves with these pillows from the forest.

It is very probable that many of my readers will consider it **barbarous** to make slaves lie down naked upon a board, but let me inform them that native Africans are not familiar with the use of feather-beds, nor do any but the free and rich in their mother country indulge in the luxury even of a mat or raw-hide. Among the Mandingo chiefs,— the most industrious and civilized of Africans,—the beds, divans, and sofas, are heaps of mud, covered with untanned skins for cushions, while logs of wood serve for bolsters! I am of opinion, therefore, that emigrant slaves experience very slight inconvenience in lying down on the deck.

But *ventilation* is carefully attended to. The hatches and bulkheads of every slaver are grated, and apertures are cut about the deck for ampler circulation of air. Wind-sails, too, are constantly pouring a steady draft into the hold, except during a chase, when, of course, every comfort is temporarily sacrificed for safety. During calms or in light and baffling winds, when the suffocating air of the tropics makes ventilation impossible, the gratings are always removed, and portions of the slaves allowed to repose at night on deck, while the crew is armed to watch the sleepers.

....

barbarous cruel; brutal
ventilation air flow

Handcuffs are rarely used on shipboard. It is the common custom to secure slaves in the **barracoons**, and while shipping, by chaining *ten* in a gang; but as these platoons would be extremely inconvenient at sea, the manacles are immediately taken off and replaced by leg-irons, which fasten them in pairs by the feet. Shackles are never used but for *full-grown men*, while *women* and *boys* are set at liberty as soon as they embark. It frequently happens that when the behavior of *male* slaves warrants their freedom, they are released from all fastenings long before they arrive. Irons are altogether dispensed with on many *Brazilian* slavers, as negroes from Anjuda, Benin, and Angola, are mild; and unaddicted to revolt like those who dwell east of the Cape or north of the Gold Coast.

Indeed, a knowing trader will never use chains but when compelled, for the longer a slave is ironed the more he **deteriorates**; and, as his sole object is to land a healthy cargo, **pecuniary** interest, as well as natural feeling, urges the sparing of metal.

My object in writing this **palliative** description is not to exculpate the slavers or their commerce, but to correct those exaggerated stories which have so long been current in regard to the *usual* voyage of a trader. I have always

---

barracoons enclosures used for confining slaves or convicts
deteriorates becomes lower in quality or value
pecuniary monetary, as in interest in making a profit
palliative excusing

believed that the cause of humanity, as well as any other cause, was least served by over-statement; and I am sure that if the narratives given by Englishmen are true, the voyages they detail must either have occurred before my day, or were conducted in British vessels, while her majesty's subjects still considered the traffic lawful.

As the reader may scarcely credit so large a profit, I subjoin an account of the fitting of a slave vessel from Havana in 1827, and the liquidation of her voyage in Cuba:—

1.—Expenses Out.

Cost of La Fortuna, a 90 ton schooner,	$3,700.00
Fitting out, sails, carpenter and cooper's bills,	$2,500.00
Provisions for crew and slaves,	$1,115.00
Wages advanced to 18 men before the mast,	$900.00
to captain, mates, boatswain, cook, and steward,	$440.00
200,000 cigars and 500 doubloons, cargo,	$10,900.00
Clearance and hush-money,	$200.00
	$19,755.00
Commission at 5 per cent.,	$987.00
Full cost of voyage out,	$20,742.00

2.—Expenses Home.

Captain's head-money, at $8 a head,	$1,746.00
Mate's "$4"	$873.00
Second mate and boatswain's head-money, at $2 each a head	$873.00
Captain's wages,	$219.78
First mate's wages	$175.56
Second mate and boatswain's wages,	$307.12
Cook and steward's wages,	$264.00
Eighteen sailors' wages,	$1,972.00
	$27,172.46

3.—Expenses in Havana.

Government officers, at $8 per head,	$1,736.00
My commission on 217 slaves, expenses off,	$5,565.00
Consignees' commissions,	$8,878.00
217 slave dresses, at $2 each,	$634.00
Extra expenses of all kinds, say,	$1,000.00
Total expenses,	$39,980.46

4.—Returns.

Value of vessel at auction,	$3,950.000
Proceeds of 217 slaves,	$77,469.00
	$81,419.00

Resumé.

Total Returns,	$81,419.00
Expenses,	$39,980.46
Nett profit,	**$41,438.54**

Voices and Viewpoints

The Rainy Day

by Henry Wadsworth Longfellow

The day is cold, and dark, and dreary;
It rains, and the wind is never weary;
The vine still clings to the **moldering** wall,
But at every gust the dead leaves fall,
    And the day is dark and dreary.

My life is cold, and dark, and dreary;
It rains, and the wind is never weary;
My thoughts still cling to the moldering Past,
But the hopes of youth fall thick in the **blast**,
    And the days are dark and dreary.

Be still, sad heart! and cease **repining**;
Behind the clouds is the sun still shining;
Thy fate is the common fate of all,
Into each life some rain must fall,
    Some days must be dark and dreary. ❖

....

moldering crumbling; falling apart
blast a strong gust of wind
repining feeling downcast and discontent; fretting

Invictus

by William Ernest Henley

Out of the night that covers me,
    Black as **the Pit** from pole to pole,
I thank whatever gods may be
    For my unconquerable soul.

In the **fell** clutch of circumstance
    I have not winced nor cried aloud.
Under the **bludgeonings** of chance
    My head is bloody, but unbowed.

Beyond this place of wrath and tears
    Looms but the Horror of the **shade**,
And yet the **menace** of the years
    Finds, and shall find, me unafraid.

It matters not how **strait** the gate,
    How charged with punishments the scroll,
I am the master of my fate;
    I am the captain of my soul. ❖

---

the Pit hell
fell cruel; sinister; fierce
bludgeonings brutal beatings, as with a heavy club
shade the realm of the dead
menace threat
strait narrow

We Real Cool

by Gwendolyn Brooks

The Pool Players.
Seven at the Golden Shovel.

We real cool. We
Left school. We

Lurk late. We
Strike straight. We

Sing sin. We
Thin gin. We

Jazz June. We
Die soon. ❖

The Negro Speaks of Rivers

by Langston Hughes

I've known rivers:
I've known rivers ancient as the world and older than the
    flow of human blood in human veins.

My soul has grown deep like the rivers.

I bathed in the Euphrates when dawns were young.
I built my hut near the Congo and it lulled me to sleep.
I looked upon the Nile and raised the pyramids above it.
I heard the singing of the Mississippi when Abe Lincoln
    went down to New Orleans, and I've seen its muddy
    bosom turn all golden in the sunset.

I've known rivers:
Ancient, dusky rivers.

My soul has grown deep like the rivers. ❖

Mending Wall

by Robert Frost

Something there is that doesn't love a wall,
That sends the frozen-ground-swell under it,
And spills the upper boulders in the sun,
And makes gaps even two can pass **abreast**.
The work of hunters is another thing:
I have come after them and made repair
Where they have left not one stone on a stone,
But they would have the rabbit out of hiding,
To please the yelping dogs. The gaps I mean,
No one has seen them made or heard them made,
But at spring mending-time we find them there.
I let my neighbor know beyond the hill;
And on a day we meet to walk the line
And set the wall between us once again.
We keep the wall between us as we go.
To each the boulders that have fallen to each.
And some are loaves and some so nearly balls
We have to use a spell to make them balance:
"Stay where you are until our backs are turned!"
We wear our fingers rough with handling them.
Oh, just another kind of outdoor game,

mending fixing; repairing
abreast side by side

One on a side. It comes to little more:
There where it is we do not need the wall:
He is all pine and I am apple orchard.
My apple trees will never get across
And eat the cones under his pines, I tell him.
He only says, "Good fences make good neighbors."
Spring is the mischief in me, and I wonder
If I could put a notion in his head:
"*Why* do they make good neighbors? Isn't it
Where there are cows? But here there are no cows.
Before I built a wall I'd ask to know
What I was walling in or walling out,
And to whom I was like to give offence.
Something there is that doesn't love a wall,
That wants it down." I could say "Elves" to him,
But it's not elves exactly, and I'd rather
He said it for himself. I see him there
Bringing a stone grasped firmly by the top
In each hand, like an old-stone savage armed.
He moves in darkness as it seems to me,
Not of woods only and the shade of trees.
He will not go behind his father's saying,
And he likes having thought of it so well
He says again, "Good fences make good neighbors." ❖

I Have a Dream

a speech delivered by Dr. Martin Luther King Jr.
on the steps of the Lincoln Memorial, Washington, D.C.
August 28, 1963

I am happy to join with you today in what will go down in history as the greatest demonstration for freedom in the history of our nation.

Five score years ago, a great American, in whose symbolic shadow we stand today, signed the **Emancipation Proclamation**. This momentous **decree** came as a great beacon light of hope to millions of Negro slaves who had been **seared** in the flames of **withering** injustice. It came as a joyous daybreak to end the long night of their captivity.

But one hundred years later, the Negro still is not free. One hundred years later, the life of the Negro is still sadly crippled by the **manacles** of segregation and the chains of discrimination. One hundred years later, the Negro lives on a lonely island of poverty in the midst of a vast ocean of material prosperity. One hundred years later, the Negro is still **languished** in the corners of American society and

....

five score 100 (one score is equal to 20)
Emancipation Proclamation a document signed during the Civil War in 1862 by President Abraham Lincoln, freeing the slaves in the Confederacy
decree an order; a command
seared burned
withering devastating
manacles metal rings and chains used to confine a person's hands
languished left neglected and in a miserable state

finds himself an exile in his own land. And so we've come here today to dramatize a shameful condition.

In a sense we've come to our nation's capital to cash a check. When the architects of our republic wrote the magnificent words of the Constitution and the Declaration of Independence, they were signing a **promissory note** to which every American was to fall heir. This note was a promise that all men—yes, black men as well as white men—would be guaranteed the **unalienable** rights of life, liberty, and the pursuit of happiness.

It is obvious today that America has **defaulted** on this promissory note insofar as her citizens of color are concerned. Instead of honoring this sacred obligation, America has given the Negro people a bad check, a check that has come back marked "insufficient funds."

But we refuse to believe that the bank of justice is bankrupt. We refuse to believe that there are insufficient funds in the great vaults of opportunity of this nation. And so we've come to cash this check, a check that will give us upon demand the riches of freedom and security of justice.

We have also come to his **hallowed** spot to remind America of the fierce urgency of now. This is no time to engage in the luxury of cooling off or to take the

....

promissory note a written promise for a future payment; a binding agreement
unalienable incapable of being taken away
defaulted failed to meet an obligation; failed to make a payment
hallowed holy; sacred

tranquilizing drug of **gradualism**. Now is the time to make real the promises of democracy. Now is the time to rise from the dark and **desolate** valley of segregation to the sunlit path of racial justice. Now is the time to lift our nation from the quicksands of racial injustice to the solid rock of brotherhood. Now is the time to make justice a reality for all of God's children.

It would be fatal for the nation to overlook the urgency of the moment. This sweltering summer of the Negro's legitimate discontent will not pass until there is an **invigorating** autumn of freedom and equality. Nineteen sixty-three is not an end but a beginning. Those who hoped that the Negro needed to blow off steam and will now be content will have a rude awakening if the nation returns to business as usual. There will be neither rest nor tranquility in America until the Negro is granted his citizenship rights. The whirlwinds of revolt will continue to shake the foundations of our nation until the bright day of justice emerges.

But there is something that I must say to my people who stand on the warm threshold which leads into the palace of justice. In the process of gaining our rightful place we must not be guilty of wrongful deeds. Let us not seek to satisfy our thirst for freedom by drinking from the cup of bitterness

gradualism moving toward a goal through a series of small steps; little by little
desolate dismal; dreary; forsaken
invigorating filling with strength or energy

Dr. Martin Luther King Jr. acknowledging the crowd in front of the Lincoln Memorial

and hatred. We must forever conduct our struggle on the high plane of dignity and discipline. We must not allow our creative protest to **degenerate** into physical violence. Again and again we must rise to the majestic heights of meeting physical force with soul force. The marvelous new **militancy** which has engulfed the Negro community must not lead us to a distrust of all white people, for many of our white brothers, as evidenced by their presence here today, have come to realize that their destiny is tied up with our destiny. And they have come to realize that their freedom is **inextricably** bound to our freedom. We cannot walk alone.

degenerate to decline; to sink to a lower state
militancy an aggressive, fighting spirit or attitude
inextricably inseparably

And as we walk, we must make the pledge that we shall always march ahead. We cannot turn back. There are those who are asking the devotees of civil rights, "When will you be satisfied?" We can never be satisfied as long as the Negro is the victim of the unspeakable horrors of police brutality. We can never be satisfied as long as our bodies, heavy with the fatigue of travel, cannot gain lodging in the motels of the highways and the hotels of the cities. We cannot be satisfied as long as the Negro's basic mobility is from a smaller ghetto to a larger one. We can never be satisfied as long as our children are stripped of their selfhood and robbed of their dignity by signs stating "for whites only." We cannot be satisfied as long as a Negro in Mississippi cannot vote and a Negro in New York believes he has nothing for which to vote. No, no we are not satisfied and we will not be satisfied until justice rolls down like waters and righteousness like a mighty stream.

I am not **unmindful** that some of you have come here out of great trials and **tribulations**. Some of you have come fresh from narrow jail cells. Some of you have come from areas where your quest for freedom left you battered by storms of persecution and staggered by the winds of police brutality. You have been the veterans of creative suffering. Continue to work with the faith that unearned suffering is **redemptive**.

---

unmindful not attentive; unaware
tribulations suffering; great troubles
redemptive tending to redeem—that is, to save, rescue, or liberate

Go back to Mississippi, go back to Alabama, go back to South Carolina, go back to Georgia, go back to Louisiana, go back to the slums and ghettos of our northern cities, knowing that somehow this situation can and will be changed.

Let us not wallow in the valley of despair. I say to you today my friends—so even though we face the difficulties of today and tomorrow, I still have a dream. It is a dream deeply rooted in the American dream.

I have a dream that one day this nation will rise up and live out the true meaning of its creed: "We hold these truths to be self-evident, that all men are created equal."

I have a dream that one day on the red hills of Georgia the sons of former slaves and the sons of former slave owners will be able to sit down together at the table of brotherhood.

I have a dream that one day even the state of Mississippi, a state sweltering with the heat of injustice, sweltering with the heat of oppression, will be transformed into an oasis of freedom and justice.

I have a dream that my four little children will one day live in a nation where they will not be judged by the color of their skin but by the content of their character.

I have a dream today.

I have a dream that one day down in Alabama, with its vicious racists, with its governor having his lips dripping with the words of **interposition** and **nullification**—one day right there in Alabama little black boys and black girls will be able to join hands with little white boys and white girls as sisters and brothers.

I have a dream today.

I have a dream that one day every valley shall be exalted, and every hill and mountain shall be made low, the rough places will be made plain, and the crooked places will be made straight, and the glory of the Lord shall be revealed and all flesh shall see it together.

This is our hope. This is the faith that I go back to the South with. With this faith we will be able to hew out of the mountain of despair a stone of hope. With this faith we will be able to transform the jangling discords of our nation into a beautiful symphony of brotherhood. With this faith we will be able to work together, to pray together, to struggle together, to go to jail together, to stand up for freedom together, knowing that we will be free one day.

This will be the day, this will be the day when all of God's children will be able to sing with new meaning, "My country 'tis of thee, sweet land of liberty, of thee I sing. Land where my fathers died, land of the Pilgrim's pride, from every mountainside, let freedom ring!"

....

interposition the act of a state putting itself between the federal government and its citizens

nullification the action of a state attempting to prevent the enforcement of a U.S. law within its borders

And if America is to be a great nation, this must become true. And so let freedom ring from the **prodigious** hilltops of New Hampshire. Let freedom ring from the mighty mountains of New York. Let freedom ring from the heightening **Alleghenies** of Pennsylvania.

Let freedom ring from the snow-capped Rockies of Colorado. Let freedom ring from the curvaceous slopes of California.

But not only that: Let freedom ring from **Stone Mountain** of Georgia.

Let freedom ring from **Lookout Mountain** of Tennessee.

Let freedom ring from every hill and molehill of Mississippi.

From every mountainside, let freedom ring.

And when this happens, and when we allow freedom [to] ring—when we let it ring from every village and every **hamlet**, from every state and every city, we will be able to speed up that day when all of God's children—black men and white men, Jews and **Gentiles**, Protestants and Catholics—will be able to join hands and sing in the words of the old Negro spiritual: "Free at last! Free at last! Thank God Almighty, we are free at last!" ❖

....

prodigious extremely impressive; causing amazement
Alleghenies a mountain range that runs from northern Pennsylvania to southern Virginia
Stone Mountain a massive granite mountain with a monument to those Confederate soldiers who died during the Civil War
Lookout Mountain a mountain on the border of Tennessee, Georgia, and Alabama that was the site of a famous Civil War battle
hamlet a small village
Gentiles non-Jewish people

President George W. Bush's First Inaugural Address

January 20, 2001

President Clinton, distinguished guests and my fellow citizens, the peaceful transfer of authority is rare in history, yet common in our country. With a simple oath, we affirm old traditions and make new beginnings.

As I begin, I thank President Clinton for his service to our nation.

And I thank Vice President Gore for a contest conducted with spirit and ended with grace.

I am honored and humbled to stand here, where so many of America's leaders have come before me, and so many will follow.

We have a place, all of us, in a long story—a story we continue, but whose end we will not see. It is the story of a new world that became a friend and liberator of the old, a story of a slave-holding society that became a servant of freedom, the story of a power that went into the world to protect but not possess, to defend but not to conquer.

It is the American story—a story of flawed and **fallible** people, united across the generations by grand and enduring ideals.

....

fallible imperfect

The grandest of these ideals is an unfolding American promise that everyone belongs, that everyone deserves a chance, that no insignificant person was ever born.

Americans are called to enact this promise in our lives and in our laws. And though our nation has sometimes halted, and sometimes delayed, we must follow no other course.

Through much of the last century, America's faith in freedom and democracy was a rock in a raging sea. Now it is a seed upon the wind, taking root in many nations.

Our democratic faith is more than the creed of our country, it is the inborn hope of our humanity, an ideal we carry but do not own, a trust we bear and pass along. And even after nearly 225 years, we have a long way yet to travel.

While many of our citizens prosper, others doubt the promise, even the justice, of our own country. The ambitions of some Americans are limited by failing schools and hidden prejudice and the circumstances of their birth. And sometimes our differences run so deep, it seems we share a continent, but not a country.

We do not accept this, and we will not allow it. Our unity, our union, is the serious work of leaders and citizens in every generation. And this is my solemn pledge: I will work to build a single nation of justice and opportunity.

I know this is in our reach because we are guided by a power larger than ourselves who creates us equal in His image.

President George W. Bush delivering his first inaugural address, overlooking the National Mall in Washington, D.C.

And we are confident in principles that unite and lead us onward.

America has never been united by blood or birth or soil. We are bound by ideals that move us beyond our backgrounds, lift us above our interests and teach us what it means to be citizens. Every child must be taught these principles. Every citizen must uphold them. And every immigrant, by embracing these ideals, makes our country more, not less, American.

Today, we affirm a new commitment to live out our nation's promise through civility, courage, compassion, and character.

America, at its best, matches a commitment to principle with a concern for civility. A civil society demands from each of us good will and respect, fair dealing and forgiveness.

Some seem to believe that our politics can afford to be petty because, in a time of peace, the stakes of our debates appear small.

But the stakes for America are never small. If our country does not lead the cause of freedom, it will not be led. If we do not turn the hearts of children toward knowledge and character, we will lose their gifts and undermine their idealism. If we permit our economy to drift and decline, the vulnerable will suffer most.

We must live up to the calling we share. Civility is not a tactic or a sentiment. It is the determined choice of trust over cynicism, of community over chaos. And this commitment, if we keep it, is a way to shared accomplishment.

America, at its best, is also courageous.

Our national courage has been clear in times of depression and war, when defending common dangers defined our common good. Now we must choose if the example of our fathers and mothers will inspire us or condemn us. We must show courage in a time of blessing by confronting problems instead of passing them on to future generations.

Together, we will reclaim America's schools, before ignorance and apathy claim more young lives.

We will reform Social Security and Medicare, sparing our children from struggles we have the power to prevent. And we will reduce taxes, to recover the momentum of our economy and reward the effort and enterprise of working Americans.

We will build our defenses beyond challenge, lest weakness invite challenge.

We will confront weapons of mass destruction, so that a new century is spared new horrors.

The enemies of liberty and our country should make no mistake: America remains engaged in the world by history and by choice, shaping a balance of power that favors freedom. We will defend our allies and our interests. We will show purpose without arrogance. We will meet aggression and bad faith with resolve and strength. And to all nations, we will speak for the values that gave our nation birth.

America, at its best, is compassionate. In the quiet of American conscience, we know that deep, persistent poverty is unworthy of our nation's promise.

And whatever our views of its cause, we can agree that children at risk are not at fault. Abandonment and abuse are not acts of God, they are failures of love.

And the proliferation of prisons, however necessary, is no substitute for hope and order in our souls.

Where there is suffering, there is duty. Americans in need are not strangers, they are citizens, not problems, but priorities. And all of us are diminished when any are hopeless.

Government has great responsibilities for public safety and public health, for civil rights and common schools. Yet compassion is the work of a nation, not just a government.

And some needs and hurts are so deep they will only respond to a mentor's touch or a pastor's prayer. Church and charity, synagogue and mosque lend our communities their humanity, and they will have an honored place in our plans and in our laws.

Many in our country do not know the pain of poverty, but we can listen to those who do.

And I can pledge our nation to a goal: When we see that wounded traveler on the road to Jericho, we will not pass to the other side.

America, at its best, is a place where personal responsibility is valued and expected.

Encouraging responsibility is not a search for scapegoats, it is a call to conscience. And though it requires sacrifice, it brings a deeper fulfillment. We find the fullness of life not only in options, but in commitments. And we find that children and community are the commitments that set us free.

Our public interest depends on private character, on civic duty and family bonds and basic fairness, on uncounted, unhonored acts of decency which give direction to our freedom.

Sometimes in life we are called to do great things. But as a saint of our times has said, every day we are called to do small things with great love. The most important tasks of a democracy are done by everyone.

I will live and lead by these principles: to advance my convictions with civility, to pursue the public interest with courage, to speak for greater justice and compassion, to call for responsibility and try to live it as well.

In all these ways, I will bring the values of our history to the care of our times.

What you do is as important as anything government does. I ask you to seek a common good beyond your comfort; to defend needed reforms against easy attacks; to serve your nation, beginning with your neighbor. I ask you to be citizens: citizens, not spectators; citizens, not subjects; responsible citizens, building communities of service and a nation of character.

Americans are generous and strong and decent, not because we believe in ourselves, but because we hold beliefs beyond ourselves. When this spirit of citizenship is missing, no government program can replace it. When this spirit is present, no wrong can stand against it.

After the Declaration of Independence was signed, Virginia statesman John Page wrote to Thomas Jefferson: "We know the race is not to the swift nor the battle to the strong. Do you not think an angel rides in the whirlwind and directs this storm?"

Much time has passed since Jefferson arrived for his inauguration. The years and changes accumulate. But the themes of this day he would know: our nation's grand story of courage and its simple dream of dignity.

We are not this story's author, who fills time and eternity with his purpose. Yet his purpose is achieved in our duty, and our duty is fulfilled in service to one another.

Never tiring, never yielding, never finishing, we renew that purpose today, to make our country more just and generous, to affirm the dignity of our lives and every life.

This work continues. This story goes on. And an angel still rides in the whirlwind and directs this storm.

God bless you all, and God bless America. ❖

Lights in
the Darkness

If Anne Frank Only Knew

by Rebecca Leung

If you want to hear "hate" coming out of the mouths of school kids, go to the schools of North Korea, as a Dutch television crew did, and you'll hear hate from that country's teenagers directed at the United States.

Western television reporters rarely get into North Korea, but remarkably they let a Dutch television crew in to see how they're using Holland's most famous book, *The Diary of Anne Frank*.

That diary, of her life in hiding during World War II, is now being studied in North Korea's schools. But Anne Frank's plea for peace and freedom got lost in translation.

North Korea is using her diary, not to teach how Anne suffered at the hands of the German Nazis, but to warn the students how they could suffer at the hands of those they call "American Nazis." Correspondent Mike Wallace reports.

"After reading this book, I had a hatred for the American **imperialists**," says one student.

"That warmonger Bush is just as bad as Hitler. Because of him we will always live in fear of war," says another student.

But Anne Frank did not preach hate. Her diary is an enchanting, if horrific, day-by-day account of the time this

---

imperialists people who support or help build an empire in which one nation unfairly rules over others

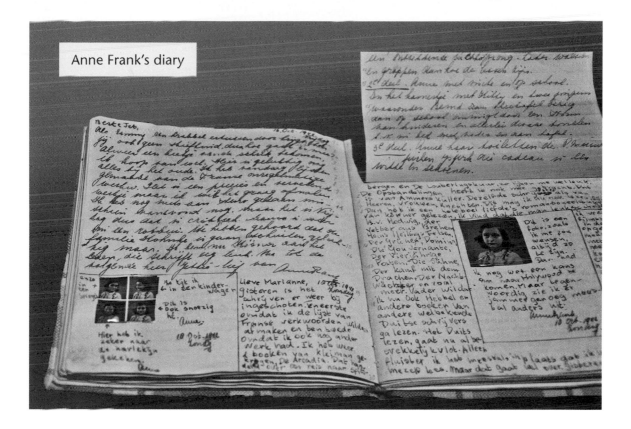

Anne Frank's diary

Dutch teenager and her Jewish family spent hiding from the Germans who had invaded and occupied Holland.

Anne, her parents, and sister hid in a small apartment in an attic in Amsterdam for more than two years. A bookcase concealed their secret stairway, but the Nazis eventually discovered them, and Anne died in a concentration camp when she was only 15.

Now, Anne Frank's house is a shrine to the courage she displayed, and the fear she lived with, under Hitler. Her diary has been translated into more than a 100 languages. Most recently, it was published in North Korea, where it's now part of the curriculum in their junior high schools.

Anne's plea for peace is a curious message for these students, because North Korea is constantly preparing for war. Dictator Kim Jong Il spends the country's meager resources maintaining a powerful military. And it turns out that North Korea is using Anne's diary to tell students they must sacrifice for the military—because war with America is inevitable.

"The Americans enjoy war. It excites them. It's part of their nature," says one student.

Here, they teach that today's Nazis are the Americans—and that today's Hitler is George W. Bush. And, to hammer that home, whenever North Korean students refer to President Bush, or to other Americans, they're taught to call them "Nazis," or "warmongers."

"As long as the warmonger Bush and the Nazi Americans live, who are worse than Hitler's fascists, world peace will be impossible to achieve," says another student.

But of course, that **bellicose** message runs counter to what Anne wrote in her diary: "You will understand that here in the attic, the desperate question is often asked: Why, oh why, go to war? Why can't people live in peace and why must we destroy everything?"

Why do the North Korean students think there are still wars in the world? "Because the cruel Americans want war," replies one student.

....

bellicose aggressive

All this came as a shock to Miriam Bartelsman, the reporter from Dutch television who received rare permission to come to the capital city of Pyongyang to see how North Korea is using Anne's diary.

For her report, she was allowed to talk with students about what they're learning from the book. After returning to Amsterdam, she told us that North Korea is simply turning Anne's message on its head.

"Anne Frank's diary is a big plea or a big cry for freedom, and for peace. But I think in North Korea, the diary is being used to promote war," says Bartelsman.

These students sympathize with Anne, but according to Bartelsman, they do not respect her.

"She didn't win. She was not a hero, and North Korea, they are learning, the children, we all want to be a hero, and we don't want to be killed," says Bartelsman.

"We know that Nazi America is certain to start a war with us, but we will win that war," says one student.

"Our students will fight with a pen in one hand and a weapon in the other until the last American is dead," adds another student.

These youngsters parrot the words of North Korea's deputy minister of education, who uses Anne's diary to teach students that North Korea's top priority is to build a stronger military to defeat the Americans.

And to make sure the students give that same answer, Dutch television caught one teacher whispering to her students, telling them just what to say to the Dutch reporter:

Teacher: Say that we don't want war, but that that is impossible as long as our enemy lives. So for us war is inevitable. We are not going to beg for peace. Instead, we must crush our enemy without mercy.

Student: You should not beg for peace. As long as the imperialists live, there will be no end to war.

"The most shocking thing is their comparison for President Bush with Hitler. That is absolutely disgusting," says Anne's cousin, Buddy Elias, who was her playmate and her last living direct relative.

Elias was the one who approved giving North Korea the rights to publish her diary, for a symbolic payment of less than $2,000.

"We were not told that it would be misused in schools. That, we had no idea," says Elias, who considers today's Hitler to be Kim Jong Il, North Korea's supreme leader. Kim insists that whenever anyone mentions his name, they must first call him respected or beloved.

And, in North Korea, teachers don't decide what their students will read. Those instructions come down from the top.

Why do the students think they were asked to read this diary? "According to our respected leader Kim Jong Il,

Students in class at a revolutionary school outside Pyongyang, North Korea

The Diary of Anne Frank is one of the great classics of the world," says one student. "That is why we read the diary—out of great respect for our leader Kim Jong Il."

"Our respected Gen. Kim Jong Il, with his warm and caring love for us students, gives us different foreign literature every year in hope that we can expand our intellectual development," adds another student. "*The Diary of Anne Frank* is part of that."

In North Korea, all art, all music, all pageants are created to praise Kim Jong Il or his father, Kim Il Sung, North Korea's first leader.

But while these children of the elite sing of their leader in Pyongyang, youngsters in the countryside are starving, reveal pictures that were smuggled out of North Korea by a German doctor. According to the World Food Program, almost half of North Korea's children under the age of 7 suffer from chronic malnutrition. But not the children of the establishment in Pyongyang.

"I'm certain that thanks to our beloved Gen. Kim Jong Il, we will never experience hunger like Anne did," says one boy.

Another student read from the diary: "Why is there hunger when food rots away elsewhere? Why are people so crazy?"

When Bartelsman asked students if they could answer Anne's question, again their teacher told them just what to say: "Why isn't food distributed everywhere? Because the imperialist **bourgeoisie** take it—that's why there is nothing left for the **proletariat**. Just say that."

The student's response: "Food is taken by the imperialist bourgeoisie, which is why there is nothing left for the proletariat."

Apparently, these students don't know that in their socialist paradise, up to a million people are now held in slave labor camps. But thanks to Anne Frank, they do know a lot about Nazi concentration camps.

Do they think that concentration camps like that still exist?

....

bourgeoisie an insulting name for members of the middle class
proletariat members of the working class

"Yes, I think such camps still exist. As long as there are American Nazis, there will be secret places where innocent people are murdered," says one student. "Places like that exist in America. The prisons in America are comparable to concentration camps."

And apparently, these students have learned what they were supposed to learn from Anne Frank's diary: When war with America comes, don't be a loser like her.

Could they live in hiding the way that Anne and her family did? "No," says one student. "I would go and fight, instead of living like a beggar as Anne did."

"For world peace, America will have to be destroyed," adds another student. "Only then, will Anne's wonderful dream of peace come true." ❖

Kindertransport

courtesy of the National Archives (United Kingdom)

The Kindertransport was a British scheme to rescue nearly 10,000 **predominantly** Jewish children from Nazi occupied territories. As a result of Nazi persecution, there was a rise in the number of Jews wanting to **emigrate** as circumstances for Jews in Germany and its annexed countries changed. The Kindertransport scheme was an opportunity for some of these children to leave their homes and families and seek temporary refuge in Britain.

Realising that the British public were keen to see some action, the scheme to bring over a large number of children was given the go-ahead. Visa and passport restrictions were lifted and children of seventeen and younger were able to enter Britain with a "white card". The majority of children had "guarantors" who would cover the re-emigration costs. These guarantors were mostly people who had some kind of connection with the families of the refugees or who had responded to the many advertisements in the newspaper, the *Jewish Chronicle*, from families seeking help. But, at a time of uncertainty in employment and with the country on the brink of war, few households could pay the sum of

predominantly mostly
emigrate to relocate from one's home country and permanently settle in a new one

Jewish children arriving from Germany as refugees in London

£50 required, the equivalent of £2000 today. Financing the "unguaranteed" children, those who did not have a previously arranged place of stay, became the responsibility of the Movement for the Care of Children in Germany, later known as the Refugee Children's Movement. The R.C.M. relied on charitable donations alone as it had been previously agreed with the Home Secretary that no refugee child would become a burden on state finances.

The children arrived from December 1938 to September 1939. With the outbreak of war, borders were closed and all transports ceased. The most reported reason for the ending of transports was that the R.C.M. had run out of funds.

Rising unemployment, anti-semitism and the concern that German refugees were now regarded as "enemy aliens" were issues which concerned the Government. Britain's policy of internment came into force in May 1940. This affected older child refugees who had reached the age of 16 before 1940. These children found work in agriculture and domestic service or joined the Pioneer Corps and other Auxiliary Services. Only a small number were interned.

Each year presented the R.C.M. with new challenges which meant changes in policies and changes within the organisation. Questions of finance, welfare and religious upbringing were issues which aroused criticism and conflict. Although its main aim was to re-unite the refugee children with their parents, as the war continued and news of the **persecution** and mass murder of the Jews reached the United Kingdom, it became apparent this was becoming increasingly unlikely. Re-emigration became uncertain.

The priorities of the R.C.M. now focused on the administration and care of those children who had arrived before the outbreak of war. By April 1943 the number of children according to the R.C.M.'s annual report totalled 8274. The Guardianship Act was passed in 1944 to provide care for those children who were not adopted, unmarried or under the age of 21. This was to ensure that those children

persecution hostility and harassment

who arrived in Britain to escape Nazi persecution would continue to be supported.

In very few cases the refugees were united with their loved ones. This action to rescue refugee children from Nazi persecution later became known as "Kindertransport".

Contains public sector information licensed under the Open Government Licence v2.0. ❖

excerpt from

First Annual Report for the Movement for the Care of Children from Germany Limited

courtesy of the National Archives (United Kingdom)
November 1938–1939 (HO 213/302)

Letter describing life at Barham House, addressed to Lord Baldwin

IN THE WORKSHOP

I work in the workshop. The workshop has to do all the craftsmen's work in and outside the house. We have a lot to do. For we live in a very old house, which was built in 1766.

There are floors broken in the house, which we have to repair. In another place a piece of the ceiling has come down which must be **mended**. Broken chairs and benches are repaired by us, windows put in, doors planed for the winter. In between one of the housemasters come running along asking for some paint or nails or tools. At the moment we are just doing the tailoring shop. It is a very large room, in which nothing has been repaired for a long time. From an old niche [recess] we have made a cupboard; and an old cupboard in the wall with stones and **rubbish**

mended fixed
rubbish trash

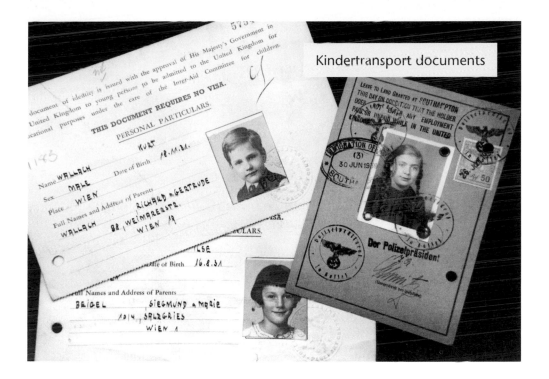

Kindertransport documents

we have cleaned; we have stopped the holes in the walls, pulled out old nails, put in new boards and painted it.

We collect all the old wood in the camp and cut out all good pieces; the rubbish we use for making fires. The Blackout is also the work of the carpenter's shop; in the dormitories we have put in blue bulbs and painted the windows, on the staircases we nailed some of them; in the common-room we have blacked out with cardboard on wooden frames.

I like the workshop.

Gunter B., 14 years old.

Contains public sector information licensed under the Open Government Licence v2.0. ❖

Report by Women's Voluntary Services

courtesy of the National Archives (United Kingdom)
12 January 1939 (MH 55/689)

Report on a vistit to Dovercourt Refugee Camp

On January 12th I visited Dovercourt Camp for refugee children, near Harwich, with Lady Marion Phillips. The camp belongs to Butlins Company, who built it for the purpose of **letting** huts to town people in summer at the rate of £2 a week. These people enjoy the communal life, they eat in the main building, and are near the sea in the country. The camp at Dovercourt has been taken on from Butlins at an all rate per head, and on the understanding that they do the catering. It is used as a kind of clearing station for German and Austrian Jewish and non-Aryan refugee children until arrangements can be made for their future. These children are from 5–18 years of age, and their parents are mostly dead or in concentration camps. The Nazi authorities are apparently only too glad to get rid of the children, with the exception of boys of 17 and over, whom they require for labour. They come into England in batches of varying numbers (80–120).

---

letting renting

Camp leader ringing the dinner bell at Dovercourt Refugee Camp

Conclusions. The camp leaders are very keen, full of human kindness, vitality and **emanating** a cheerful atmosphere. Great efforts are made to stress the future hopes of the children and so help them to forget the past. They seem wonderfully happy, considering all they had been through. The arrangements for heating, clothing, sanitation and health were very good, and the occupation of time as regards leisure seemed fairly satisfactory for an emergency measure. Better organisation for lessons and

....

emanating giving off; exuding

more variety in games would no doubt be possible over longer periods and in camps for boys or girls only. The one glaring defect appears to be the profiteering on catering, which should be remedied. The excuse for this would seem to be the difficulty of finding suitable accommodation in a short time, which necessitated using the easiest available.

N. de Selincourt

Contains public sector information licensed under the Open Government Licence v2.0. ❖

Letter to Lord Halifax, Foreign Secretary

courtesy of the National Archives (United Kingdom)
31 October 1938 (HO 213/302)

The Haven
Exley Gardens
Halifax
Oct. 31st 1938

Lord Halifax,
Dear Sir,

I am deeply concerned for the plight of the German girls and boys, who, after leaving school find life made **intolerable** for them owing to the racial and religious differences in their own country. That feeling of concern is my only excuse for taking up the valuable time of one whose onerous duties render inexcusable any intrusion of lesser import.

If I could succeed in **eliciting** your support in any one of the following schemes I feel that it's [sic] ultimate success would be assured:

1. Would migration to England of these young people be **facilitated** by their temporary adoption by English families?

---

intolerable unbearable
eliciting gaining; drawing out
facilitated made easier

2. Is it possible to arouse the interest of a body of voluntary workers to form an institution for providing food, refuge or employment for them?

3. Would you, sir, give permission for a broadcast appeal for co-operation from British families, or an appeal to local authorities to give friendly aid in the housing, clothing & employment of them?

4. Would you, sir, give assistance in obtaining visas for them?

5. Would you, sir, assist the writer in his efforts by placing with him your written full approval of the scheme?

If, in your wider experience of such matters you consider the above suggestions impracticable, would you advise me as to how these unfortunate young people can best be helped by young English people?

Needless to state, any assistance or advice that you can offer to me will not be undervalued.

I beg to remain,

Yours respectfully,
J H Harker

Letter to
the Chief Medical Officer
of Health at the Ministry of Health

courtesy of the National Archives (United Kingdom)
16 February 1939 (MH 55/709)

Borough of Hampstead
PUBLIC HEALTH DEPARTMENT
Town Hall, Haverstock Hill
Hampstead, N.W.3

H. Leslie Oldershaw, M.D. (Lon) D.P.H.

Medical Officer of Health

Telephone No Primrose 4421

All communication to be addressed to the Medical Officer
of Health O/H/A

16th Feburary 1939

Dear Sir,

I have been considerably concerned during the last few weeks in respect of the large numbers of Refugees, particularly children, who have arrived in my Borough. You will appreciate that I have received no information as to number, nor the addresses to which they have gone. However, I have discovered that certain houses are being used as hostels (e.g. one house is now used as a hostel for

17 German-Jewish boys) and other private boarding schools are taking in numbers of these children, functioning thereby, as clearing houses.

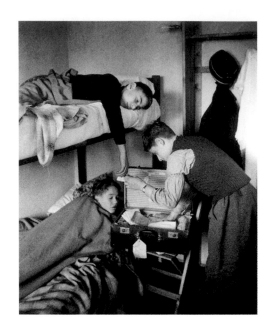

Is it your wish that I should exercise any special control or supervision over their Refugees in so far as they might possibly occasion the importation and spread of infectious disease, etc. It appears to me that unless some measure of registration is effected, a medical officer of health will remain **ignorant** of the existence of such premises to which I have referred.

Yours faithfully,
H. Leslie Oldershaw

Medical Officer of Health
The Chief Medical Officer,
Ministry of Health,
Whitehall, S.W.1.

....
ignorant unaware

The Date of Infamy

courtesy of the National Park Service

The attack on Pearl Harbor was the **culmination** of a decade of deteriorating relations between Japan and the United States over the status of China and the security of Southeast Asia. The breakdown began in 1931 when Japanese army extremists, in defiance of government policy, invaded and overran the northernmost Chinese province of Manchuria. Japan ignored American protests, and launched a full-scale attack on the rest of China in the summer of 1937. Although alarmed by this action, neither the United States, nor any other nation with interests in the Far East, was willing to use military force to halt Japanese expansion.

Over the next three years, war broke out in Europe, and Japan joined Nazi Germany in the Axis Alliance. The United States applied both diplomatic and economic pressures to try to resolve the Sino-Japanese conflict. The Japanese government viewed these measures, especially an **embargo** on oil, as threats to their nation's security. By the summer of 1941, both countries had taken positions from which they could not retreat without a serious loss of national prestige. Although both governments continued to negotiate their differences, Japan had already decided on war.

....

culmination the climax or pinnacle
embargo a ban on the trade of a commodity

The attack on Pearl Harbor was part of a grand strategy of conquest in the Western Pacific. The objective was to **immobilize** the Pacific Fleet so that the United States could not interfere with these invasion plans. The principal architect of the attack was Admiral Isoroku Yamamoto, Commander-in-Chief of the Japanese Combined Fleet. Though personally opposed to war with America, Admiral Yamamoto knew that Japan's only hope of success in such a war was to achieve quick and decisive victory. America's superior economic and industrial might would tip the scales in her favor during a prolonged conflict.

On November 26, the Japanese attack fleet of 33 warships and auxiliary craft, including 6 aircraft carriers, sailed from northern Japan for the Hawaiian Islands. The fleet followed a route that took it far to the north of the normal shipping lanes. By early morning, December 7, 1941, the ships had reached their launch position, 230 miles north of Oahu. At 6:00 a.m., the first wave of fighters, bombers, and torpedo planes took off. The night before, some 10 miles outside the entrance to Pearl Harbor, five midget submarines carrying two crewmen and two torpedoes each were launched from larger "mother" subs. Their mission: enter Pearl Harbor before the air strike, remain submerged until the attack got underway, then cause as much damage as possible.

....

immobilize to prevent movement or normal operations

Fire and smoke pouring from the battleships *Arizona* (right) and *West Virginia* (left), December 7, 1941

Meanwhile, at Pearl Harbor, the 130 vessels of the U.S. Pacific Fleet lay calm and serene. Seven of the fleet's nine battleships were tied up along "Battleship Row" on the southeast shore of Ford Island. Naval aircraft were lined up at Ford Island and Kaneohe Bay Naval Air Stations, and at Ewa Marine Corps Air Station. The aircraft belonging to the U.S. Army Air Corps were parked in groups as defense against possible saboteurs at Hickam, Wheeler, and Bellows airfields.

While the attack on Pearl Harbor intensified, other military installations on Oahu were hit. Hickam, Wheeler, and Bellows airfields; Ewa Marine Corps Air Station; Kaneohe Bay Naval Air Station; and Schofield Barracks suffered varying degrees of damage, with hundreds of planes destroyed on the ground and hundreds of men killed or wounded.

At 6:40 a.m., the crew of the destroyer USS *Ward* spotted the conning tower of one of the midget subs headed for the entrance to Pearl Harbor. The *Ward* sank the sub with depth charges and gunfire, then radioed the information to headquarters.

Before 7 a.m., the radar station at Opana Point picked up a signal indicating a large flight of planes approaching from the north. These were thought to be either aircraft flying in from the carrier USS *Enterprise* or an anticipated flight of B-17s from the mainland, so no action was taken.

The first wave of Japanese aircraft arrived over their target areas shortly before 7:55 a.m. Their leader, Commander Mitsuo Fuchida, sent the coded messages "To, To, To" and "Tora, Tora, Tora," telling the fleet that the attack had begun and that complete surprise had been achieved.

At approximately 8:10 a.m., the USS *Arizona* exploded, having been hit by a 1,760-pound, armor-piercing bomb that slammed through her deck and ignited her forward ammunition magazine. In less than nine minutes, she sank with 1,177 of her crew, a total loss. The USS *Oklahoma*, hit by several torpedoes, rolled completely over, trapping over

Fighting fires on the sunken USS *West Virginia*

400 men inside. The USS *California* and USS *West Virginia* sank at their moorings, while the USS *Utah*, converted to a training ship, capsized with over 50 of her crew. The USS *Maryland*, USS *Pennsylvania*, and USS *Tennessee*, all suffered significant damage. The USS *Nevada* attempted to run out to sea but took several hits and had to be beached to avoid sinking and blocking the harbor entrance.

After about five minutes, American anti-aircraft fire began to register hits, although many of the shells that had been improperly fused fell on Honolulu, where residents assumed them to be Japanese bombs. After a lull at about 8:40 a.m., the second wave of attacking planes focused on continuing the destruction inside the harbor, destroying the USS *Shaw*, USS *Sotoyomo*, a dry dock, and heavily damaging the *Nevada*, forcing her aground. They also attacked Hickam and Kaneohe airfields, causing heavy loss of life and reducing American ability to retaliate.

The forward magazine of the USS *Shaw* exploding

Army Air Corps pilots managed to take off in a few fighters and may have shot down 12 enemy planes. At 10 a.m. the second wave withdrew to the north, and the attack was over. The Japanese lost a total of 29 planes and 5 midget submarines, one of which was captured when it ran aground off Bellows Field. The commander of this midget submarine, Ensign Sakamaki, became the first U.S.-captured prisoner of the pacific war.

The attack was a great, but not total, success. Although the U.S. Pacific Fleet was shattered, its aircraft carriers (not in port at the time of the attack) were still afloat and Pearl Harbor was surprisingly intact. The shipyards, fuel storage areas, and submarine base suffered no more than slight damage. More importantly, the American people, previously divided over the issue of U.S. involvement in World War II, rallied together with a total commitment to victory over Japan and her Axis partners. ❖

Japanese Americans at Manzanar

courtesy of the National Park Service

"We had about one week to dispose of what we owned, except what we could pack and carry for our departure by bus … for Manzanar." William Hohri

Japan's attack on Pearl Harbor December 7, 1941, led the United States into World War II and radically changed the lives of 120,000 men, women, and children of Japanese ancestry living in the United States. The attack intensified racial prejudices and led to fear of potential sabotage and espionage by Japanese Americans among some in the government, military, news media, and public. In February 1942, President Franklin D. Roosevelt signed Executive Order 9066 authorizing the Secretary of War to establish Military Areas and to remove from those areas anyone who might threaten the war effort. Without due process, the government gave everyone of Japanese ancestry living on the West Coast only days to decide what to do with their houses, farms, businesses, and other possessions. Most families sold their belongings at a significant loss. Some rented their properties to neighbors. Others left possessions with friends or religious groups. Some abandoned their property. They did not know where they were going or

Japanese Americans lining up for buses to internment camps *NPS photo*

for how long. Each family was assigned an identification number and loaded into cars, buses, trucks, and trains, taking only what they could carry. Japanese Americans were transported under military guard to 17 temporary assembly centers located at racetracks, fairgrounds, and similar facilities in Washington, Oregon, California, and Arizona. Then they were moved to one of 10 **hastily** built relocation centers. By November 1942, the relocation was complete.

....

hastily quickly

Life at Manzanar

Ten war relocation centers were built in remote deserts, plains, and swamps of seven states: Arkansas, Arizona, California, Colorado, Idaho, Utah, and Wyoming. Manzanar, located in the Owens Valley of California between the Sierra Nevada on the west and the Inyo mountains on the east, was typical in many ways of the 10 camps.

About two-thirds of all Japanese Americans interned at Manzanar were American citizens by birth. The remainder were aliens, many of whom had lived in the United States for decades, but who, by law, were denied citizenship.

The first Japanese Americans to arrive at Manzanar, in March 1942, were men and women who volunteered to help build the camp. On June 1 the War Relocation Authority (WRA) took over operation of Manzanar from the U.S. Army.

The 500-acre housing section was surrounded by barbed wire and eight guard towers with searchlights and patrolled by military police. Outside the fence, military police housing, a reservoir, a sewage treatment plant, and agricultural fields occupied the remaining 5,500 acres. By September 1942, more than 10,000 Japanese Americans were crowded into 504 barracks organized into 36 blocks. There was little or no privacy in the barracks—and not much outside. The 200 to 400 people living in each block, consisting of 14 barracks each divided into four

National Archives and Records Administration, Clem Albers, photographer

rooms, shared men's and women's toilets and showers, a laundry room, and a mess hall. Any combination of eight individuals was allotted a 20-by-25-foot room. An oil stove, a single hanging light bulb, cots, blankets, and mattresses filled with straw were the only furnishings provided.

Coming from Los Angeles and other communities in California and Washington, Manzanar's internees were unaccustomed to the harsh desert environment. Summer temperatures soared as high as 110°F. In winter, temperatures frequently plunged below freezing.

Throughout the year strong winds swept through the valley, often blanketing the camp with dust and sand. Internees covered knotholes in the floors with tin can lids, but dust continued to blow in between the floorboards until linoleum was installed in late 1942.

"...one of the hardest things to endure was the communal latrines, with no partitions; and showers with no stalls."
Rosie Kakuuchi

Overcoming Adversity

Internees attempted to make the best of a bad situation. The WRA formed an advisory council of internee-elected block managers. Internees established churches, temples, and boys and girls clubs. They developed sports, music, dance, and other recreational programs; built gardens and ponds; and published a newspaper, the *Manzanar Free Press*.

Most internees worked in the camp. They dug irrigation canals and ditches; tended acres of fruits and vegetables; and raised chickens, hogs, and cattle. They made clothes and furniture for themselves and camouflage netting and experimental rubber for the military. They served as mess hall workers, doctors, nurses, police officers, firefighters, and teachers.

Professionals were paid $19 per month, skilled workers received $16, and nonskilled workers got $12. Many pooled their resources and created a consumer cooperative that

Sports, a welcome diversion at camp *Francis Stewart*

published the *Manzanar Free Press* and operated a general store, beauty parlor, barbershop, and bank. As the war turned in America's favor, restrictions were lifted, and Japanese Americans were allowed to leave the camps. Church groups, service organizations, and some camp administrators helped find sponsors and jobs in the Midwest and the East. From all 10 camps, 4,300 people received permission to attend college, and about 10,000 were allowed to leave temporarily to harvest sugar beets in Idaho, Montana, Utah, and Wyoming.

A total of 11,070 Japanese Americans were processed through Manzanar. From a peak of 10,046 in September 1942, the population dwindled to 6,000 by 1944. The last few hundred internees left in November 1945, three months after the war ended. Many of them had spent three-and-a-half years at Manzanar.

The removal of all Japanese Americans from the West Coast was based on widespread distrust of their loyalty after Pearl Harbor. Yet, no Japanese Americans were charged with espionage.

"Manzanar has its first gold star mother. We had dreaded the day when some family in Manzanar would receive the fateful telegram ...." Manzanar Free Press *article on Pfc. Frank Arikawa's death*

Loyalty and Service

About 5,000 Japanese Americans were serving in the U.S. Army when Japan attacked Pearl Harbor in December 1941. The U.S. military soon called for another 5,000 volunteers from the mainland and Hawaii. In January 1942, however, the Selective Service reclassified Japanese Americans as "enemy aliens" and stopped drafting them.

Emotions were intense during 1942 as the United States entered the war and Japanese Americans were moved to the relocation centers. Various protests and disturbances occurred at some centers over political differences, wages, and rumors of informers and black marketing. At Manzanar two people were killed and 10 were wounded by military police during the "Manzanar Riot" in December 1942.

Tensions intensified in 1943 when the government required internees to answer a "loyalty questionnaire." They were asked if they would serve in combat and if they would swear unqualified allegiance to the United States. Some older internees answered "no" because they were not allowed to become U.S. citizens. Others refused to serve while their families were behind barbed wire. Those who answered "yes" were considered "loyal" and became eligible for indefinite leave outside the West Coast military areas. Those who answered "no" were sent to a segregation center at Tule Lake, California.

In January 1944 the draft was reinstated for Japanese Americans. Most of those who were drafted or volunteered joined the 442nd Regimental Combat Team. Combined with the 100th Infantry Battalion of the Hawaiian Territorial Guard, the 442nd fought with distinction in North Africa, France, and Italy. With 9,846 casualties, the 100th/442nd had the highest casualty rate and was the most highly decorated Army unit for its size and length of service. Nearly 26,000 Japanese Americans served in the U.S. military during World War II. ❖

Manzanar ID Card Booklet

courtesy of the National Park Service

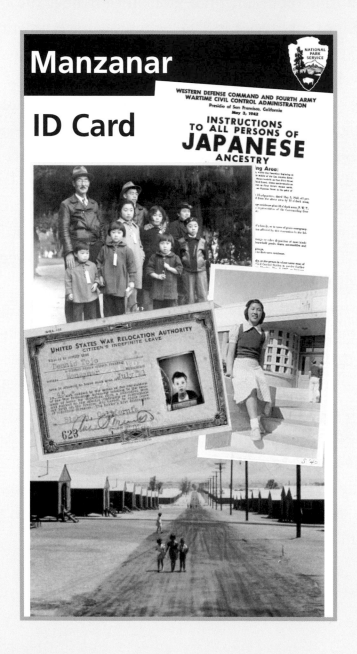

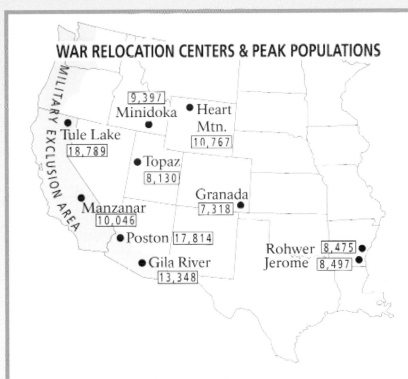

WAR RELOCATION CENTERS & PEAK POPULATIONS

MILITARY EXCLUSION AREA

Minidoka 9,397

Heart Mtn. 10,767

Tule Lake 18,789

Topaz 8,130

Granada 7,318

Manzanar 10,046

Poston 17,814

Rohwer 8,475
Jerome 8,497

Gila River 13,348

In 1942 the United States Government
ordered over 110,000 men, women,
and children to leave their homes and
detained them in **remote**, military-style
camps. Two-thirds of them were born
in America. Not one was convicted of
espionage or sabotage.

In this booklet, you will read the story
of a person who lived this history,
in his or her own words.

remote distant

LILIAN BANNAI
Family # 1107
Camp: Manzanar, CA
Address: 5-5-1

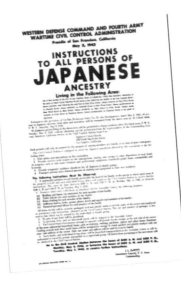

I was born on April 5, 1922 in Storrs, Utah, the second child of Shino and Sakui (Sam) Bannai. At the time of the mass evacuation of all American-Japanese from the West Coast, I was a 19 year old secretary to the principal of Gardena Elementary School.

After joining my family in Manzanar, my work was with the Board of Education. Because many others have described the disillusionment they felt, the humiliation of the crude conditions, I will omit my feelings, which were essentially much like the theirs. The greatest grief we felt was for

The greatest grief we felt was for the anxiety of our parents....

My goal was to overcome the situation by trying for the earliest possible release from camp.

the anxiety of our parents, and the uncertainty of our future as an intact family. My goal was to overcome the situation by trying for the earliest possible release from camp.

I relocated to Chicago, Ill. as executive secretary to the Dean of the Chicago Theological Seminary. In Jan., 1944, I was able to call my sister, Rose, so she could find work to eventually enroll in the University of Minnesota. The following year I brought out my youngest sister, Sharlen, so she could complete her final year of high school.

On my free weekends I was often asked to speak to outlying church groups who were interested in what was happening on the West Coast. As I described the sad situations, I asked the people to try and give the unfortunate victims of wartime **hysteria** an opportunity to resume their studies and lives in a welcoming community.

> **I asked the people to try and give the unfortunate victims of wartime hysteria an opportunity to resume their studies and lives in a welcoming community.**

> **My brother, Paul, who was training at Camp Shelby, Mississippi became very concerned for the young Hawaiian boys he met...**

My brother, Paul, who was training at Camp Shelby, Mississippi became very concerned for the young Hawaiian boys he met, ready soon to be sent into combat, too far from their Island homes for a

Nisei Troops Training at Camp Shelby

hysteria extreme irrationality or unreasonableness

final visit. He passed out our address to all his new buddies, told them to ring his sister's doorbell and expect a hearty Japanese dinner. Suddenly we began to get a steady stream of weekend visitors with funny accents. Wherever they wanted to go,

Nisei Troops with USO Hostesses

we took them— dancing at the Aragon Ballroom, baseball at Wrigley Field, stage shows of one or more of the great bands. Those who survived the Italian campaign came by Chicago to say goodbye. Not one came home intact. We could never forget these brave young men who lived up to their motto of "GO FOR BROKE" and held nothing back in the way they dedicated their lives to the cause of America,

> **Those who survived the Italian campaign came by Chicago to say goodbye. Not one came home intact.**

even while the constitutional rights of many of their citizens were being misinterpreted.

With the end of the war and the closure of the camps, my final goal was to help my parents get out of the shabby trailer camp where they had been sent. With the return of my brother from the South Pacific, we were able to locate into a normal neighborhood so our younger brother could resume his junior high school education.

> ...these brave young men... held nothing back in the way they dedicated their lives to the cause of America, even while the constitutional rights of many of their citizens were being misinterpreted.

Nisei Troops Training at Camp Shelby

Eventually my career as manager of a travel agency saw me visiting many distant places around the world, a great contrast to the two years I was imprisoned behind barbed wire and armed sentry posts, wondering if I would ever see anything but endless miles of desolate desert.

...two years I was imprisoned behind barbed wire and armed sentry posts, wondering if I would ever see anything but endless miles of desolate desert.

MANZANAR

Location: Inyo County, California, at the eastern base of the Sierra Nevada.

Environmental Conditions: Temperatures can be over 100 degrees in summer and below freezing in winter. Strong winds & dust storms are frequent.

Acreage: 6,000

Opened: March 21, 1942 as a Reception Center and June 1, 1942 as a War Relocation Center.

Closed: November 21, 1945

Max. Population: 10,046 (September 1942)

Demographics: Most internees were from the Los Angeles area, Terminal Island, and the San Fernando Valley. Others came from the San Joaquin Valley and Bainbridge Island.

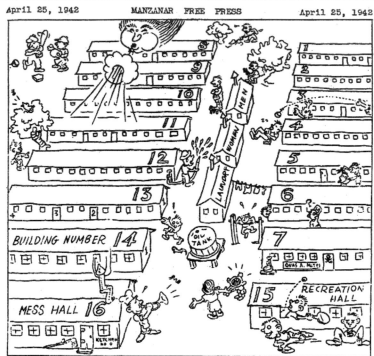

April 25, 1942   MANZANAR FREE PRESS   April 25, 1942

LIFE IN A MANZANAR BLOCK

Wind and Dust

This wind and dust I have to bear
How hard it blows I do not care.
But when the wind begins to blow –
My morale is pretty low.
I know that I can see it through
Because others have to bear it too.
So I will bear it with the rest
And hope the outcome is the best.

-- *George Nishimura, age 16 (1943)*

Manzanar Cemetery, Winter 2002.

This booklet was developed by the park rangers at Manzanar National Historic Site in partnership with the individuals profiled and their families.

The National Park Service cares for special places saved by the American people so that all may experience our heritage. To learn more about your national parks, visit the National Park Service website at www.nps.gov. To learn more about Manzanar National Historic Site, please visit our website at www.nps.gov/manz.

Manzanar National Historic Site
P.O. Box 426, Independence, CA 93526
Tel. 760-878-2194
E-mail: manz_superintendent@nps.gov

Printing was made possible by a grant from the California Civil Liberties Public Education Program.

3/08

EXPERIENCE YOUR AMERICA

Telling Tales

Rules of the Game

by Amy Tan

I was six when my mother taught me the art of invisible strength. It was a strategy for winning arguments, respect from others, and eventually, though neither of us knew it at the time, chess games.

"Bite back your tongue," scolded my mother when I cried loudly, yanking her hand toward the store that sold bags of salted plums. At home, she said, "Wise guy, he not go against wind. In Chinese we say, Come from South, blow with wind—poom!—North will follow. Strongest wind cannot be seen." The next week I bit back my tongue as we entered the store with the forbidden candies. When my mother finished her shopping, she quietly plucked a small bag of plums from the rack and put it on the counter with the rest of the items.

My mother imparted her daily truths so she could help my older brothers and me rise above our circumstances. We lived in San Francisco's Chinatown. Like most of the other Chinese children who played in the back alleys of restaurants and curio shops, I didn't think we were poor. My bowl was always full, three five-course meals every day, beginning with a soup of mysterious things I didn't want to know the names of.

We lived on Waverly Place, in a warm, clean, two-bedroom flat that sat above a small Chinese bakery specializing in steamed pastries and **dim sum**. In the early morning, when the alley was still quiet, I could smell fragrant red beans as they were cooked down to a pasty sweetness. By daybreak, our flat was heavy with the odor of fried sesame balls and sweet curried chicken crescents. From my bed, I would listen as my father got ready for work, then locked the door behind him, one-two-three clicks.

At the end of our two-block alley was a small sandlot playground with swings and slides well-shined down the middle with use. The play area was bordered by wood-slat benches where old-country people sat cracking roasted watermelon seeds with their golden teeth and scattering the husks to an impatient gathering of gurgling pigeons.

dim sum Chinese dumplings

The best playground, however, was the dark alley itself. It was crammed with daily mysteries and adventures. My brothers and I would peer into the medicinal herb shop, watching old Li dole out onto a stiff sheet of white paper the right amount of insect shells, saffron-colored seeds, and **pungent** leaves for his ailing customers. It was said that he once cured a woman dying of an ancestral curse that had eluded the best of American doctors. Next to the pharmacy was a printer who specialized in gold-embossed wedding invitations and festive red banners.

Farther down the street was Ping Yuen Fish Market. The front window displayed a tank crowded with doomed fish and turtles struggling to gain footing on the slimy green-tiled sides. A hand-written sign informed tourists, "Within this store, is all for food, not for pet." Inside, the butchers with their bloodstained white smocks **deftly** gutted the fish while customers cried out their orders and shouted, "Give me your freshest," to which the butchers always protested, "All are freshest." On less crowded market days, we would inspect the crates of live frogs and crabs which we were warned not to poke, boxes of dried cuttlefish, and row upon row of iced prawns, squid, and slippery fish. The sanddabs made me shiver each time; their eyes lay on one flattened side and reminded me of my mother's story of a careless

....

pungent having a sharp point or an intense odor
deftly skillfully

girl who ran into a crowded street and was crushed by a cab. "Was smash flat," reported my mother.

At the corner of the alley was Hong Sing's, a four-table cafe with a recessed stairwell in front that led to a door marked "Tradesmen." My brothers and I believed the bad people emerged from this door at night. Tourists never went to Hong Sing's, since the menu was printed only in Chinese. A Caucasian man with a big camera once posed me and my playmates in front of the restaurant. He had us move to the side of the picture window so the photo would capture the roasted duck with its head dangling from a juice-covered rope. After he took the picture, I told him he should go into Hong Sing's and eat dinner. When he smiled and asked me what they served, I shouted, "Guts and duck's feet and octopus gizzards!" Then I ran off with my friends, shrieking with laughter as we scampered across the alley and hid in the entryway grotto of the China Gem Company, my heart pounding with hope that he would chase us.

My mother named me after the street that we lived on: Waverly Place Jong, my official name for important American documents. But my family called me Meimei, "Little Sister." I was the youngest, the only daughter. Each morning before school, my mother would twist and yank on my thick black hair until she had formed two tightly wound pigtails. One day, as she struggled to weave a hard-toothed comb through my disobedient hair, I had a sly thought.

I asked her, "Ma, what is Chinese torture?" My mother shook her head. A bobby pin was wedged between her lips. She wetted her palm and smoothed the hair above my ear, then pushed the pin in so that it nicked sharply against my scalp.

"Who say this word?" she asked without a trace of knowing how wicked I was being. I shrugged my shoulders and said, "Some boy in my class said Chinese people do Chinese torture."

"Chinese people do many things," she said simply. "Chinese people do business, do medicine, do painting. Not lazy like American people. We do torture. Best torture."

My older brother Vincent was the one who actually got the chess set. We had gone to the annual Christmas party held at the First Chinese Baptist Church at the end of the alley. The missionary ladies had put together a Santa bag of gifts donated by members of another church. None of the gifts had names on them. There were separate sacks for boys and girls of different ages.

One of the Chinese parishioners had donned a Santa Claus costume and a stiff paper beard with cotton balls glued to it. I think the only children who thought he was the real thing were too young to know that Santa Claus was not Chinese. When my turn came up, the Santa man asked me how old I was. I thought it was a trick question; I was seven according to the American formula and eight by the Chinese calendar. I said I was born on March 17, 1951.

That seemed to satisfy him. He then solemnly asked if I had been a very, very good girl this year and did I believe in Jesus Christ and obey my parents. I knew the only answer to that. I nodded back with equal solemnity.

Having watched the older children opening their gifts, I already knew that the big gifts were not necessarily the nicest ones. One girl my age got a large coloring book of biblical characters, while a less greedy girl who selected a smaller box received a glass vial of lavender toilet water. The sound of the box was also important. A ten-year-old boy had chosen a box that jangled when he shook it. It was a tin globe of the world with a slit for inserting money. He must have thought it was full of dimes and nickels, because when he saw that it had just ten pennies, his face fell with such undisguised disappointment that his mother slapped the side of his head and led him out of the church hall, apologizing to the crowd for her son who had such bad manners he couldn't appreciate such a fine gift.

As I peered into the sack, I quickly fingered the remaining presents, testing their weight, imagining what they contained. I chose a heavy, compact one that was wrapped in shiny silver foil and a red satin ribbon. It was a twelve-pack of Life Savers and I spent the rest of the party arranging and rearranging the candy tubes in the order of my favorites. My brother Winston chose wisely as well. His present turned out to be a box of intricate plastic parts; the instructions on the box proclaimed that when they were properly assembled he would have an authentic miniature replica of a World War II submarine.

Vincent got the chess set, which would have been a very decent present to get at a church Christmas party, except it was obviously used and, as we discovered later, it was missing a black pawn and a white knight. My mother graciously thanked the unknown **benefactor**, saying, "Too good. Cost too much." At which point, an old lady with fine white, wispy hair nodded toward our family and said with a whistling whisper, "Merry, merry Christmas."

When we got home, my mother told Vincent to throw the chess set away. "She not want it. We not want it," she said, tossing her head stiffly to the side with a tight, proud smile. My brothers had deaf ears. They were already lining up the chess pieces and reading from the dog-eared instruction book. I watched Vincent and Winston play during Christmas week. The chessboard seemed to hold elaborate secrets waiting to be untangled. The chessmen were more powerful than old Li's magic herbs that cured ancestral curses. And my brothers wore such serious faces that I was sure something was at stake that was greater than avoiding the tradesmen's door to Hong Sing's.

"Let me! Let me!" I begged between games when one brother or the other would sit back with a deep sigh of relief and victory, the other annoyed, unable to let go of the

....

benefactor someone who donates to help a person or group outcome. Vincent at first refused to let me play, but when I offered my Life Savers as replacements for the buttons that filled in for the missing pieces, he relented. He chose the flavors: wild cherry for the black pawn and peppermint for the white knight. Winner could eat both.

As our mother sprinkled flour and rolled out small doughy circles for the steamed dumplings that would be our dinner that night, Vincent explained the rules, pointing to each piece. "You have sixteen pieces and so do I. One king and queen, two bishops, two knights, two castles, and eight pawns. The pawns can only move forward one step, except on the first move. Then they can move two. But they can only take men by moving crossways like this, except in the beginning, when you can move ahead and take another pawn."

"Why?" I asked as I moved my pawn. "Why can't they move more steps?"

"Because they're pawns," he said.

"But why do they go crossways to take other men? Why aren't there any women and children?"

"Why is the sky blue? Why must you always ask stupid questions?" asked Vincent. "This is a game. These are the rules. I didn't make them up. See. Here in the book." He jabbed a page with a pawn in his hand. "Pawn. P-A-W-N. Pawn. Read it yourself."

My mother patted the flour off her hands. "Let me see book," she said quietly. She scanned the pages quickly, not reading the foreign English symbols, seeming to search **deliberately** for nothing in particular.

"This American rules," she concluded at last. "Every time people come out from foreign country, must know rules. You not know, judge say, Too bad, go back. They not telling you why so you can use their way go forward. They say, Don't know why, you find out yourself. But they knowing all the time. Better you take it, find out why yourself." She tossed her head back with a satisfied smile.

I found out about all the whys later. I read the rules and looked up all the big words in a dictionary. I borrowed books from the Chinatown library. I studied each chess piece, trying to absorb the power each contained.

I learned about opening moves and why it's important to control the center early on; the shortest distance between two points is straight down the middle. I learned about the middle game and why tactics between two **adversaries** are like clashing ideas; the one who plays better has the clearest plans for both attacking and getting out of traps. I learned why it is essential in the endgame to have foresight, a mathematical understanding of all possible moves, and patience; all weaknesses and advantages become evident to a strong adversary and are **obscured** to

deliberately carefully, on purpose
adversaries opponents or enemies
obscured hidden

a tiring opponent. I discovered that for the whole game one must gather invisible strengths and see the endgame before the game begins.

I also found out why I should never reveal "why" to others. A little knowledge withheld is a great advantage one should store for future use. That is the power of chess. It is a game of secrets in which one must show and never tell.

I loved the secrets I found within the sixty-four black and white squares. I carefully drew a handmade chessboard and pinned it to the wall next to my bed, where I would stare for hours at imaginary battles. Soon I no longer lost any games or Life Savers, but I lost my adversaries. Winston and Vincent decided they were more interested in roaming the streets after school in their Hopalong Cassidy cowboy hats.

On a cold spring afternoon, while walking home from school, I detoured through the playground at the end of our alley. I saw a group of old men, two seated across a folding table playing a game of chess, others smoking pipes, eating peanuts, and watching. I ran home and grabbed Vincent's chess set, which was bound in a cardboard box with rubber bands. I also carefully selected two prized rolls of Life Savers. I came back to the park and approached a man who was observing the game.

"Want to play?" I asked him. His face widened with surprise and he grinned as he looked at the box under my arm.

"Little sister, been a long time since I play with dolls," he said, smiling benevolently. I quickly put the box down next to him on the bench and displayed my **retort**.

Lau Po, as he allowed me to call him, turned out to be a much better player than my brothers. I lost many games and many Life Savers. But over the weeks, with each diminishing roll of candies, I added new secrets. Lau Po gave me the names. The Double Attack from the East and West Shores. Throwing Stones on the Drowning Man. The Sudden Meeting of the Clan. The Surprise from the Sleeping Guard. The Humble Servant Who Kills the King. Sand in the Eyes of Advancing Forces. A Double Killing Without Blood.

There were also the fine points of chess etiquette. Keep captured men in neat rows, as well-tended prisoners. Never announce "Check" with vanity, lest someone with an unseen sword slit your throat. Never hurl pieces into the sandbox after you have lost a game, because then you must find them again, by yourself, after apologizing to all around you. By the end of the summer, Lau Po had taught me all he knew, and I had become a better chess player.

A small weekend crowd of Chinese people and tourists would gather as I played and defeated my opponents one by one. My mother would join the crowds during these outdoor exhibition games. She sat proudly on the bench, telling my admirers with proper Chinese humility, "Is luck."

....

retort response

A man who watched me play in the park suggested that my mother allow me to play in local chess tournaments. My mother smiled graciously, an answer that meant nothing. I desperately wanted to go, but I bit back my tongue. I knew she would not let me play among strangers. So as we walked home I said in a small voice that I didn't want to play in the local tournament. They would have American rules. If I lost, I would bring shame on my family.

"Is shame you fall down nobody push you," said my mother.

During my first tournament, my mother sat with me in the front row as I waited for my turn. I frequently bounced my legs to unstick them from the cold metal seat of the folding chair. When my name was called, I leapt up. My mother unwrapped something in her lap. It was her chang, a small tablet of red jade which held the sun's fire. "Is luck," she whispered, and tucked it into my dress pocket. I turned to my opponent, a fifteen-year-old boy from Oakland. He looked at me, wrinkling his nose.

As I began to play, the boy disappeared, the color ran out of the room, and I saw only my white pieces and his black ones waiting on the other side. A light wind began blowing past my ears. It whispered secrets only I could hear.

"Blow from the South," it murmured. "The wind leaves no trail." I saw a clear path, the traps to avoid. The crowd rustled. "Shhh! Shhh!" said the corners of the room. The wind blew stronger. "Throw sand from the East to distract him." The knight came forward ready for the sacrifice. The wind hissed, louder and louder. "Blow, blow, blow. He cannot see. He is blind now. Make him lean away from the wind so he is easier to knock down."

"Check," I said, as the wind roared with laughter. The wind died down to little puffs, my own breath. My mother placed my first trophy next to a new plastic chess set that the neighborhood Tao society had given to me. As she wiped each piece with a soft cloth, she said, "Next time win more, lose less."

"Ma, it's not how many pieces you lose," I said. "Sometimes you need to lose pieces to get ahead."

"Better to lose less, see if you really need."

At the next tournament, I won again, but it was my mother who wore the triumphant grin. "Lost eight piece this time. Last time was eleven. What I tell you? Better off lose less!" I was annoyed, but I couldn't say anything.

I attended more tournaments, each one farther away from home. I won all games, in all divisions. The Chinese bakery downstairs from our flat displayed my growing collection of trophies in its window, amidst the dust-covered cakes that were never picked up. The day after I won an important regional tournament, the window encased a fresh sheet cake with whipped-cream frosting and red script saying "Congratulations, Waverly Jong, Chinatown Chess Champion." Soon after that, a flower shop, headstone engraver, and funeral parlor offered to sponsor me in national tournaments. That's when my mother decided I no longer had to do the dishes. Winston and Vincent had to do my chores.

"Why does she get to play and we do all the work," complained Vincent.

"Is new American rules," said my mother. "Meimei play, squeeze all her brains out for win chess. You play, worth squeeze towel."

By my ninth birthday, I was a national chess champion. I was still some 429 points away from grand-master status, but I was touted as the Great American Hope, a child prodigy and a girl to boot. They ran a photo of me in *Life* magazine next to a quote in which Bobby Fischer said, "There will never be a woman grand master." "Your move, Bobby," said the caption.

The day they took the magazine picture I wore neatly plaited braids clipped with plastic barrettes trimmed with rhinestones. I was playing in a large high school auditorium that echoed with **phlegmy** coughs and the squeaky rubber knobs of chair legs sliding across freshly waxed wooden floors. Seated across from me was an American man, about the same age as Lau Po, maybe fifty. I remember that his sweaty brow seemed to weep at my every move. He wore a dark, **malodorous** suit. One of his pockets was stuffed with a great white kerchief on which he

phlegmy having mucus in the throat
malodorous having a bad smell

wiped his palm before sweeping his hand over the chosen chess piece with great flourish.

In my crisp pink-and-white dress with scratchy lace at the neck, one of two my mother had sewn for these special occasions, I would clasp my hands under my chin, the delicate points of my elbows poised lightly on the table in the manner my mother had shown me for posing for the press. I would swing my patent leather shoes back and forth like an impatient child riding on a school bus. Then I would pause, suck in my lips, twirl my chosen piece in midair as if undecided, and then firmly plant it in its new threatening place, with a triumphant smile thrown back at my opponent for good measure.

I no longer played in the alley of Waverly Place. I never visited the playground where the pigeons and old men gathered. I went to school, then directly home to learn new chess secrets, cleverly concealed advantages, more escape routes.

But I found it difficult to concentrate at home. My mother had a habit of standing over me while I plotted out my games. I think she thought of herself as my protective ally. Her lips would be sealed tight, and after each move I made, a soft "Hmmmmph" would escape from her nose.

"Ma, I can't practice when you stand there like that," I said one day. She retreated to the kitchen and made loud noises with the pots and pans. When the crashing stopped, I could see out of the corner of my eye that she was standing in the doorway. "Hmmmmph!" Only this one came out of her tight throat.

My parents made many concessions to allow me to practice. One time I complained that the bedroom I shared was so noisy that I couldn't think. Thereafter, my brothers slept in a bed in the living room facing the street. I said I couldn't finish my rice; my head didn't work right when my stomach was too full. I left the table with half-finished bowls and nobody complained. But there was one duty I couldn't avoid. I had to accompany my mother on Saturday market days when I had no tournament to play. My mother would proudly walk with me, visiting many shops, buying very little. "This my daughter Wave-ly Jong," she said to whoever looked her way.

One day after we left a shop I said under my breath, "I wish you wouldn't do that, telling everybody I'm your daughter." My mother stopped walking. Crowds of people with heavy bags pushed past us on the sidewalk, bumping into first one shoulder, than another.

"Aii-ya. So shame be with mother?" She grasped my hand even tighter as she glared at me.

I looked down. "It's not that, it's just so obvious. It's just so embarrassing."

"Embarrass you be my daughter?" Her voice was cracking with anger.

"That's not what I meant. That's not what I said."

"What you say?"

I knew it was a mistake to say anything more, but I heard my voice speaking, "Why do you have to use me to show off? If you want to show off, then why don't you learn to play chess?"

My mother's eyes turned into dangerous black slits. She had no words for me, just sharp silence. I felt the wind rushing around my hot ears. I jerked my hand out of my mother's tight grasp and spun around, knocking into an old woman. Her bag of groceries spilled to the ground.

"Aii-ya! Stupid girl!" my mother and the woman cried. Oranges and tin cans careened down the sidewalk. As my mother stooped to help the old woman pick up the escaping food, I took off.

I raced down the street, dashing between people, not looking back as my mother screamed shrilly, "Meimei! Meimei!" I fled down an alley, past dark, curtained shops and merchants washing the grime off their windows. I sped into the sunlight, into a large street crowded with tourists examining trinkets and souvenirs. I ducked into another dark alley, down another street, up another alley. I ran until it hurt and I realized I had nowhere to go, that I was not running from anything. The alleys contained no escape routes.

My breath came out like angry smoke. It was cold. I sat down on an upturned plastic pail next to a stack of empty boxes, cupping my chin with my hands, thinking hard. I imagined my mother, first walking briskly down one street or another looking for me, then giving up and returning home to await my arrival. After two hours, I stood up on creaking legs and slowly walked home. The alley was quiet and I could see the yellow lights shining from our flat like two tiger's eyes in the night. I climbed the sixteen steps to the door, advancing quietly up each so as not to make any warning sounds. I turned the knob; the door was locked. I heard a chair moving, quick steps, the locks turning—click! click! click!—and then the door opened.

"About time you got home," said Vincent. "Boy, are you in trouble."

He slid back to the dinner table. On a platter were the remains of a large fish, its fleshy head still connected to bones swimming upstream in vain escape. Standing there waiting for my punishment, I heard my mother speak in a dry voice.

"We not concerning this girl. This girl not have concerning for us." Nobody looked at me. Bone chopsticks clinked against the inside of bowls being emptied into hungry mouths.

I walked into my room, closed the door, and lay down on my bed. The room was dark, the ceiling filled with shadows from the dinnertime lights of neighboring flats.

In my head, I saw a chessboard with sixty-four black and white squares. Opposite me was my opponent, two angry black slits. She wore a triumphant smile. "Strongest wind cannot be seen," she said.

Her black men advanced across the plane, slowly marching to each successive level as a single unit. My white pieces screamed as they scurried and fell off the board one by one. As her men drew closer to my edge, I felt myself growing light. I rose up into the air and flew out the window. Higher and higher, above the alley, over the tops of tiled roofs, where I was gathered up by the wind and pushed up toward the night sky until everything below me disappeared and I was alone.

I closed my eyes and pondered my next move. ❖

Gumption

by Langston Hughes

You young folks don't remember the depression, but I
do. No jobs for nobody. That winter there wasn't a soul
working in our house but my wife, and she was evil as she
could be. She was doing a few washings now and then for
the white folks—before hand laundry went out of style—so
we kinder made out. But she didn't like to see me sitting
around, even if I couldn't find a job. There wasn't no work
to be got in our town, nor any other place, for that matter.
We had a couple of roomers, a man and his girl friend; but
they were out of a job also. And, like me and my wife, they
hadn't been in town long enough to get any consideration,
since the **relief** folks were hard on strangers. All of us was
just managing to get by on beans and mush all winter.

One cold February morning we was sitting around the
stove in the kitchen trying to keep warm, the roomers and
me, my wife was ironing, when who should pass by outside
in the alley but old man Oyster and his son.

"There goes Oyster and that boy of his," I said, "ragged
as a jay-bird, both of 'em."

"They ain't even on relief work, is they?" Jack, the
roomer, asked.

....

gumption spunk; boldness; initiative
relief public program to assist people in need

"They did have a few hours' work a month," I answered. "They messed up, though."

"Messed up, you call it, heh?" my wife put in, in her nervous way. "Well, they got gumption, anyhow. They told them white folks up yonder in the office just what they thought of 'em. That's what they did."

"And look at 'em now," I said, "going through the alley looking for something to eat."

"Well, they got gumption," my wife yelled, "and that's something."

"You can't eat gumption," Jack remarked, which made my wife mad.

"You can't eat sitting-around-on-your-rumpus, neither," she broke out, slamming her iron down on the white man's shirt and looking real hard at our roomer—a look that said, You oughtn't to talk, cause you ain't paid your rent for a month.

I sure was glad I hadn't said nothing, boy.

"What's it all about?" Jack's girl asked. "What's old man Oyster done to get in bad with them relief folks, Miss Clara?"

She had heard about it before from me, but she just wanted to get my wife to running her mouth—and keep her mind off the fact that they hadn't paid their rent that month.

"You ain't heard?" my wife said, choosing a new hot iron. "It's a story worth telling, to my mind, cause they got *gumption*—them Oysters." She looked hard at Jack and me. "Now, old man Oyster—this story goes way back, child—he ain't never amounted to much, just poor and honest. But he always did want to make something out of that boy o' his'n, Charlie—little and runty as he was. He worked hard to do it, too. He **portered**, **bellhopped**, did road work, did anything he could get to do. Kept that boy in school after his wife died, washed his ears, kept him clean, tried to make a gentleman out of him—and that boy did pretty well. Grew up and took a commercial bookkeeping-typewriter course in the school, and come out Grade A. *Grade A*, I'm telling you. Graduated and got a job with the white folks. Yes, sir! First time I ever heard tell of a colored boy typewriting or keeping books or anything like that in this white man's town. But Mr. Bartelson what owned the coalyard and fuel office where young Oyster worked, he was from Maine and didn't have no prejudice to speak of, so he gave this colored boy a chance in his place. And was them white truck drivers jealous—seeing a Negro working in the office and they out driving trucks! But old man Oyster's boy was *prepared*. I'm telling you, *prepared*! He had a good education and could do the work, black as he was. And he was lucky to find somebody to give him a break, because you know and I know you don't see no colored men working in white folks' offices nowhere hardly.

....

portered carried bags at a train or bus station
bellhopped carried bags at a hotel

"Well, sir, old man Oyster was proud as he could be of his boy. We was all proud. The church was proud. The white business school what graduated him was proud. Everything went fine for two or three years. Oyster and Charlie even started to buy a little house, cause the old man was working on the road digging for forty cents a hour. Then the depression came. They stopped building roads, and folks stopped buying fuel to keep warm by. Poor old man Bartelson what owned the coalyard finally had to close up, bankrupted and broke—which left young Oyster without a job, like the rest of us. Old man Oyster was jobless, too, cause the less roads they built and sewers they laid, the less work they gave to colored folks, and give it to the white instead. You know how it is—first to be fired and last to be hired."

Clara was just a-ironing and a-talking. "Then along come this Government relief and **WPA** and everybody thought times was surely gonna get better. Well, they ain't got no better, leastwise not for colored. Everybody in this town's on relief now but me and you-all—what ain't been here long enough to be in it. I've still got a few washings to do and a little house cleaning now and then, thank God! But look at Sylvester," pointing at me. "They have done cut every porter off at the bus station but one. And Syl is jobless as a greyhound.

....

WPA Works Progress Administration, a government program created during the Depression to help provide jobs

"Anyhow, to go ahead with Oyster, it were a crying shame to see this poor old man and that fine young colored boy out of work—and they both ambitious, and steady, and good race men. Well, when relief opened up and they started giving out so many hours of work a month, they put old man Oyster back on the road. Now, his boy, Charlie, ain't never done no kind of work like road work, being a office man. But he thought he'd have to do it, too, and Charlie wasn't objecting, mind you—when the Government opened up a office for what they calls white-collar workers. All the white folks what's been doing office work in good times, insurance people and store clerks and such, they went there to get the kind o' work they was used to doing. Oyster's son went, too. But don't you know they discriminated against him! Yes, sir—the Government discriminating him because he were black! They said, 'You're not no office worker,' in spite of all the proofs Charlie had that he were in Mr. Bartelson's office for three years—the letter Bartelson gave him and all. But they sent old man Oyster's boy right on out yonder to work on the road with his father.

"Well, that made the old man mad. He said, 'What am I working all these years for you, educating you to come out here and dig on the road with me, and you with a education?'

"The old man stopped his work then and there that morning, laid off, and went right on up to that government office to see the white man about it. And that's where the trouble commenced!"

Clara was just a-talking and a-ironing. "The government white man said, 'You ought to be glad for your boy to get any kind o' work, these days and times. You can't be picking and choosing now.'

"But old man Oyster stood there and argued with the man for his son's rights. That's why I say he's got *gumption*. He said, 'I ain't asking to be picking and choosing, and I ain't asked nothing for *myself*. I'm speaking about that boy o' mine. Charlie's got a education. True, he's colored, but he's worked for three years in a office for one of the finest white men that ever lived and breathed, Mr. Bartelson. Charlie's got experience. My boy's a typewriter and a bookkeeper. What for you send him out to work on a road with me? Ain't this the place what's giving all the white folks jobs doing what they used to doing and know how to do? My boy ain't know nothing about no pick and shovel. Why don't you treat Charlie Oyster like you do the rest of the people and give him some o' his kind o' work?'

"'We have no office jobs here for Negroes,' said the man, right flat out like that. That's why I sent your son over where they give out road work. I classify all Negroes as laborers on our relief rolls.'

"Well, that made old man Oyster mad as hell. He said, 'Drat it, I'm a citizen! Is that what WPA is for—to bring more discrimination than what is? I want to know why my boy can't be a typewriter like the rest of 'em what's got training, even if it is on relief. If he could work in a white man's office, ain't he good enough to get work from you—and you the gobernment?'

"Well, this made the white man mad, and he yelled, 'You must be one o' them Communists, ain't you?' And he pressed some kind o' buzzer and sent out for a cop.

"Now, old man Oyster ain't never had no trouble of any kind in this town before, but when them cops started to put their hands on him and throw him out o' that office, he raised sand. He was right, too! But them cops didn't see it that way, and one of 'em brought his stock down on that old man's head and knocked him out.

"When Oyster come to, he was in jail.

"Then old man Oyster's son showed he was a man! Charlie heard about the trouble when he come home from off the road that evening, and he went to the jail to see his papa, boiling mad. When he heard how it was, that white man calling the cops in to beat up his father, he said, 'Pa, I'll be in jail here with you tomorrow.' And sure enough, he was. He went up to that there white-collar relief office the next morning and beat that white man so bad, he ain't got over it yet.

"'The idea,' young Oyster said, 'of you having my father knocked down and dragged out because he came here to talk to you like a citizen about our rights! Who are you anyway, any more'n me? Try to throw me out o' here and I'll beat you to a pulp first!'

"Well, that man reached for the buzzer again to call some more cops. When he reached, young Oyster had him! It would a-done me good to see the way that black boy give that white man a fit—cause he turned him every way but loose. When the cops come, they put Charlie in jail all right—but that white man was beat by then! The idea of relief coming here adding prejudice to what we already got, and times as hard as they is."

Clara planked down her iron on the stove. "Anyhow, they didn't keep them Oysters in jail very long, neither father or son. Old Judge Murray give 'em a month apiece, suspended sentence, and let 'em out. But when they got out o' jail, don't you know them relief people wouldn't give Oyster and his boy no more work a-tall! No, sir! They told 'em they wasn't feeding no black **reds**. Now old man Oyster nor Charlie neither ain't never heard o' Communists—but that's what they called 'em just cause they went up there and fought for what they ought to have. They didn't win— they're out there in the alleys now hauling trash. But they got gumption!"

"You can't live on gumption," I said, trying to be practical.

....
reds slang term for "communists"

"No, but you can choke on shame!" my wife yelled, looking hard at Jack and me. "I ain't never seen you-all fighting for nothing yet. Lord knows you both bad enough off to go out and raise hell somewhere and get something!" She put the iron down with a bang. "If I had a young boy, I'd want him to be like Oyster's son, and not take after none of you—sitting around behind the stove talking 'bout you 'can't live on gumption.' You can't live on it cause you ain't got none, that's why! Get up from behind that stove, get out o' here, both of you, and bring me something back I can use— bread, money, or a job, I don't care which. Get up and go on! Scat!"

She waved her iron in the air and looked like she meant to bring it down on my head instead of on a shirt. So Jack and me had to leave that nice warm house and go out in the cold and scuffle. There was no peace at home that morning, I mean. I had to try and work up a little gumption. ❖

To Build a Fire

by Jack London

Day had broken cold and grey, exceedingly cold and
grey, when the man turned aside from the main **Yukon**
trail and climbed the high earth-bank, where a dim and
little-traveled trail led eastward through the fat spruce
timberland. It was a steep bank, and he paused for breath
at the top, excusing the act to himself by looking at his
watch. It was nine o'clock. There was no sun nor hint of
sun, though there was not a cloud in the sky. It was a clear
day, and yet there seemed an **intangible pall** over the face

Yukon a territory in northwestern Canada; also, a river that runs through the region
intangible incapable of being touched
pall something that covers and produces a gloomy effect; a heavy cloth thrown
over a coffin

of things, a subtle gloom that made the day dark, and that was due to the absence of sun. This fact did not worry the man. He was used to the lack of sun. It had been days since he had seen the sun, and he knew that a few more days must pass before that cheerful orb, due south, would just peep above the sky-line and dip immediately from view.

The man flung a look back along the way he had come. The Yukon lay a mile wide and hidden under three feet of ice. On top of this ice were as many feet of snow. It was all pure white, rolling in gentle **undulations** where the ice jams of the freeze-up had formed. North and south, as far as his eye could see, it was unbroken white, save for a dark hairline that curved and twisted from around the spruce-covered island to the south, and that curved and twisted away into the north, where it disappeared behind another spruce-covered island. This dark hairline was the trail—the main trail—that led south five hundred miles to the **Chilcoot Pass**, **Dyea**, and salt water; and that led north seventy miles to **Dawson**, and still on to the north a thousand miles to **Nulato**, and finally to **St. Michael** on **Bering Sea**, a thousand miles and half a thousand more.

....

undulations wave-like appearances; wavy, curving forms
Chilcoot Pass (also spelled *Chilkoot*) a pass in the mountains on the border between British Columbia and Alaska
Dyea at one time, a town south of the Chilcoot Pass
Dawson a town on the Yukon River in the western Yukon Territory
Nulato a town in Alaska
St. Michael a port in Alaska
Bering Sea a body of water that extends from the Pacific Ocean northward between Siberia and Alaska

But all this—the mysterious, far-reaching hairline trail, the absence of sun from the sky, the tremendous cold, and the strangeness and weirdness of it all—made no impression on the man. It was not because he was long used to it. He was a newcomer in the land, a **chechaquo**, and this was his first winter. The trouble with him was that he was without imagination. He was quick and alert in the things of life, but only in the things, and not in the significances. Fifty degrees below zero meant eighty-odd degrees of frost. Such fact impressed him as being cold and uncomfortable, and that was all. It did not lead him to **meditate** upon his frailty as a creature of temperature, and upon man's frailty in general, able only to live within certain narrow limits of heat and cold; and from there on it did not lead him to the **conjectural** field of immortality and man's place in the universe. Fifty degrees below zero stood for a bite of frost that hurt and that must be guarded against by the use of mittens, ear-flaps, warm moccasins, and thick socks. Fifty degrees below zero was to him just precisely fifty degrees below zero. That there should be anything more to it than that was a thought that never entered his head.

....

chechaquo a newcomer; a tenderfoot
meditate to think about; to reflect on
conjectural based on guesswork; concluded without evidence or proof

As he turned to go on, he spat **speculatively**. There was a sharp, explosive crackle that startled him. He spat again. And again, in the air, before it could fall to the snow, the spittle crackled. He knew that at fifty below spittle crackled on the snow, but this spittle had crackled in the air. Undoubtedly it was colder than fifty below—how much colder he did not know. But the temperature did not matter. He was bound for the old claim on the left fork of Henderson Creek, where the boys were already. They had come over across the divide from the Indian Creek country, while he had come the roundabout way to take a look at the possibilities of getting out logs in the spring from the islands in the Yukon. He would be in to camp by six o'clock; a bit after dark, it was true, but the boys would be there, a fire would be going, and a hot supper would be ready. As for lunch, he pressed his hand against the **protruding** bundle under his jacket. It was also under his shirt, wrapped up in a handkerchief and lying against the naked skin. It was the only way to keep the biscuits from freezing. He smiled agreeably to himself as he thought of those biscuits, each cut open and sopped in bacon grease, and each enclosing a generous slice of fried bacon.

He plunged in among the big spruce trees. The trail was faint. A foot of snow had fallen since the last sled

---

speculatively in a manner intended to test an idea or theory
protruding jutting out; pushing forward

had passed over, and he was glad he was without a sled, traveling light. In fact, he carried nothing but the lunch wrapped in the handkerchief. He was surprised, however, at the cold. It certainly was cold, he concluded, as he rubbed his numbed nose and cheekbones with his mittened hand. He was a warm-whiskered man, but the hair on his face did not protect the high cheekbones and the eager nose that thrust itself aggressively into the frosty air.

At the man's heels trotted a dog, a big native husky, the proper wolf dog, grey-coated and without any visible or **temperamental** difference from its brother, the wild wolf. The animal was depressed by the tremendous cold. It knew that it was no time for traveling. Its instinct told it a truer tale than was told to the man by the man's judgment. In reality, it was not merely colder than fifty below zero; it was colder than sixty below, than seventy below. It was seventy-five below zero. Since the freezing point is thirty-two above zero, it meant that one hundred and seven degrees of frost obtained. The dog did not know anything about thermometers. Possibly in its brain there was no sharp consciousness of a condition of very cold such as was in the man's brain. But the brute had its instinct. It experienced a vague but **menacing apprehension** that subdued it and

----

temperamental relating to one's disposition, one's way of thinking and behaving
menacing threatening
apprehension suspicion of fear; foreboding

made it slink along at the man's heels, and that made it question eagerly every **unwonted** movement of the man as if expecting him to go into camp or to seek shelter somewhere and build a fire. The dog had learned fire, and it wanted fire, or else to burrow under the snow and cuddle its warmth away from the air.

The frozen moisture of its breathing had settled on its fur in a fine powder of frost, and especially were its jowls, muzzle, and eyelashes whitened by its crystalled breath. The man's red beard and moustache were likewise frosted, but more solidly, the deposit taking the form of ice and increasing with every warm, moist breath he exhaled. Also, the man was chewing tobacco, and the muzzle of ice held his lips so rigidly that he was unable to clear his chin when he expelled the juice. The result was that a crystal beard of the color and solidity of amber was increasing its length on his chin. If he fell down it would shatter itself, like glass, into brittle fragments. But he did not mind the **appendage**. It was the penalty all tobacco chewers paid in that country, and he had been out before in two cold snaps. They had not been so cold as this, he knew, but by the spirit thermometer at Sixty Mile he knew they had been registered at fifty below and at fifty-five.

....

unwonted not usual; out of the ordinary
appendage something attached to a larger thing, such as a limb of a body

He held on through the level stretch of woods for several miles, crossed a wide flat, and dropped down a bank to the frozen bed of a small stream. This was Henderson Creek, and he knew he was ten miles from the forks. He looked at his watch. It was ten o'clock. He was making four miles an hour, and he calculated that he would arrive at the forks at half-past twelve. He decided to celebrate that event by eating his lunch there.

The dog dropped in again at his heels, with a tail drooping discouragement, as the man swung along the creek bed. The furrow of the old sled trail was plainly visible, but a dozen inches of snow covered the marks of the last runners. In a month no man had come up or down that silent creek. The man held steadily on. He was not much given to thinking, and just then particularly he had nothing to think about save that he would eat lunch at the forks and that at six o'clock he would be in camp with the boys. There was nobody to talk to and, had there been, speech would have been impossible because of the ice muzzle on his mouth. So he continued **monotonously** to chew tobacco and to increase the length of his amber beard.

Once in a while the thought **reiterated** itself that it was very cold and that he had never experienced such cold. As he walked along he rubbed his cheekbones and nose with the back of his mittened hand. He did this automatically,

monotonously in a tiresome and unvarying way
reiterated repeated

now and again changing hands. But rub as he would, the instant he stopped his cheekbones went numb, and the following instant the end of his nose went numb. He was sure to frost his cheeks; he knew that, and experienced a pang of regret that he had not devised a nose strap of the sort Bud wore in cold snaps. Such a strap passed across the cheeks, as well, and saved them. But it didn't matter much, after all. What were frosted cheeks? A bit painful, that was all; they were never serious.

Empty as the man's mind was of thoughts, he was keenly observant, and he noticed the changes in the creek, the curves and bends and timber jams, and always he sharply noted where he placed his feet. Once, coming around a bend, he shied abruptly, like a startled horse, curved away from the place where he had been walking, and retreated several paces back along the trail. The creek he knew was frozen clear to the bottom—no creek could contain water in that arctic winter—but he knew also that there were springs that bubbled out from the hillsides and ran along under the snow and on top of the ice of the creek. He knew that the coldest snaps never froze these springs, and he knew likewise their danger. They were traps. They hid pools of water under the snow that might be three inches deep, or three feet. Sometimes a skin of ice half an inch thick covered them, and in turn was covered by the snow. Sometimes there were alternate layers of water and ice-skin, so that when one broke through he kept on breaking through for a while, sometimes wetting himself to the waist.

That was why he had shied in such panic. He had felt the give under his feet and heard the crackle of a snow-hidden ice-skin. And to get his feet wet in such a temperature meant trouble and danger. At the very least it meant delay, for he would be forced to stop and build a fire, and under its protection to bare his feet while he dried his socks and moccasins. He stood and studied the creek bed and its banks, and decided that the flow of water came from the right. He reflected awhile, rubbing his nose and cheeks, then skirted to the left, stepping **gingerly** and testing the footing for each step. Once clear of the danger, he took a fresh chew of tobacco and swung along at his four-mile gait.

In the course of the next two hours he came upon several similar traps. Usually the snow above the hidden pools had a sunken, candied appearance that advertised the danger. Once again, however, he had a close call; and once, suspecting danger, he **compelled** the dog to go on in front. The dog did not want to go. It hung back until the man shoved it forward, and then it went quickly across the white, unbroken surface. Suddenly it broke through, floundered to one side, and got away to firmer footing. It

....

gingerly cautiously; very carefully
compelled forced; urged

had wet its forefeet and legs, and almost immediately the water that clung to it turned to ice. It made quick efforts to lick the ice off its legs, then dropped down in the snow and began to bite out the ice that had formed between the toes. This was a matter of instinct. To permit the ice to remain would mean sore feet. It did not know this. It merely obeyed the mysterious prompting that arose from the deep crypts of its being. But the man knew, having achieved a judgment on the subject, and he removed the mitten from his right hand and helped tear out the ice particles. He did not expose his fingers more than a minute, and was astonished at the swift numbness that **smote** them.

....

smote struck suddenly

It certainly was cold. He pulled on the mitten hastily, and beat the hand savagely across his chest.

At twelve o'clock the day was at its brightest. Yet the sun was too far south on its winter journey to clear the horizon. The bulge of the earth intervened between it and Henderson Creek, where the man walked under a clear sky at noon and cast no shadow. At half-past twelve, to the minute, he arrived at the forks of the creek. He was pleased at the speed he had made. If he kept it up, he would certainly be with the boys by six. He unbuttoned his jacket and shirt and drew forth his lunch. The action consumed no more than a quarter of a minute, yet in that brief moment the numbness laid hold of the exposed fingers. He did not put the mitten on, but, instead, struck the fingers a dozen sharp smashes against his leg. Then he sat down on a snow-covered log to eat. The sting that followed upon the striking of his fingers against his leg ceased so quickly that he was startled, he had had no chance to take a bite of biscuit. He struck the fingers repeatedly and returned them to the mitten, baring the other hand for the purpose of eating. He tried to take a mouthful, but the ice-muzzle prevented. He had forgotten to build a fire and thaw out. He chuckled at his foolishness, and as he chuckled he noted the numbness creeping into the exposed fingers. Also, he noted that the stinging which had first come to his toes when he sat down was already passing away. He wondered whether the toes were warm or numbed. He moved them inside the moccasins and decided that they were numbed.

He pulled the mitten on hurriedly and stood up. He was a bit frightened. He stamped up and down until the stinging returned into the feet. It certainly was cold, was his thought. That man from Sulphur Creek had spoken the truth when telling how cold it sometimes got in the country. And he had laughed at him at the time! That showed one must not be too sure of things. There was no mistake about it, it was cold. He strode up and down, stamping his feet and threshing his arms, until reassured by the returning warmth. Then he got out matches and proceeded to make a fire. From the undergrowth, where high water of the previous spring had lodged a supply of seasoned twigs, he got his firewood. Working carefully from a small beginning, he soon had a roaring fire, over which he thawed the ice from his face and in the protection of which he ate his biscuits. For the moment the cold of space was outwitted. The dog took satisfaction in the fire, stretching out close enough for warmth and far enough away to escape being singed.

When the man had finished, he filled his pipe and took his comfortable time over a smoke. Then he pulled on his mittens, settled the ear flaps of his cap firmly about his ears, and took the creek trail up the left fork. The dog was disappointed and yearned back toward the fire. This man did not know cold. Possibly all the generations of his ancestry had been ignorant of cold, of real cold, of cold one hundred and seven degrees below freezing point. But the dog knew; all its ancestry knew, and it had inherited the knowledge. And it knew that it was not good to walk abroad in such fearful cold. It was the time to lie snug in a hole in the snow and wait for a curtain of cloud to be drawn across the face of outer space whence this cold came. On the other hand, there was no keen **intimacy** between the dog and the man. The one was the toil slave of the other, and the only caresses it had ever received were the caresses of the whip lash and of harsh and menacing throat sounds that threatened the whip lash. So the dog made no effort to communicate its apprehension to the man. It was not concerned in the welfare of the man; it was for its own sake that it yearned back toward the fire. But the man whistled, and spoke to it with the sound of whip lashes, and the dog swung in at the man's heels and followed after.

The man took a chew of tobacco and proceeded to start a new amber beard. Also, his moist breath quickly powdered with white his moustache, eyebrows, and lashes. There did not seem to be so many springs on the left fork of the Henderson, and for half an hour the man saw no signs of any. And then it happened. At a place where there

intimacy close familiarity

were no signs, where the soft, unbroken snow seemed to advertise solidity beneath, the man broke through. It was not deep. He wetted himself half-way to the knees before he floundered out to the firm crust.

He was angry, and cursed his luck aloud. He had hoped to get into camp with the boys at six o'clock, and this would delay him an hour, for he would have to build a fire and dry out his footgear. This was **imperative** at that low temperature—he knew that much; and he turned aside to the bank, which he climbed. On top, tangled in the underbrush about the trunks of several small spruce trees, was a high-water deposit of dry firewood—sticks and twigs principally, but also larger portions of seasoned branches and fine, dry, last-year's grasses. He threw down several large pieces on top of the snow. This served for a foundation and prevented the young flame from drowning itself in the snow it otherwise would melt. The flame he got by touching a match to a small shred of birch bark that he took from his pocket. This burned even more readily than paper. Placing it on the foundation, he fed the young flame with wisps of dry grass and with the tiniest dry twigs.

He worked slowly and carefully, keenly aware of his danger. Gradually, as the flame grew stronger, he increased the size of the twigs with which he fed it. He squatted in the snow, pulling the twigs out from their entanglement

---

imperative necessary

in the brush and feeding directly to the flame. He knew there must be no failure. When it is seventy-five below zero, a man must not fail in his first attempt to build a fire—that is, if his feet are wet. If his feet are dry, and he fails, he can run along the trail for half a mile and restore his circulation. But the circulation of wet and freezing feet cannot be restored by running when it is seventy-five below. No matter how fast he runs, the wet feet will freeze the harder.

All this the man knew. The old-timer on Sulphur Creek had told him about it the previous fall, and now he was appreciating the advice. Already all sensation had gone out of his feet. To build the fire he had been forced to remove his mittens, and the fingers had quickly gone numb. His pace of four miles an hour had kept his heart pumping blood to the surface of his body and to all the **extremities**. But the instant he stopped, the action of the pump eased down. The cold of space smote the unprotected tip of the planet, and he, being on that unprotected tip, received the full force of the blow. The blood of his body recoiled before it. The blood was alive, like the dog, and like the dog it wanted to hide away and cover itself up from the fearful cold. So long as he walked four miles an hour, he pumped that blood, willy-nilly, to the surface; but now it ebbed away and sank down into the recesses of his body.

....

extremities limbs of the body

The extremities were the first to feel its absence. His wet feet froze the faster, and his exposed fingers numbed the faster, though they had not yet begun to freeze. Nose and cheeks were already freezing, while the skin of all his body chilled as it lost its blood.

But he was safe. Toes and nose and cheeks would be only touched by the frost, for the fire was beginning to burn with strength. He was feeding it with twigs the size of his finger. In another minute he would be able to feed it with branches the size of his wrist, and then he could remove his wet footgear, and, while it dried, he could keep his naked feet warm by the fire, rubbing them at first, of course, with snow. The fire was a success. He was safe. He remembered the advice of the old-timer on Sulphur Creek, and smiled. The old-timer had been very serious in laying down the law that no man must travel alone in the **Klondike** after fifty below. Well, here he was; he had had the accident; he was alone; and he had saved himself. Those old-timers were rather womanish, some of them, he thought. All a man had to do was to keep his head, and he was all right. Any man who was a man could travel alone. But it was surprising, the rapidity with which his cheeks and nose were freezing. And he had not thought his fingers could go lifeless in so short a time. Lifeless they were, for he could scarcely make them move together to grip a twig, and

....

Klondike a region of the Yukon Territory in northwest Canada, on the Alaska border they seemed remote from his body and from him. When he touched a twig, he had to look and see whether or not he had hold of it. The wires were pretty well down between him and his finger-ends.

All of which counted for little. There was the fire, snapping and crackling and promising life with every dancing flame. He started to untie his moccasins. They were coated with ice; the thick German socks were like sheaths of iron halfway to the knees; and the moccasin strings were like rods of steel all twisted and knotted as by some **conflagration**. For a moment he tugged with his numbed fingers, then, realizing the folly of it, he drew his sheath knife.

But before he could cut the strings, it happened. It was his own fault or, rather, his mistake. He should not have built the fire under the spruce tree. He should have built it in the open. But it had been easier to pull the twigs from the brush and drop them directly on the fire. Now the tree under which he had done this carried a weight of snow on its boughs. No wind had blown for weeks, and each bough was fully freighted. Each time he had pulled a twig he had communicated a slight **agitation** to the tree—an **imperceptible** agitation, so far as he was concerned, but an agitation sufficient to bring about the disaster. High

conflagration a raging, destructive fire
agitation motion
imperceptible not noticeable

up in the tree one bough **capsized** its load of snow. This fell on the boughs beneath, capsizing them. This process continued, spreading out and involving the whole tree. It grew like an avalanche, and it descended without warning upon the man and the fire, and the fire was blotted out! Where it had burned was a mantle of fresh and disordered snow.

The man was shocked. It was as though he had just heard his own sentence of death. For a moment he sat and stared at the spot where the fire had been. Then he grew very calm. Perhaps the old-timer on Sulphur Creek was right. If he had only had a trail-mate he would have been in no danger now. The trail-mate could have built the fire. Well, it was up to him to build the fire over again, and this second time there must be no failure. Even if he succeeded, he would most likely lose some toes. His feet must be badly frozen by now, and there would be some time before the second fire was ready.

Such were his thoughts, but he did not sit and think them. He was busy all the time they were passing through his mind. He made a new foundation for a fire, this time in the open, where no treacherous tree could blot it out. Next, he gathered dry grasses and tiny twigs from the high-water **flotsam**. He could not bring his fingers together to pull

capsized caused to tip over; overturned
flotsam floating debris (or in this case, the material left behind by waters that have receded)

them out, but he was able to gather them by the handful. In this way he got many rotten twigs and bits of green moss that were undesirable, but it was the best he could do. He worked methodically, even collecting an armful of the larger branches to be used later when the fire gathered strength. And all the while the dog sat and watched him, a certain yearning wistfulness in its eyes, for it looked upon him as the fire provider, and the fire was slow in coming.

When all was ready, the man reached in his pocket for a second piece of birch bark. He knew the bark was there, and, though he could not feel it with his fingers, he could hear its crisp rustling as he fumbled for it. Try as he would, he could not clutch hold of it. And all the time, in his consciousness, was the knowledge that each instant his feet were freezing. This thought tended to put him in a panic, but he fought against it and kept calm. He pulled on his mittens with his teeth, and threshed his arms back and forth, beating his hands with all his might against his sides. He did this sitting down, and he stood up to do it; and all the while the dog sat in the snow, its wolf brush of a tail curled around warmly over its forefeet, its sharp wolf ears pricked forward intently as it watched the man. And the man as he beat and threshed with his arms and hands, felt a great surge of envy as he regarded the creature that was warm and secure in its natural covering.

After a time he was aware of the first far-away signals of sensation in his beaten fingers. The faint tingling grew stronger till it evolved into a stinging ache that was **excruciating**, but which the man hailed with satisfaction. He stripped the mitten from his right hand and fetched forth the birch bark. The exposed fingers were quickly going numb again. Next he brought out his bunch of sulphur matches. But the tremendous cold had already driven the life out of his fingers. In his effort to separate one match from the others, the whole bunch fell in the snow. He tried to pick it out of the snow, but failed. The dead fingers could neither touch nor clutch. He was very careful. He drove the thought of his freezing feet, and nose, and cheeks, out of his mind, devoting his whole soul to the matches. He watched, using the sense of vision in place of that of touch, and when he saw his fingers on each side of the bunch, he closed them—that is, he willed to close them, for the wires were drawn, and the fingers did not obey. He pulled the mitten on the right hand, and beat it fiercely against his knee. Then, with both mittened hands, he scooped the bunch of matches, along with much snow, into his lap. Yet he was no better off.

After some manipulation he managed to get the bunch between the heels of his mittened hands. In this fashion he carried it to his mouth. The ice crackled and snapped when by a violent effort he opened his mouth. He drew the lower jaw in, curled the upper lip out of the way, and scraped the

....

excruciating extremely painful

bunch with his upper teeth in order to separate a match. He succeeded in getting one, which he dropped on his lap. He was no better off. He could not pick it up. Then he devised a way. He picked it up in his teeth and scratched it on his leg. Twenty times he scratched before he succeeded in lighting it. As it flamed he held it with his teeth to the birch bark. But the burning **brimstone** went up his nostrils and into his lungs, causing him to cough **spasmodically**. The match fell into the snow and went out.

The old-timer on Sulphur Creek was right, he thought in the moment of controlled despair that ensued: after fifty below, a man should travel with a partner. He beat his hands, but failed in exciting any sensation. Suddenly he bared both hands, removing the mittens with his teeth. He caught the whole bunch between the heels of his hands. His arm muscles not being frozen enabled him to press the hand heels tightly against the matches. Then he scratched the bunch along his leg. It flared into flame, seventy sulphur matches at once! There was no wind to blow them out. He kept his head to one side to escape the strangling fumes, and held the blazing bunch to the birch bark. As he so held it, he became aware of sensation in his hand. His flesh was burning. He could smell it. Deep down below the surface he could feel it. The sensation developed into pain

....

brimstone sulfur (used in matches)
spasmodically fitfully; in sharp jerks

that grew acute. And still he endured it, holding the flame of the matches clumsily to the bark that would not light readily because his own burning hands were in the way, absorbing most of the flame.

At last, when he could endure no more, he jerked his hands apart. The blazing matches fell sizzling into the snow, but the birch bark was alight. He began laying dry grasses and the tiniest twigs on the flame. He could not pick and choose, for he had to lift the fuel between the heels of his hands. Small pieces of rotten wood and green moss clung to the twigs, and he bit them off as well as he could with his teeth. He cherished the flame carefully and awkwardly. It meant life, and it must not perish. The withdrawal of blood from the surface of his body now made him begin to shiver, and he grew more awkward. A large piece of green moss fell squarely on the little fire. He tried to poke it out with his fingers, but his shivering frame made him poke too far, and he disrupted the **nucleus** of the little fire, the burning grasses and tiny twigs separating and scattering. He tried to poke them together again, but in spite of the tenseness of the effort, his shivering got away with him, and the twigs were hopelessly scattered. Each twig gushed a puff of smoke and went out. The fire provider had failed. As he looked **apathetically** about him, his eyes

....

nucleus central part; core
apathetically indifferently; in a way showing little interest or concern

chanced on the dog, sitting across the ruins of the fire from him, in the snow, making restless, hunching movements, slightly lifting one forefoot and then the other, shifting its weight back and forth on them with wistful eagerness.

The sight of the dog put a wild idea into his head. He remembered the tale of the man, caught in a blizzard, who killed a steer and crawled inside the carcass, and so was saved. He would kill the dog and bury his hands in the warm body until the numbness went out of them. Then he could build another fire. He spoke to the dog, calling it to him; but in his voice was a strange note of fear that frightened the animal, who had never known the man to speak in such way before. Something was the matter, and its suspicious nature sensed danger—it knew not what danger but somewhere, somehow, in its brain arose an apprehension of the man. It flattened its ears down at the sound of the man's voice, and its restless, hunching movements and the liftings and shiftings of its forefeet became more pronounced; but it would not come to the man. He got on his hands and knees and crawled toward the dog. This unusual posture again excited suspicion, and the animal **sidled** mincingly away.

The man sat up in the snow for a moment and struggled for calmness. Then he pulled on his mittens, by means of his teeth, and got upon his feet. He glanced

....

sidled edged away

down at first in order to assure himself that he was really standing up, for the absence of sensation in his feet left him unrelated to the earth. His erect position in itself started to drive the webs of suspicion from the dog's mind; and when he spoke **peremptorily**, with the sound of whip lashes in his voice, the dog rendered its customary allegiance and came to him. As it came within reaching distance, the man lost his control. His arms flashed out to the dog, and he experienced genuine surprise when he discovered that his hands could not clutch, that there was neither bend nor feeling in the fingers. He had forgotten for the moment that they were frozen and that they were freezing more and more. All this happened quickly, and before the animal could get away, he encircled its body with his arms. He sat down in the snow, and in this fashion held the dog, while it snarled and whined and struggled.

But it was all he could do, hold its body encircled in his arms and sit there. He realized that he could not kill the dog. There was no way to do it. With his helpless hands he could neither draw nor hold his sheath knife nor throttle the animal. He released it, and it plunged wildly away, with tail between its legs, and still snarling. It halted forty feet away and surveyed him curiously, with ears sharply pricked forward. The man looked down at his hands in order to locate them, and found them hanging on the

....

peremptorily in a curt and commanding manner

ends of his arms. It struck him as curious that one should have to use his eyes in order to find out where his hands were. He began threshing his arms back and forth, beating the mittened hands against his sides. He did this for five minutes, violently, and his heart pumped enough blood up to the surface to put a stop to his shivering. But no sensation was aroused in the hands. He had an impression that they hung like weights on the ends of his arms, but when he tried to run the impression down, he could not find it.

A certain fear of death, dull and **oppressive**, came to him. This fear quickly became **poignant** as he realized that it was no longer a mere matter of freezing his fingers and toes, or of losing his hands and feet, but that it was a matter of life and death with the chances against him. This threw him into a panic, and he turned and ran up the creek bed along the old, dim trail. The dog joined in behind and kept up with him. He ran blindly, without intention, in fear such as he had never known in his life. Slowly, as he plowed and floundered through the snow, he began to see things again—the banks of the creek, the old timber jams, the leafless aspens, and the sky. The running made him feel better. He did not shiver. Maybe, if he ran on, his feet would thaw out; and, anyway, if he ran far enough, he would

....

oppressive depressing; heavily weighing on the spirit
poignant deeply emotional; affecting the emotions in a sharp, painful way

reach camp and the boys. Without doubt he would lose some fingers and toes and some of his face; but the boys would take care of him, and save the rest of him when he got there. And at the same time there was another thought in his mind that said he would never get to the camp and the boys; that it was too many miles away, that the freezing had too great a start on him, and that he would soon be stiff and dead. This thought he kept in the background and refused to consider. Sometimes it pushed itself forward and demanded to be heard, but he thrust it back and strove to think of other things.

It struck him as curious that he could run at all on feet so frozen that he could not feel them when they struck the earth and took the weight of his body. He seemed to himself to skim along above the surface and to have no connection with the earth. Somewhere he had once seen a winged **Mercury**, and he wondered if Mercury felt as he felt when skimming over the earth.

His theory of running until he reached camp and the boys had one flaw in it: he lacked the endurance. Several times he stumbled, and finally he tottered, crumpled up, and fell. When he tried to rise, he failed. He must sit and rest, he decided, and next time he would merely walk and keep on going. As he sat and regained his breath, he noted

....

Mercury in ancient Roman mythology, the messenger god, often pictured wearing a winged cap and sandals that he was feeling quite warm and comfortable. He was not shivering, and it even seemed that a warm glow had come to his chest and trunk. And yet, when he touched his nose or cheeks, there was no sensation. Running would not thaw them out. Nor would it thaw out his hands and feet. Then the thought came to him that the frozen portions of his body must be extending. He tried to keep this thought down, to forget it, to think of something else; he was aware of the panicky feeling that it caused, and he was afraid of the panic. But the thought asserted itself, and persisted, until it produced a vision of his body totally frozen. This was too much, and he made another wild run along the trail. Once he slowed down to a walk, but the thought of the freezing extending itself made him run again.

And all the time the dog ran with him, at his heels. When he fell down a second time, it curled its tail over its forefeet and sat in front of him facing him curiously eager and intent. The warmth and security of the animal angered him, and he cursed it till it flattened down its ears **appeasingly**. This time the shivering came more quickly upon the man. He was losing in his battle with the frost. It was creeping into his body from all sides. The thought of it drove him on, but he ran no more than a hundred feet, when he staggered and pitched headlong. It was his last panic. When he had recovered his breath and control,

....

appeasingly in a manner intended to calm, soothe, or pacify he sat up and entertained in his mind the conception of meeting death with dignity. However, the conception did not come to him in such terms. His idea of it was that he had been making a fool of himself, running around like a chicken with its head cut off– such was the simile that occurred to him. Well, he was bound to freeze anyway, and he might as well take it decently. With this newfound peace of mind came the first glimmerings of drowsiness. A good idea, he thought, to sleep off to death. It was like taking an **anesthetic**. Freezing was not so bad as people thought. There were lots worse ways to die.

He pictured the boys finding his body next day. Suddenly he found himself with them, coming along the trail and looking for himself. And, still with them, he came around a turn in the trail and found himself lying in the snow. He did not belong with himself any more, for even then he was out of himself, standing with the boys and looking at himself in the snow. It certainly was cold, was his thought. When he got back to the States he could tell the folks what real cold was. He drifted on from this to a vision of the old-timer on Sulphur Creek. He could see him quite clearly, warm and comfortable, and smoking a pipe.

"You were right, old hoss; you were right," the man mumbled to the old-timer of Sulphur Creek.

....

anesthetic something that produces a loss of sensation

Then the man drowsed off into what seemed to him the most comfortable and satisfying sleep he had ever known. The dog sat facing him and waiting. The brief day drew to a close in a long, slow twilight. There were no signs of a fire to be made, and, besides, never in the dog's experience had it known a man to sit like that in the snow and make no fire. As the twilight drew on, its eager yearning for the fire mastered it, and with a great lifting and shifting of forefeet, it whined softly, then flattened its ears down in anticipation of being **chidden** by the man. But the man remained silent. Later, the dog whined loudly. And still later it crept close to the man and caught the scent of death. This made the animal bristle and back away. A little longer it delayed, howling under the stars that leaped and danced and shone brightly in the cold sky. Then it turned and trotted up the trail in the direction of the camp it knew, where were the other food providers and fire providers. ❖

---

chidden scolded

The Secret Life of Walter Mitty

by James Thurber

"We're going through!" The Commander's voice was like thin ice breaking. He wore his full-dress uniform, with the heavily braided white cap pulled down **rakishly** over one cold gray eye. "We can't make it, sir. It's spoiling for a hurricane, if you ask me." "I'm not asking you, Lieutenant Berg," said the Commander. "Throw on the power lights! Rev her up to 8500! We're going through!" The pounding of the cylinders increased: ta-pocketa-pocketa-pocketa-*pocketa-pocketa*. The Commander stared at the ice forming on the pilot window. He walked over and twisted a row of complicated dials. "Switch on No. 8 **auxiliary**!" he shouted. "Switch on No. 8 auxiliary!" repeated Lieutenant Berg. "Full strength in No. 3 **turret**!" shouted the Commander.

---

rakishly in a careless, jaunty way
auxiliary a reserve or backup
turret an armored structure that protects the gunmen on a warship

"Full strength in No. 3 turret!" The crew, bending to their various tasks in the huge, hurtling eight-engined Navy **hydroplane**, looked at each other and grinned. "The Old Man'll get us through," they said to one another. "The Old Man ain't afraid of hell!"…

"Not so fast! You're driving too fast!" said Mrs. Mitty. "What are you driving so fast for?"

"Hmm?" said Walter Mitty. He looked at his wife, in the seat beside him, with shocked astonishment. She seemed grossly unfamiliar, like a strange woman who had yelled at him in a crowd. "You were up to fifty-five," she said. "You know I don't like to go more than forty. You were up to fifty-five." Walter Mitty drove on toward Waterbury in silence, the roaring of the SN202 through the worst storm in twenty years of Navy flying fading in the remote, intimate airways of his mind. "You're tensed up again," said Mrs. Mitty. "It's one of your days. I wish you'd let Dr. Renshaw look you over."

Walter Mitty stopped the car in front of the building where his wife went to have her hair done. "Remember to get those overshoes while I'm having my hair done," she said. "I don't need overshoes," said Mitty. She put her mirror back into her bag. "We've been all through that," she said, getting out of the car. "You're not a young man any longer." He raced the engine a little. "Why don't you

....

hydroplane an airplane designed to take off from and land on water wear your gloves? Have you lost your gloves?" Walter Mitty reached in a pocket and brought out the gloves. He put them on, but after she had turned and gone into the building and he had driven on to a red light, he took them off again. "Pick it up, brother!" snapped a cop as the light changed, and Mitty hastily pulled on his gloves and lurched ahead. He drove around the streets aimlessly for a time, and then he drove past the hospital on his way to the parking lot.

…"It's the millionaire banker, Wellington McMillan," said the pretty nurse. "Yes?" said Walter Mitty, removing his gloves slowly. "Who has the case?" "Dr. Renshaw and Dr. Benbow, but there are two specialists here, Dr. Remington from New York and Dr. Pritchard-Mitford from London. He flew over." A door opened down a long, cool corridor and Dr. Renshaw came out. He looked **distraught** and **haggard**. "Hello, Mitty," he said. "We're having the devil's own time with McMillan, the millionaire banker and close personal friend of **Roosevelt. Obstreosis of the ductal tract. Tertiary**. Wish you'd take a look at him." "Glad to," said Mitty.

In the operating room there were whispered introductions: "Dr. Remington, Dr. Mitty. Dr. Pritchard-Mitford, Dr. Mitty."

distraught extremely upset
haggard appearing worn out or exhausted
Roosevelt Franklin D. Roosevelt, president of the United States from 1933–1945
"Obstreosis of the ductal tract. Tertiary" a combination of made-up and real (but misused) words, here used humorously to sound like medical terms

"I've read your book on **streptothricosis**," said Pritchard-Mitford, shaking hands. "A brilliant performance, sir." "Thank you," said Walter Mitty. "Didn't know you were in the States, Mitty," grumbled Remington. "**Coals to Newcastle**, bringing Mitford and me up here for a tertiary." "You are very kind," said Mitty. A huge, complicated machine, connected to the operating table, with many tubes and wires, began at this moment to go pocketa-pocketa-pocketa. "The new anesthetizer is giving away!" shouted an intern. "There is no one in the East who knows how to fix it!" "Quiet, man!" said Mitty, in a low, cool voice. He sprang to the machine, which was now going pocketa-pocketa-queep-pocketa-queep. He began fingering delicately a row of glistening dials. "Give me a fountain pen!" he snapped. Someone handed him a fountain pen. He pulled a faulty **piston** out of the machine and inserted the pen in its place. "That will hold for ten minutes," he said. "Get on with the operation." A nurse hurried over and whispered to Renshaw, and Mitty saw the man turn pale. "**Coreopsis** has set in," said Renshaw nervously. "If you would take over, Mitty?" Mitty looked at him and at the craven figure of Benbow, who drank, and at the grave,

....

streptothricosis a kind of bacterial infection, usually of cattle or other animals, here used humorously as a medical term
"Coals to Newcastle" an expression meaning "completely unnecessary and pointless," since Newcastle is a coal-mining region in England
piston a moving cylinder in a machine
Coreopsis a kind of flower, here used humorously to sound like a medical term

uncertain faces of the two great specialists. "If you wish," he said. They slipped a white gown on him, he adjusted a mask and drew on thin gloves; nurses handed him shining …

"Back it up, Mac! Look out for that Buick!" Walter Mitty jammed on the brakes. "Wrong lane, Mac," said the parking-lot attendant, looking at Mitty closely. "Gee. Yeh," muttered Mitty. He began cautiously to back out of the lane marked "Exit Only." "Leave her sit there," said the attendant. "I'll put her away." Mitty got out of the car. "Hey, better leave the key." "Oh," said Mitty, handing the man the ignition key. The attendant vaulted into the car, backed it up with **insolent** skill, and put it where it belonged.

They're so darn cocky, thought Walter Mitty, walking along Main Street; they think they know everything. Once he had tried to take his chains off, outside New Milford, and he had got them wound around the axles. A man had had to come out in a wrecking car and unwind them, a young, grinning garageman. Since then Mrs. Mitty always made him drive to a garage to have the chains taken off. The next time, he thought, I'll wear my right arm in a sling; they won't grin at me then. I'll have my right arm in a sling and they'll see I couldn't possibly take the chains off myself. He kicked at the slush on the sidewalk.

....

insolent cocky; arrogant

"Overshoes," he said to himself, and he began looking for a shoe store.

When he came out into the street again, with the overshoes in a box under his arm, Walter Mitty began to wonder what the other thing was his wife had told him to get. She had told him, twice before they set out from their house for Waterbury. In a way he hated these weekly trips to town—he was always getting something wrong. Kleenex, he thought. Squibb's, razor blades? No. Toothpaste, toothbrush, **bicarbonate**, **carborundum**, initiative and referendum? He gave it up. But she would remember it. "Where's the what's-its-name?" she would ask. "Don't tell me you forgot the what's-its-name." A newsboy went by shouting something about the Waterbury trial.

…"Perhaps this will refresh your memory." The District Attorney suddenly thrust a heavy automatic at the quiet figure on the witness stand. "Have you ever seen this before?" Walter Mitty took the gun and examined it expertly. "This is my Webley-Vickers 50.80," he said calmly. An excited buzz ran around the courtroom. The Judge rapped for order. "You are a crack shot with any sort of firearms, I believe?" said the District Attorney, **insinuatingly**. "Objection!" shouted Mitty's attorney. "We have shown that the defendant could not have fired the

----

bicarbonate baking soda
carborundum a substance used for scouring or wearing down a surface
insinuatingly in a way that casts doubt or suspicion

shot. We have shown that he wore his right arm in a sling on the night of the fourteenth of July." Walter Mitty raised his hand briefly and the bickering attorneys were stilled. "With any known make of gun," he said evenly, "I could have killed Gregory Fitzhurst at three hundred feet with my left hand." **Pandemonium** broke loose in the courtroom. A woman's scream rose above the **bedlam** and suddenly a lovely, dark-haired girl was in Walter Mitty's arms. The District Attorney struck at her savagely. Without rising from his chair, Mitty let the man have it on the point of the chin. "You miserable **cur**!"...

"Puppy biscuit," said Walter Mitty. He stopped walking and the buildings of Waterbury rose up out of the misty courtroom and surrounded him again. A woman who was passing laughed. "He said 'Puppy biscuit,'" she said to her companion. "That man said 'Puppy biscuit' to himself." Walter Mitty hurried on. He went into an A&P, not the first one he came to but a smaller one farther up the street. "I want some biscuit for small, young dogs," he said to the clerk. "Any special brand, sir?" The greatest pistol shot in the world thought a moment. "It says 'Puppies Bark for It' on the box," said Walter Mitty.

His wife would be through at the hairdresser's in fifteen minutes, Mitty saw in looking at his watch, unless they

....

pandemonium chaos; complete disorder
bedlam a state of confusion and uproar
cur a mongrel dog; a cowardly person

had trouble drying it; sometimes they had trouble drying it. She didn't like to get to the hotel first; she would want him to be there waiting for her as usual. He found a big leather chair in the lobby, facing a window, and he put the overshoes and the puppy biscuit on the floor beside it. He picked up an old copy of *Liberty* and sank down into the chair. "Can Germany Conquer the World Through the Air?" Walter Mitty looked at the pictures of bombing planes and of ruined streets.

…"The **cannonading** has got the wind up in young Raleigh, sir," said the sergeant. Captain Mitty looked up at him through **tousled** hair. "Get him to bed," he said wearily, "with the others. I'll fly alone." "But you can't, sir," said the sergeant anxiously. "It takes two men to handle that bomber and the Archies are pounding hell out of the air. Von Richtman's circus is between here and Saulier." "Somebody's got to get that ammunition dump," said Mitty. "I'm going over. Spot of brandy?" He poured a drink for the sergeant and one for himself. War thundered and whined around the dugout and battered at the door. There was a rending of wood and splinters flew through the room. "A bit of a near thing," said Captain Mitty carelessly. "The box **barrage** is closing in," said the sergeant. "We only live once, Sergeant," said Mitty, with his faint, fleeting smile.

··

cannonading heavy gunfire
tousled disarranged; rumpled
barrage heavy artillery fire

"Or do we?" He poured another brandy and tossed it off. "I never see a man could hold his brandy like you, sir," said the sergeant. "Begging your pardon, sir." Captain Mitty stood up and strapped on his huge Webley-Vickers automatic. "It's forty kilometers through hell, sir," said the sergeant. Mitty finished one last brandy. "After all," he said softly, "what isn't?" The pounding of the cannon increased; there was the rat-tat-tatting of machine guns, and from somewhere came the menacing pocketa-pocketa-pocketa of the new flame throwers. Walter Mitty walked to the door of the dugout humming "Auprès de Ma Blonde." He turned and waved to the sergeant. "Cheerio!" he said ....

Something struck his shoulder. "I've been looking all over this hotel for you," said Mrs. Mitty. "Why do you have to hide in this old chair? How did you expect me to find you?" "Things close in," said Walter Mitty vaguely. "What?" Mrs. Mitty said. "Did you get the what's-its-name? The puppy biscuit? What's in that box?" "Overshoes," said Mitty. "Couldn't you have put them on in the store?" "I was thinking," said Walter Mitty. "Does it ever occur to you that I am sometimes thinking?" She looked at him. "I'm going to take your temperature when I get you home," she said.

They went out through the revolving doors that made a faintly **derisive** whistling sound when you pushed them. It was two blocks to the parking lot. At the drugstore on

---

derisive mocking; expressing ridicule

the corner she said, "Wait here for me. I forgot something. I won't be a minute." She was more than a minute. Walter Mitty lighted a cigarette. It began to rain, rain with sleet in it. He stood up against the wall of the drugstore, smoking . . . .

He put his shoulders back and his heels together. "To hell with the handkerchief," said Walter Mitty scornfully. He took one last drag on his cigarette and snapped it away. Then, with that faint, fleeting smile playing about his lips, he faced the firing squad; erect and motionless, proud and **disdainful**, Walter Mitty the Undefeated, **inscrutable** to the last. ❖

---

disdainful scornful; haughty
inscrutable difficult to understand; mysterious

The Piece of String

by Guy de Maupassant
translated by Albert M. C. McMaster and others

It was market day, and from all the country round
Goderville the peasants and their wives were coming
toward the town. The men walked slowly, throwing the
whole body forward at every step of their long, crooked legs.
They were deformed from pushing the plow, which makes
the left shoulder higher, and bends their figures sideways;
from **reaping** the grain, when they have to spread their
legs so as to keep on their feet. Their starched blue blouses,
glossy as though **varnished**, ornamented at collar and cuffs
with a little embroidered design and blown out around
their bony bodies, looked very much like balloons about to
soar, from which **issued** two arms and two feet.

Some of these fellows dragged a cow or a calf at the
end of a rope. And just behind the animal followed their
wives, beating it over the back with a leaf-covered branch
to hasten its pace, and carrying large baskets out of which
protruded the heads of chickens or ducks. These women
walked more quickly and energetically than the men, with

Goderville a town in northern France, in the region of Normandy (all towns
mentioned in this story are in the same general region)
reaping harvesting
varnished coated with a liquid that dries to a hard, glossy surface
issued emerged; came forth
protruded jutted; stuck out

their erect, dried-up figures, adorned with scanty little shawls pinned over their flat bosoms, and their heads wrapped round with a white cloth, enclosing the hair and **surmounted** by a cap.

Now a wagon passed by, jogging along behind a **nag**, strangely shaking the two men on the seat and the woman at the bottom of the cart who held fast to its sides to lessen the hard jolting.

In the marketplace at Goderville there was a great crowd, a mingled multitude of men and beasts. The horns of cattle, the high, long-napped hats of wealthy peasants, the headdresses of the women rose above the surface of that sea. And the sharp, shrill, barking voices made a continuous, wild **din**, while above it occasionally rose a huge burst of laughter from the sturdy lungs of a merry peasant or a prolonged bellow from a cow tied fast to the wall of a house.

It all smelled of the stable, of milk, of hay and of perspiration, giving off that half-human, half-animal odor which is peculiar to country folks.

Maître Hauchecorne, of Breaute, had just arrived at Goderville and was making his way toward the square when he perceived on the ground a little piece of string.

....

surmounted topped by
nag an old horse
din noise
Maître French title meaning "Master"

Maître Hauchecorne, economical as are all true **Normans**,
reflected that everything was worth picking up which could
be of any use, and he stooped down, but painfully, because
he suffered from **rheumatism**. He took the bit of thin string
from the ground and was carefully preparing to roll it up
when he saw Maître Malandain, the harness maker, on
his doorstep staring at him. They had once had a quarrel
about a halter, and they had borne each other **malice** ever
since. Maître Hauchecorne was overcome with a sort of

....

Normans the inhabitants of Normandy, in northern France
rheumatism achy bones and muscles
malice ill will; the desire to see another come to harm

shame at being seen by his enemy picking up a bit of string in the road. He quickly hid it beneath his blouse and then slipped it into his **breeches** pocket, then pretended to be still looking for something on the ground which he did not discover and finally went off toward the marketplace, his head bent forward and his body almost doubled in two by rheumatic pains.

He was at once lost in the crowd, which kept moving about slowly and noisily as it **chaffered** and bargained. The peasants examined the cows, went off, came back, always in doubt for fear of being cheated, never quite daring to decide, looking the seller square in the eye in the effort to discover the tricks of the man and the defect in the beast.

The women, having placed their great baskets at their feet, had taken out the poultry, which lay upon the ground, their legs tied together, with terrified eyes and scarlet combs.

They listened to propositions, maintaining their prices in a decided manner with an **impassive** face or perhaps deciding to accept the smaller price offered, suddenly calling out to the customer who was starting to go away, "All right, I'll let you have them, Maître Anthime."

Then, little by little, the square became empty, and when the **Angelus** struck midday those who lived at a distance poured into the inns.

---

breeches pants
chaffered haggled; bargained
impassive expressionless; blank
Angelus a bell rung in Catholic churches three times a day to call people to prayer

At Jourdain's the great room was filled with eaters, just as the vast court was filled with vehicles of every sort—carts, gigs, wagons, **tilburies**, innumerable vehicles which have no name, yellow with mud, misshapen, pieced together, raising their shafts to heaven like two arms, or it may be with their nose on the ground and their rear in the air.

Just opposite the diners seated at the table, the huge fireplace, with its bright flame, gave out a burning heat on the backs of those who sat at the right. Three spits were turning, loaded with chickens, with pigeons and with joints of mutton; and a delectable odor of roast meat and of gravy flowing over crisp brown skin arose from the hearth, kindled merriment, and caused every mouth to water.

All the aristocracy of the plow were eating there at Maître Jourdain's, the innkeeper's, a dealer in horses also and a sharp fellow who had made a great deal of money in his day.

The dishes were passed round and emptied, as were the jugs of yellow cider. Everyone told of his affairs, of his purchases and his sales. They exchanged news about the crops. The weather was good for greens, but too wet for grain.

Suddenly the drum began to beat in the courtyard before the house. All except the most indifferent were on their feet at once and ran to the door, to the windows, their mouths full and napkins in hand.

---

tilburies two-seat carriages

When the public crier had finished his drum-beating, he called forth in a jerky voice, pausing in the wrong places:

"Be it known to the inhabitants of Goderville and in general to all persons present at the market that there has been lost this morning on the Benzeville road, between nine and ten o'clock, a black leather pocketbook containing five hundred **francs** and business papers. The finder is requested to return it to the mayor's office at once or to Maître Fortune Houlbreque of Manneville. There will be twenty francs reward."

Then the man went away. They heard once more at a distance the dull beating of the drum and the faint voice of the crier. Then they all began to talk of this incident, reckoning up the chances which Maître Houlbreque had of finding or of not finding his pocketbook again.

The meal went on. They were finishing their coffee when the corporal of **gendarmes** appeared on the threshold.

He asked, "Is Maître Hauchecorne of Breaute here?" Maître Hauchecorne, seated at the other end of the table, answered, "Here I am."

The officer responded, "Maître Hauchecorne, will you be so good as to accompany me to the mayor's office? The mayor would like to talk with you."

The peasant, surprised, swallowed his tiny glass of brandy, rose, and, even more bent than in the morning,

....

francs French money
gendarmes the French police force

for the first steps after each rest were especially difficult, set out, repeating, "Here I am, here I am."

The mayor was waiting for him, seated in an armchair. He was the **notary** of the place, a stout, grave man of **pompous** speech.

"Maître Hauchecorne," said he, "this morning on the Benzeville road, you were seen picking up the pocketbook lost by Maître Houlbreque, of Manneville."

The countryman looked at the mayor in amazement, frightened already at this suspicion which rested on him, he knew not why.

"Me? Me? Me pick up the pocketbook?"

"Yes, you."

"I swear I don't even know anything about it."

"You were seen."

"I was seen—me? Who says he saw me?"

"Monsieur Malandain, the harness-maker."

Then the old man remembered, understood, and, reddening with anger, said, "Ah! he saw me, did he, the rascal? He saw me picking up this string here, **M'sieu** the Mayor."

And fumbling at the bottom of his pocket, he pulled out of it the little end of string.

....

notary a public officer who is responsible for such tasks as verifying official documents

pompous self-important; pretentious

M'sieu Monsieur (French for "Mister")

But the mayor **incredulously** shook his head: "You will not make me believe, Maître Hauchecorne, that Monsieur Malandain, who is a man whose word can be relied on, has mistaken this string for a pocketbook."

The peasant, furious, raised his hand and spat on the ground beside him as if to attest his good faith, repeating, "For all that, it is God's truth, M'sieu the Mayor. There! On my soul's salvation, I repeat it."

The mayor continued: "After you picked up the object in question, you even looked about for some time in the mud to see if a piece of money had not dropped out of it."

The good man was choking with **indignation** and fear. "How can they tell—how can they tell such lies as that to **slander** an honest man! How can they?"

His protestations were in vain; he was not believed.

He was confronted with Monsieur Malandain, who repeated and sustained his testimony. They **railed** at one another for an hour. At his own request Maître Hauchecorne was searched. Nothing was found on him.

At last the mayor, much perplexed, sent him away, warning him that he would inform the public prosecutor and ask for orders.

....

incredulously with disbelief
indignation anger caused by something unjust
slander false statements made to injure someone
railed yelled angrily

The news had spread. When he left the mayor's office the old man was surrounded, interrogated with a curiosity which was serious or mocking, as the case might be, but into which no indignation entered. And he began to tell the story of the string. They did not believe him. They laughed at him.

He passed on, **buttonholed** by every one, himself buttonholing his acquaintances, beginning over and over again his tale and his protestations, showing his pockets turned inside out to prove that he had nothing in them.

They said to him: "You old **rogue**!"

He grew more and more angry, feverish, in despair at not being believed, and kept on telling his story.

The night came. It was time to go home. He left with three of his neighbors, to whom he pointed out the place where he had picked up the string, and all the way he talked of his adventure.

That evening he made the round of the village of Breaute for the purpose of telling every one. He met only unbelievers.

He felt ill about it all night long.

The next day, about one in the afternoon, Marius Paumelle, a farm hand of Maître Breton, the market gardener at Ymanville, returned the pocketbook and its contents to Maître Holbreque of Manneville.

buttonholed detained in conversation
rogue a scoundrel; an unprincipled person

This man said, indeed, that he had found it on the road, but not knowing how to read, he had carried it home and given it to his master.

The news spread through the neighborhood. Maître Hauchecorne was informed. He started off at once and began to relate his story with the **denouement**. He was triumphant.

"What grieved me," said he, "was not the thing itself, do you understand, but it was being accused of lying. Nothing does you so much harm as being in disgrace for lying."

All day he talked of his adventure. He told it on the roads to the people who passed, at the wineshop to the people drinking there, and next Sunday when they came out of church. He even stopped strangers to tell them about it. He was easy now, and yet something worried him without his knowing exactly what it was. People had a joking manner while they listened. They did not seem convinced. He seemed to feel their remarks behind his back.

On Tuesday of the following week he went to market at Goderville, prompted solely by the need of telling his story.

Malandain, standing on his doorstep, began to laugh as he saw him pass. Why?

He approached a farmer of Criquetot, who did not let him finish, and giving him a punch in the pit of the stomach cried in his face, "Oh, you great rogue!" Then he turned his heel upon him.

denouement the final outcome of a story

Maître Hauchecorne remained speechless and grew more and more uneasy. Why was he called a "great rogue"?

When seated at table in Jourdain's tavern he began again to explain the whole affair.

A horse dealer of Montivilliers shouted at him, "Get out, get out, you old **scamp**! I know all about your old string."

Hauchecorne stammered, "But since they found it again, the pocketbook!"

But the other continued, "Hold your tongue, old one; there's one who finds it and there's another who returns it. And no one the wiser."

The farmer was speechless. He understood at last. They accused him of having had the pocketbook brought back by an accomplice, by a **confederate**.

He tried to protest. The whole table began to laugh.

He could not finish his dinner, and went away amid a chorus of jeers.

He went home indignant, choking with rage, with confusion, the more cast down since with his Norman craftiness he was, perhaps, capable of having done what they accused him of and even of boasting of it as a good trick. He was dimly conscious that it was impossible to prove his innocence, his craftiness being so well known. He felt himself struck to the heart by the injustice of the suspicion.

scamp a rascal
confederate a partner

He began anew to tell his tale, lengthening his recital every day, each day adding new proofs, more energetic declarations and more sacred oaths, which he thought of and prepared in his hours of solitude, for his mind was entirely occupied with the story of the string. The more he denied it, the more complicated his arguments, the less he was believed.

"Those are liars' proofs," they said behind his back.

He felt this. It preyed upon him and he exhausted himself in useless efforts.

He was visibly wasting away.

Jokers would make him tell the story of "the piece of string" to amuse them, just as you make a soldier who has been on a campaign tell his story of the battle. His mind kept growing weaker, and about the end of December he took to his bed.

He passed away early in January, and, in the ravings of death agony, he protested his innocence, repeating: "A little bit of string—a little bit of string. See, here it is, M'sieu the Mayor." ❖

The Tell-Tale Heart

by Edgar Allan Poe

True! nervous—very, very dreadfully nervous I had been and am; but why *will* you say that I am **mad**? The disease had sharpened my senses—not destroyed—not dulled them. Above all was the sense of hearing **acute**. I heard all things in the heaven and in the earth. I heard many things in hell. How, then, am I mad? **Hearken**! and observe how healthily—how calmly I can tell you the whole story.

It is impossible to say how first the idea entered my brain; but once conceived, it haunted me day and night. **Object** there was none. **Passion** there was none. I loved the old man. He had never wronged me. He had never given me insult. For his gold I had no desire. I think it was his eye! yes, it was this! He had the eye of a vulture—a pale blue eye, with a film over it. Whenever it fell upon me, my blood ran cold; and so by degrees—very gradually—I made up my mind to take the life of the old man, and thus rid myself of the eye forever.

Now this is the point. You **fancy** *me* mad. Madmen know nothing. But you should have seen me. You should

mad insane
acute sharp; keen; extremely perceptive
hearken to listen
object a goal
passion powerful emotion
fancy to imagine; to suppose

have seen how wisely I proceeded—with what caution—with what foresight—with what **dissimulation** I went to work! I was never kinder to the old man than during the whole week before I killed him. And every night, about midnight, I turned the latch of his door and opened it—oh so gently! And then, when I had made an opening sufficient for my head, I put in a dark lantern, all closed, closed, that no light shone out, and then I thrust in my head. Oh, you would have laughed to see how **cunningly** I thrust it in! I moved it slowly—very, very slowly, so that I might not disturb the old man's sleep. It took me an hour to place my whole head within the opening so far that I could see him as he lay upon his bed. Ha!—would a madman have been so wise as this? And then, when my head was well in the room, I undid the lantern cautiously—oh, so cautiously—cautiously (for the hinges creaked)—I undid it just so much that a single thin ray fell upon the vulture eye. And this I did for seven long nights—every night just at midnight—but I found the eye always closed; and so it was impossible to do the work; for it was not the old man who **vexed** me, but his Evil Eye. And every morning, when the day broke, I went boldly into the chamber, and spoke courageously to him, calling him by name in a hearty tone, and inquiring how he had passed

....

dissimulation deception; concealment of one's true intentions
cunningly deceptively
vexed troubled; distressed

the night. So you see he would have been a very profound old man, indeed, to suspect that every night, just at twelve, I looked in upon him while he slept.

Upon the eighth night I was more than usually cautious in opening the door. A watch's minute hand moves more quickly than did mine. Never before that night had I *felt* the extent of my own powers—of my **sagacity**. I could scarcely contain my feelings of triumph. To think that there I was, opening the door, little by little, and he not even to dream of my secret deeds or thoughts. I fairly chuckled at the idea; and perhaps he heard me; for he moved on the bed suddenly, as if startled. Now you may think that I drew back—but no. His room was as black as pitch with the thick darkness (for the shutters were close fastened, through fear of robbers), and so I knew that he could not see the opening of the door, and I kept pushing it on steadily, steadily.

I had my head in, and was about to open the lantern, when my thumb slipped upon the tin fastening, and the old man sprang up in bed, crying out, "Who's there?"

I kept quite still and said nothing. For a whole hour I did not move a muscle, and in the meantime I did not hear him lie down. He was still sitting up in the bed listening— just as I have done, night after night, hearkening to the death watches in the wall.

....

sagacity wisdom; keen judgment and understanding

Presently I heard a slight groan, and I knew it was the groan of mortal terror. It was not a groan of pain or of grief—oh, no!—it was the low stifled sound that arises from the bottom of the soul when **overcharged** with awe. I knew the sound well. Many a night, just at midnight, when all the world slept, it has welled up from my own bosom, deepening, with its dreadful echo, the terrors that distracted me. I say I knew it well. I knew what the old man felt, and pitied him, although I chuckled at heart. I knew that he had been lying awake ever since the first slight noise, when he had turned in the bed. His fears had been ever since growing upon him. He had been trying to fancy them causeless, but could not. He had been saying to himself—"It is nothing but the wind in the chimney—it is only a mouse crossing the floor," or "It is merely a cricket which has made a single chirp." Yes, he had been trying to comfort himself with these **suppositions**: but he had found all in vain. *All in vain*; because Death, in approaching him, had stalked with his black shadow before him, and **enveloped** the victim. And it was the mournful influence of the unperceived shadow that caused him to feel—although he neither saw nor heard—to *feel* the presence of my head within the room.

----

overcharged filled to overflowing
suppositions assumptions; beliefs without evidence
enveloped enclosed; surrounded totally

When I had waited a long time, very patiently, without hearing him lie down, I resolved to open a little—a very, very little crevice in the lantern. So I opened it—you cannot imagine how stealthily, stealthily—until, at length a simple dim ray, like the thread of the spider, shot from out the crevice and fell full upon the vulture eye.

It was open—wide, wide open—and I grew furious as I gazed upon it. I saw it with perfect distinctiveness—all a dull blue, with a hideous veil over it that chilled the very marrow in my bones; but I could see nothing else of the old man's face or person: for I had directed the ray as if by instinct, precisely upon the damned spot.

And have I not told you that what you mistake for madness is but overacuteness of the senses?—now, I say, there came to my ears a low, dull, quick sound, such as a watch makes when enveloped in cotton. I knew that sound well, too. It was the beating of the old man's heart. It increased my fury, as the beating of a drum stimulates the soldier into courage.

But even yet I refrained and kept still. I scarcely breathed. I held the lantern motionless. I tried how steadily I could maintain the ray upon the eye. Meantime the hellish tattoo of the heart increased. It grew quicker and quicker, and louder and louder every instant. The old

crevice a narrow opening or crack
stealthily in a cautious, secretive way
distinctiveness clarity
tattoo a rhythmic tapping sound, as of a drum

man's terror *must* have been extreme! It grew louder, I say, louder every moment!—do you mark me well? I have told you that I am nervous: so I am. And now at the dead hour of the night, amid the dreadful silence of that old house, so strange a noise as this excited me to uncontrollable terror. Yet, for some minutes longer I refrained and stood still. But the beating grew louder, louder! I thought the heart must burst. And now a new anxiety seized me—the sound would be heard by a neighbor! The old man's hour had come! With a loud yell, I threw open the lantern and leaped into the room. He shrieked once—once only. In an instant I dragged him to the floor, and pulled the heavy bed over him. I then smiled gaily, to find the deed so far done. But, for many minutes, the heart beat on with a muffled sound. This, however, did not vex me; it would not be heard through the wall. At length it ceased. The old man was dead. I removed the bed and examined the corpse. Yes, he was stone, stone dead. I placed my hand upon the heart and held it there many minutes. There was no **pulsation**. He was stone dead. His eye would trouble me no more.

If still you think me mad, you will think so no longer when I describe the wise precautions I took for the concealment of the body. The night **waned**, and I worked hastily, but in silence. First of all I dismembered the corpse. I cut off the head and the arms and the legs.

....

pulsation beating; throbbing
waned decreased; approached an end

He shrieked once—once only.

I then took up three planks from the flooring of the chamber, and deposited all between the **scantlings**. I then replaced the boards so cleverly, so cunningly, that no human eye—not even *his*—could have detected anything wrong. There was nothing to wash out—no stain of any kind—no blood spot whatever. I had been too wary for that. A tub had caught all—ha! ha!

When I had made an end of these labors, it was four o'clock—still dark as midnight. As the bell sounded the hour, there came a knocking at the street door. I went down to open it with a light heart—for what had I *now* to fear? There entered three men, who introduced themselves, with perfect **suavity**, as officers of the police. A shriek had been heard by a neighbor during the night; suspicion of foul play had been aroused; information had been lodged at the police office, and they (the officers) had been deputed to search the premises.

I smiled—for *what* had I to fear? I bade the gentlemen welcome. The shriek, I said, was my own in a dream. The old man, I mentioned, was absent in the country. I took my visitors all over the house. I bade them search—search well. I led them, at length, to *his* chamber. I showed them his treasures, secure, undisturbed. In the enthusiasm of my confidence, I brought chairs into the room, and desired them *here* to rest from their fatigues, while I myself, in the

scantlings small pieces of lumber
suavity pleasantness; politeness

wild **audacity** of my perfect triumph, placed my own seat upon the very spot beneath which **reposed** the corpse of the victim.

The officers were satisfied. My *manner* had convinced them. I was singularly at ease. They sat, and while I answered cheerily, they chatted of familiar things. But, **erelong**, I felt myself getting pale and wished them gone. My head ached, and I fancied a ringing in my ears: but still they sat and still chatted. The ringing became more distinct—it continued and became more distinct; I talked more freely to get rid of the feeling; but it continued and gained definiteness—until, at length, I found that the noise was *not* within my ears.

No doubt I now grew *very* pale;—but I talked more **fluently**, and with a heightened voice. Yet the sound increased—and what could I do? It was a *low, dull, quick sound—much such a sound as a watch makes when enveloped in cotton.* I gasped for breath—and yet the officers heard it not. I talked more quickly—more **vehemently**; but the noise steadily increased. I arose and argued about **trifles**, in a high key and with violent **gesticulations**; but the

---

audacity reckless, daring boldness
reposed lay at rest
erelong soon
fluently smoothly; in an effortless, flowing manner
vehemently forcefully; with strong emotion
trifles unimportant things
gesticulations excited and forceful gestures

noise steadily increased. Why *would* they not be gone? I paced the floor to and fro with heavy strides, as if excited to fury by the observations of the men—but the noise steadily increased. Oh God! what *could* I do? I foamed—I raved—I swore! I swung the chair upon which I had been sitting, and grated it upon the boards, but the noise arose over all and continually increased. It grew louder—louder—*louder*! And still the men chatted pleasantly, and smiled. Was it possible they heard not? Almighty God!—no, no! They heard!—they suspected!—they *knew*!—they were making a mockery of my horror!—this I thought, and this I think. But anything was better than this agony! Anything was more tolerable than this **derision**! I could bear those **hypocritical** smiles no longer! I felt that I must scream or die! and now—again!—hark! louder! louder! louder! *louder*!

"Villains!" I shrieked, "**dissemble** no more! I admit the deed!—tear up the planks! here, here!—it is the beating of his hideous heart!" ❖

---

derision scorn
hypocritical false; deceptive; showing or saying one thing but meaning another
dissemble to deceive; to conceal

The Lottery

by Shirley Jackson

The morning of June 27th was clear and sunny, with
the fresh warmth of a full-summer day; the flowers were
blossoming **profusely** and the grass was richly green. The
people of the village began to gather in the square, between
the post office and the bank, around ten o'clock; in some
towns there were so many people that the lottery took two
days and had to be started on June 26th, but in this village,
where there were only about three hundred people, the
whole lottery took less than two hours, so it could begin at
ten o'clock in the morning and still be through in time to
allow the villagers to get home for noon dinner.

The children assembled first, of course. School was
recently over for the summer, and the feeling of liberty sat
uneasily on most of them; they tended to gather together
quietly for a while before they broke into **boisterous** play,
and their talk was still of the classroom and the teacher, of
books and **reprimands**. Bobby Martin had already stuffed
his pockets full of stones, and the other boys soon followed
his example, selecting the smoothest and roundest stones;
Bobby and Harry Jones and Dickie Delacroix—the villagers

....

profusely abundantly; in great amounts
boisterous noisy and rowdy
reprimands sharp criticisms; severe scoldings

pronounced this name "Dellacroy"—eventually made a great pile of stones in one corner of the square and guarded it against the raids of the other boys. The girls stood aside, talking among themselves, looking over their shoulders at the boys, and the very small children rolled in the dust or clung to the hands of their older brothers or sisters.

Soon the men began to gather, **surveying** their own children, speaking of planting and rain, tractors and taxes. They stood together, away from the pile of stones in the corner, and their jokes were quiet and they smiled rather than laughed. The women, wearing faded house dresses and sweaters, came shortly after their menfolk. They greeted one another and exchanged bits of gossip as they went to join their husbands. Soon the women, standing by their husbands, began to call to their children, and the children came reluctantly, having to be called four or five times. Bobby Martin ducked under his mother's grasping hand and ran, laughing, back to the pile of stones. His father spoke up sharply, and Bobby came quickly and took his place between his father and his oldest brother.

The lottery was conducted—as were the square dances, the teen-age club, the Halloween program—by Mr. Summers, who had time and energy to devote to civic activities. He was a round-faced, jovial man and he ran the coal business, and people were sorry for him, because he

....

surveying watching over

had no children and his wife was a **scold**. When he arrived in the square, carrying the black wooden box, there was a murmur of conversation among the villagers, and he waved and called, "Little late today, folks." The postmaster, Mr. Graves, followed him, carrying a three-legged stool, and the stool was put in the center of the square and Mr. Summers set the black box down on it. The villagers kept their distance, leaving a space between themselves and the stool, and when Mr. Summers said, "Some of you fellows want to give me a hand?" there was a hesitation before two men, Mr. Martin and his oldest son, Baxter, came forward to hold the box steady on the stool while Mr. Summers stirred up the papers inside it.

The original **paraphernalia** for the lottery had been lost long ago, and the black box now resting on the stool had been put into use even before Old Man Warner, the oldest man in town, was born. Mr. Summers spoke frequently to the villagers about making a new box, but no one liked to upset even as much tradition as was represented by the black box. There was a story that the present box had been made with some pieces of the box that had preceded it, the one that had been constructed when the first people settled down to make a village here. Every year, after the lottery, Mr. Summers began talking again about a new box, but every year the subject was allowed to fade off without

scold one who habitually nags and criticizes
paraphernalia equipment; items needed for a task

anything's being done. The black box grew shabbier each year; by now it was no longer completely black but splintered badly along one side to show the original wood color, and in some places faded or stained.

Mr. Martin and his oldest son, Baxter, held the black box securely on the stool until Mr. Summers had stirred the papers thoroughly with his hand. Because so much of the ritual had been forgotten or discarded, Mr. Summers had been successful in having slips of paper substituted for the chips of wood that had been used for generations. Chips of wood, Mr. Summers had argued, had been all very well when the village was tiny, but now that the population was more than three hundred and likely to keep on growing, it was necessary to use something that would fit more easily into the black box. The night before the lottery, Mr. Summers and Mr. Graves made up the slips of paper and put them in the box, and it was then taken to the safe of Mr. Summers's coal company and locked up until Mr. Summers was ready to take it to the square next morning. The rest of the year, the box was put away, sometimes one place, sometimes another: it had spent one year in Mr. Graves's barn and another year underfoot in the post office, and sometimes it was set on a shelf in the Martin grocery and left there.

There was a great deal of fussing to be done before Mr. Summers declared the lottery open. There were the lists to make up—of heads of families, heads of households in each family, members of each household in each family. There was the proper swearing-in of Mr. Summers by the postmaster, as the official of the lottery; at one time, some people remembered, there had been a recital of some sort, performed by the official of the lottery, a **perfunctory**, tuneless chant that had been rattled off duly each year; some people believed that the official of the lottery used to stand just so when he said or sang it, others believed that he was supposed to walk among the people, but years and years ago this part of the ritual had been allowed to lapse. There had been, also, a ritual salute, which the official of the lottery had had to use in addressing each person who came up to draw from the box, but this also changed with time, until now it was felt necessary only for the official to speak to each person approaching. Mr. Summers was very good at all this; in his clean white shirt and blue jeans, with one hand resting carelessly on the black box, he seemed very proper and important as he talked **interminably** to Mr. Graves and the Martins.

Just as Mr. Summers finally left off talking and turned to the assembled villagers, Mrs. Hutchinson came hurriedly along the path to the square, her sweater thrown over her shoulders, and slid into place in the back of the crowd. "Clean forgot what day it was," she said to Mrs. Delacroix,

....

perfunctory indifferent; routine; done in a careless, inattentive, hasty way
interminably seemingly endless; wearisome

who stood next to her, and they both laughed softly. "Thought my old man was out back stacking wood," Mrs. Hutchinson went on, "and then I looked out the window and the kids was gone, and then I remembered it was the twenty-seventh and came a-running." She dried her hands on her apron, and Mrs. Delacroix said, "You're in time though. They're still talking away up there."

Mrs. Hutchinson craned her neck to see through the crowd and found her husband and children standing near the front. She tapped Mrs. Delacroix on the arm as a farewell and began to make her way through the crowd, "Here comes your Missus, Hutchinson," and "Bill, she made it after all." Mrs. Hutchinson reached her husband, and Mr. Summers, who had been waiting, said cheerfully, "Thought we were going to have to get on without you, Tessie." Mrs. Hutchinson said, grinning, "Wouldn't have me leave m'dishes in the sink, now, would you Joe?" and soft laughter ran through the crowd as the people stirred back into position after Mrs. Hutchinson's arrival.

"Well, now," Mr. Summers said soberly, "guess we better get started, get this over with, so's we can go back to work. Anybody ain't here?"

"Dunbar," several people said. "Dunbar, Dunbar."

Mr. Summers consulted his list. "Clyde Dunbar," he said. "That's right. He's broke his leg, hasn't he. Who's drawing for him?"

"Me, I guess," a woman said, and Mr. Summers turned to look at her. "Wife draws for her husband," Mr. Summers said. "Don't you have a grown boy to do it for you, Janey?"

Although Mr. Summers and everyone else in the village knew the answer perfectly well, it was the business of the official of the lottery to ask such questions formally. Mr. Summers waited with an expression of polite interest while Mrs. Dunbar answered.

"Horace's not but sixteen yet," Mrs. Dunbar said regretfully. "Guess I gotta fill in for the old man this year."

"Right," Mr. Summers said. He made a note on the list he was holding. Then he asked, "Watson boy drawing this year?"

A tall boy in the crowd raised his hand. "Here," he said. "I'm drawing for m'mother and me." He blinked his eyes nervously and ducked his head as several voices in the crowd said things like "Good fellow, Jack," and "Glad to see your mother's got a man to do it."

"Well," Mr. Summers said, "guess that's everyone. Old Man Warner make it?"

"Here," a voice said, and Mr. Summers nodded.

A sudden hush fell on the crowd as Mr. Summers cleared his throat and looked at the list. "All ready?" he called. "Now, I'll read the names—heads of families first—and the men come up and take a paper out of the box. Keep the paper folded in your hand without looking at it until everyone has had a turn. Everything clear?"

The people had done it so many times that they only half listened to the directions; most of them were quiet, wetting their lips, not looking around. Then Mr. Summers raised one hand high and said, "Adams." A man disengaged himself from the crowd and came forward. "Hi, Steve," Mr. Summers said, and Mr. Adams said, "Hi, Joe." They grinned at one another humorlessly and nervously. Then Mr. Adams reached into the black box and took out a folded paper. He held it firmly by one corner as he turned and went hastily back to his place in the crowd, where he stood a little apart from his family, not looking down at his hand.

"Allen," Mr. Summers said. "Anderson . . . . Bentham."

"Seems like there's no time at all between lotteries any more," Mrs. Delacroix said to Mrs. Graves in the back row. "Seems like we got through with the last one only last week."

"Time sure goes fast," Mrs. Graves said.

"Clark . . . . Delacroix."

"There goes my old man," Mrs. Delacroix said. She held her breath while her husband went forward.

"Dunbar," Mr. Summers said, and Mrs. Dunbar went steadily to the box while one of the women said, "Go on, Janey," and another said, "There she goes."

"We're next," Mrs. Graves said. She watched while Mr. Graves came around from the side of the box, greeted Mr. Summers gravely, and selected a slip of paper from the box. By now, all through the crowd there were men holding the small folded papers in their large hands, turning them over and over nervously. Mrs. Dunbar and her two sons stood together, Mrs. Dunbar holding the slip of paper.

"Harburt....Hutchinson."

"Get up there, Bill," Mrs. Hutchinson said, and the people near her laughed.

"Jones."

"They do say," Mr. Adams said to Old Man Warner, who stood next to him, "that over in the north village they're talking of giving up the lottery."

Old Man Warner snorted. "Pack of crazy fools," he said. "Listening to the young folks, nothing's good enough for *them*. Next thing you know, they'll be wanting to go back to living in caves, nobody work any more, live *that* way for a while. Used to be a saying about 'Lottery in June, corn be heavy soon.' First thing you know, we'd all be eating stewed chickweed and acorns. There's *always* been a lottery," he added **petulantly**. "Bad enough to see young Joe Summers up there joking with everybody."

"Some places have already quit lotteries," Mrs. Adams said. "Nothing but trouble in *that*," Old Man Warner said stoutly. "Pack of young fools."

"Martin." And Bobby Martin watched his father go forward. "Overdyke....Percy."

"I wish they'd hurry," Mrs. Dunbar said to her oldest son. "I wish they'd hurry."

---

petulantly irritably; with ill temper

"They're almost through," her son said.

"You get ready to run tell Dad," Mrs. Dunbar said. Mr. Summers called his own name and then stepped forward precisely and selected a slip from the box. Then he called, "Warner."

"Seventy-seventh year I been in the lottery," Old Man Warner said as he went through the crowd. "Seventy-seventh time."

"Watson." The tall boy came awkwardly through the crowd. Someone said, "Don't be nervous, Jack," and Mr. Summers said, "Take your time, son."

"Zanini."

After that, there was a long pause, a breathless pause, until Mr. Summers, holding his slip of paper in the air, said, "All right, fellows." For a minute, no one moved, and then all the slips of paper were opened. Suddenly, all the women began to speak at once, saying, "Who is it?" "Who's got it?" "Is it the Dunbars?" "Is it the Watsons?" Then the voices began to say, "It's Hutchinson. It's Bill." "Bill Hutchinson's got it."

"Go tell your father," Mrs. Dunbar said to her older son. People began to look around to see the Hutchinsons. Bill Hutchinson was standing quiet, staring down at the paper in his hand. Suddenly, Tessie Hutchinson shouted to Mr. Summers, "You didn't give him time enough to take any paper he wanted. I saw you. It wasn't fair!"

"Be a good sport, Tessie," Mrs. Delacroix called, and Mrs. Graves said, "All of us took the same chance."

"Shut up, Tessie," Bill Hutchinson said.

"Well, everyone," Mr. Summers said, "that was done pretty fast, and now we've got to be hurrying a little more to get done in time." He consulted his next list. "Bill," he said, "you draw for the Hutchinson family. You got any other households in the Hutchinsons?"

"There's Don and Eva," Mrs. Hutchinson yelled. "Make them take their chance!"

"Daughters draw with their husbands' families, Tessie," Mr. Summers said gently. "You know that as well as anyone else."

"It wasn't *fair*," Tessie said.

"I guess not, Joe," Bill Hutchinson said regretfully. "My daughter draws with her husband's family, that's only fair. And I've got no other family except the kids."

"Then, as far as drawing for families is concerned, it's you," Mr. Summers said in explanation, "and as far as drawing for households is concerned, that's you, too. Right?"

"Right," Bill Hutchinson said.

"How many kids, Bill?" Mr. Summers asked formally.

"Three," Bill Hutchinson said. "There's Bill Jr., and Nancy, and little Dave. And Tessie and me."

"All right, then," Mr. Summers said. "Harry, you got their tickets back?"

Mr. Graves nodded and held up the slips of paper. "Put them in the box, then," Mr. Summers directed. "Take Bill's and put it in."

"I think we ought to start over," Mrs. Hutchinson said, as quietly as she could. "I tell you it wasn't *fair*. You didn't give him time enough to choose. Everybody saw that."

Mr. Graves had selected the five slips and put them in the box, and he dropped all the papers but those onto the ground, where the breeze caught them and lifted them off.

"Listen, everybody," Mrs. Hutchinson was saying to the people around her.

"Ready, Bill?" Mr. Summers asked, and Bill Hutchinson, with one quick glance around at his wife and children, nodded.

"Remember," Mr. Summers said, "take the slips and keep them folded until each person has taken one. Harry, you help little Dave." Mr. Graves took the hand of the little boy, who came willingly with him up to the box. "Take a paper out of the box, Davy," Mr. Summers said. Davy put his hand into the box and laughed. "Take just one paper," Mr. Summers said. "Harry, you hold it for him." Mr. Graves took the child's hand and removed the folded paper from the tight fist and held it while little Dave stood next to him and looked up at him wonderingly.

"Nancy next," Mr. Summers said. Nancy was twelve, and her school friends breathed heavily as she went forward, switching her skirt, and took a slip daintily from the box. "Bill Jr.," Mr. Summers said, and Billy, his face red and his feet overlarge, nearly knocked the box over as he got a paper out. "Tessie," Mr. Summers said. She hesitated for a minute, looking around defiantly, and then set her lips and went up to the box. She snatched a paper out and held it behind her.

"Bill," Mr. Summers said, and Bill Hutchinson reached into the box and felt around, bringing his hand out at last with the slip of paper in it.

The crowd was quiet. A girl whispered, "I hope it's not Nancy," and the sound of the whisper reached the edges of the crowd.

"It's not the way it used to be," Old Man Warner said clearly. "People ain't the way they used to be."

"All right," Mr. Summers said, "Open the papers. Harry, you open little Dave's."

Mr. Graves opened the slip of paper and there was a general sigh through the crowd as he held it up and everyone could see that it was blank. Nancy and Bill Jr., opened theirs at the same time, and both beamed and laughed, turning around to the crowd and holding their slips of paper above their heads.

"Tessie," Mr. Summers said. There was a pause, and then Mr. Summers looked at Bill Hutchinson, and Bill unfolded his paper and showed it. It was blank.

"It's Tessie," Mr. Summers said, and his voice was hushed. "Show us her paper, Bill."

Bill Hutchinson went over to his wife and forced the slip of paper out of her hand. It had a black spot on it, the black spot Mr. Summers had made the night before with the heavy pencil in the coal-company office. Bill Hutchinson held it up, and there was a stir in the crowd. "All right, folks," Mr. Summers said. "Let's finish quickly."

Although the villagers had forgotten the ritual and lost the original black box, they still remembered to use stones. The pile of stones the boys had made earlier was ready; there were stones on the ground with the blowing scraps of paper that had come out of the box. Mrs. Delacroix selected a stone so large she had to pick it up with both hands and turned to Mrs. Dunbar. "Come on," she said. "Hurry up."

Mrs. Dunbar had small stones in both hands, and she said, gasping for breath, "I can't run at all. You'll have to go ahead and I'll catch up with you."

The children had stones already, and someone gave little Davy Hutchinson a few pebbles.

Tessie Hutchinson was in the center of a cleared space by now, and she held her hands out desperately as the villagers moved in on her. "It isn't fair," she said. A stone hit her on the side of the head.

Old Man Warner was saying, "Come on, come on, every-one." Steve Adams was in the front of the crowd of villagers, with Mrs. Graves beside him.

"It isn't fair, it isn't right," Mrs. Hutchinson screamed, and then they were upon her. ❖

The Lady or the Tiger?

by Frank R. Stockton

In the very olden time, there lived a **semi-barbaric** king, whose ideas, though somewhat polished and sharpened by the progressiveness of distant Latin neighbors, were still large, **florid**, and **untrammeled**, as became the half of him which was barbaric. He was a man of **exuberant** fancy, and, **withal**, of an authority so irresistible that, at his will, he turned his varied **fancies** into facts. He was greatly given to **self-communing**, and, when he and himself agreed upon anything, the thing was done. When every member of his domestic and political systems moved smoothly in its appointed course, his nature was bland and **genial**; but, whenever there was a little hitch, and some of his **orbs** got out of their orbits, he was blander and more genial still, for nothing pleased him so much as to make the crooked straight and crush down uneven places.

....

semi-barbaric partially uncivilized
florid overly elaborate; marked by emotional intensity
untrammeled not limited or restricted
exuberant unrestrained; extreme; bursting with enthusiasm
withal besides; also
fancies interests; tastes
self-communing consulting one's own thoughts; talking to oneself
genial friendly
orbs spheres; planets

Among the borrowed notions by which his barbarism had become **semified** was that of the public arena, in which, by exhibitions of manly and beastly **valor**, the minds of his subjects were refined and cultured.

But even here the exuberant and barbaric fancy asserted itself. The arena of the king was built, not to give the people an opportunity of hearing the **rhapsodies** of dying gladiators, nor to enable them to view the inevitable conclusion of a conflict between religious opinions and hungry jaws, but for purposes far better adapted to widen and develop the mental energies of the people. This vast **amphitheater**, with its encircling galleries, its mysterious vaults, and its unseen passages, was an agent of poetic justice, in which crime was punished, or virtue rewarded, by the decrees of an **impartial** and incorruptible chance.

When a subject was accused of a crime of sufficient importance to interest the king, public notice was given that on an appointed day the fate of the accused person would be decided in the king's arena—a structure which well deserved its name; for, although its form and plan were borrowed from afar, its purpose emanated solely from the brain of this man, who, every barleycorn a king,

---

semified cut in half; reduced
valor bravery
rhapsodies intensely emotional expressions in speech or song
amphitheater a round or oval arena for performances, athletic contests, etc.
impartial fair; not favoring one side or another

knew no tradition to which he owed more allegiance than pleased his fancy, and who **engrafted** on every adopted form of human thought and action the rich growth of his barbaric idealism.

When all the people had assembled in the galleries, and the king, surrounded by his court, sat high up on his throne of royal state on one side of the arena, he gave a signal, a door beneath him opened, and the accused subject stepped out into the amphitheater. Directly opposite him, on the other side of the enclosed space, were two doors, exactly alike and side by side. It was the duty and the privilege of the person on trial to walk directly to these doors and open one of them. He could open either door he pleased. He was subject to no guidance or influence but that of the aforementioned impartial and incorruptible chance. If he opened the one, there came out of it a hungry tiger, the fiercest and most cruel that could be **procured**, which immediately sprang upon him, and tore him to pieces as a punishment for his guilt. The moment that the case of the criminal was thus decided, **doleful** iron bells were clanged, great wails went up from the hired mourners posted on the outer rim of the arena, and the vast audience, with bowed heads and downcast hearts, **wended** slowly their homeward

---

engrafted fastened; attached
procured obtained
doleful sad; mournful
wended proceeded

way, mourning greatly that one so young and fair, or so old and respected, should have merited so **dire** a fate.

But if the accused person opened the other door, there came forth from it a lady, the most suitable to his years and station that his Majesty could select among his fair subjects; and to this lady he was immediately married, as a reward of his innocence. It mattered not that he might already possess a wife and family, or that his affections might be engaged upon an object of his own selection. The king allowed no such subordinate arrangements to interfere with his great scheme of **retribution** and reward. The exercises, as in the other instance, took place immediately, and in the arena. Another door opened beneath the king, and a priest, followed by a band of choristers, and dancing maidens blowing joyous airs on golden horns and treading an **epithalamic** measure, advanced to where the pair stood, side by side, and the wedding was promptly and cheerily **solemnized**. Then the gay brass bells rang forth their merry peals, the people shouted glad hurrahs, and the innocent man, preceded by children strewing flowers on his path, led his bride to his home.

This was the king's semi-barbaric method of administering justice. Its perfect fairness is obvious. The

dire terrible; having awful consequences
retribution punishment
epithalamic having to do with marriage (from *epithalamion*, a song or poem in praise of a bride or groom)
solemnized observed or performed with ceremony and ritual

criminal could not know out of which door would come the lady. He opened either he pleased, without having the slightest idea whether, in the next instant, he was to be devoured or married. On some occasions the tiger came out of one door, and on some out of the other. The decisions of this **tribunal** were not only fair—they were positively determinate. The accused person was instantly punished if he found himself guilty, and, if innocent he was rewarded on the spot, whether he liked it or not. There was no escape from the judgments of the king's arena.

The institution was a very popular one. When the people gathered together on one of the great trial days, they never knew whether they were to witness a bloody slaughter or a hilarious wedding. This element

....

tribunal a court or committee for administering justice

of uncertainty lent an interest to the occasion which it could not otherwise have attained. Thus the masses were entertained and pleased, and the thinking part of the community could bring no charge of unfairness against this plan; for did not the accused person have the whole matter in his own hands?

This semi-barbaric king had a daughter as blooming as his most florid fancies, and with a soul as **fervent** and **imperious** as his own. As is usual in such cases, she was the apple of his eye, and was loved by him above all humanity. Among his courtiers was a young man of that fineness of blood and lowness of station common to the conventional heroes of romance who love royal maidens. This royal maiden was well satisfied with her lover, for he was handsome and brave to a degree unsurpassed in all this kingdom, and she loved him with an **ardor** that had enough of barbarism in it to make it exceedingly warm and strong. This love affair moved on happily for many months, until, one day, the king happened to discover its existence. He did not hesitate nor waver in regard to his duty in the premises. The youth was immediately cast into prison, and a day was appointed for his trial in the king's arena. This, of course, was an especially important occasion, and his Majesty, as well as all the people, was

---

fervent highly emotional
imperious commanding; domineering; overbearing
ardor a warm, intense emotion

greatly interested in the workings and development of this trial. Never before had such a case occurred—never before had a subject dared to love the daughter of the king. In after years such things became commonplace enough, but then they were in no slight degree **novel** and startling.

The tiger cages of the kingdom were searched for the most savage and relentless beasts, from which the fiercest monster might be selected for the arena, and the ranks of maiden youth and beauty throughout the land were carefully surveyed by competent judges in order that the young man might have a fitting bride in case fate did not determine for him a different destiny. Of course, everybody knew that the deed with which the accused was charged had been done. He had loved the princess, and neither he, she, nor any one else, thought of denying the fact. But the king would not think of allowing any fact of this kind to interfere with the workings of the tribunal, in which he took such great delight and satisfaction. No matter how the affair turned out, the youth would be disposed of, and the king would take an **aesthetic** pleasure in watching the course of events which would determine whether or not the young man had done wrong in allowing himself to love the princess.

The appointed day arrived. From far and near the people gathered, and thronged the great galleries of the

novel new
aesthetic artistic

arena, while crowds, unable to gain admittance, massed themselves against its outside walls. The king and his court were in their places, opposite the twin doors—those fateful **portals**, so terrible in their similarity!

All was ready. The signal was given. A door beneath the royal party opened, and the lover of the princess walked into the arena. Tall, beautiful, fair, his appearance was greeted with a low hum of admiration and anxiety. Half the audience had not known so grand a youth had lived among them. No wonder the princess loved him! What a terrible thing for him to be there!

As the youth advanced into the arena, he turned, as the custom was, to bow to the king. But he did not think at all of that royal personage; his eyes were fixed upon the princess, who sat to the right of her father. Had it not been for the **moiety** of barbarism in her nature, it is probable that lady would not have been there. But her intense and **fervid** soul would not allow her to be absent on an occasion in which she was so terribly interested. From the moment that the decree had gone forth that her lover should decide his fate in the king's arena, she had thought of nothing, night or day, but this great event and the various subjects connected with it. Possessed of more power, influence, and force of character than any one who had ever before been

portals doorways
moiety half; portion
fervid passionate

interested in such a case, she had done what no other person had done—she had possessed herself of the secret of the doors. She knew in which of the two rooms that lay behind those doors stood the cage of the tiger, with its open front, and in which waited the lady. Through these thick doors, heavily curtained with skins on the inside, it was impossible that any noise or suggestion should come from within to the person who should approach to raise the latch of one of them. But gold, and the power of a woman's will, had brought the secret to the princess.

Not only did she know in which room stood the lady ready to emerge, all blushing and radiant, should her door be opened, but she knew who the lady was. It was one of the fairest and loveliest of the damsels of the court who had been selected as the reward of the accused youth, should he be proved innocent of the crime of **aspiring** to one so far above him; and the princess hated her. Often had she seen, or imagined that she had seen, this fair creature throwing glances of admiration upon the person of her lover, and sometimes she thought these glances were perceived and even returned. Now and then she had seen them talking together. It was but for a moment or two, but much can be said in a brief space. It may have been on most unimportant topics, but how could she know that? The girl was lovely, but she had dared to raise her eyes to the loved

....

aspiring eagerly desiring to achieve or attain something high or great one of the princess, and, with all the intensity of the savage blood transmitted to her through long lines of wholly barbaric ancestors, she hated the woman who blushed and trembled behind that silent door.

When her lover turned and looked at her, and his eye met hers as she sat there paler and whiter than any one in the vast ocean of anxious faces about her, he saw, by that power of quick perception which is given to those whose souls are one, that she knew behind which door crouched the tiger, and behind which stood the lady. He had expected her to know it. He understood her nature, and his soul was assured that she would never rest until she had made plain to herself this thing, hidden to all other lookers-on, even to the king. The only hope for the youth in which there was any element of certainty was based upon the success of the princess in discovering this mystery, and the moment he looked upon her, he saw she had succeeded, as in his soul he knew she had succeeded.

Then it was that his quick and anxious glance asked the question, "Which?" It was as plain to her as if he shouted it from where he stood. There was not an instant to be lost. The question was asked in a flash; it must be answered in another.

Her right arm lay on the cushioned **parapet** before her. She raised her hand, and made a slight, quick movement

....
parapet a low wall or railing around a platform

toward the right. No one but her lover saw her. Every eye but his was fixed on the man in the arena.

He turned, and with a firm and rapid step he walked across the empty space. Every heart stopped beating, every breath was held, every eye was fixed immovably upon that man. Without the slightest hesitation, he went to the door on the right, and opened it.

Now, the point of the story is this: Did the tiger come out of that door, or did the lady?

The more we reflect upon this question, the harder it is to answer. It involves a study of the human heart which leads us through **devious** mazes of passion, out of which it is difficult to find our way. Think of it, fair reader, not as if the decision of the question depended upon yourself, but upon that hot-blooded, semi-barbaric princess, her soul at a white heat beneath the combined fires of despair and jealousy. She had lost him, but who should have him?

How often, in her waking hours and in her dreams, had she started in wild horror, and covered her face with her hands as she thought of her lover opening the door on the other side of which waited the cruel fangs of the tiger!

But how much oftener had she seen him at the other door! How in her **grievous reveries** had she gnashed her

----

devious roundabout; wandering; misleading
grievous characterized by pain and extreme suffering
reveries daydreams

teeth and torn her hair when she saw his start of rapturous delight as he opened the door of the lady! How her soul had burned in agony when she had seen him rush to meet that woman, with her flushing cheek and sparkling eye of triumph; when she had seen him lead her forth, his whole frame kindled with the joy of recovered life; when she had heard the glad shouts from the multitude, and the wild ringing of the happy bells; when she had seen the priest, with his joyous followers, advance to the couple, and make them man and wife before her very eyes; and when she had seen them walk away together upon their path of flowers, followed by the tremendous shouts of the hilarious multitude, in which her one despairing shriek was lost and drowned!

Would it not be better for him to die at once, and go to wait for her in the blessed regions of semi-barbaric futurity?

And yet, that awful tiger, those shrieks, that blood!

Her decision had been indicated in an instant, but it had been made after days and nights of anguished deliberation. She had known she would be asked, she had decided what she would answer, and, without the slightest hesitation, she had moved her hand to the right.

The question of her decision is one not to be lightly considered, and it is not for me to presume to set myself up as the one person able to answer it. So I leave it with all of you: Which came out of the opened door—the lady, or the tiger? ❖

Just the Facts

Responding to Climate Change

courtesy of NASA

*NASA is a world leader in climate studies and Earth science. While its role is not to set climate policy or prescribe particular responses or solutions to climate change, its **purview** does include providing the robust scientific data needed to understand climate change. NASA then makes this information available to the global community—the public, policy- and decision-makers, and scientific and planning agencies around the world.*

....

purview range of influence; authority

Key Points

- Responding to climate change involves two possible approaches: reducing and stabilizing the levels of heat-trapping greenhouse gases in the atmosphere ("**mitigation**") and/or adapting to the climate change already in the pipeline ("**adaptation**").

- NASA's role is to make detailed climate data available to the global community, including the public, policy- and decision-makers, and scientific and planning agencies.

Climate change is one of the most complex issues facing us today. It involves many dimensions—science, economics, society, politics and moral and ethical questions—and is a global problem, felt on local scales, that will be around for decades and centuries to come. Carbon dioxide, the heat-trapping greenhouse gas that has driven recent global warming, lingers in the atmosphere for hundreds of years, and the planet (especially the oceans) takes a while to respond to warming. So even if we stopped emitting all greenhouse gases today, global warming and climate change will continue to affect future generations. In this way, humanity is "committed" to some level of climate change.

How much climate change? That will be determined by how our emissions continue and also exactly how our climate system responds to those emissions. Despite increasing awareness of climate change, our emissions of greenhouse gases continue on a relentless rise. In 2013, the daily level of carbon dioxide in the atmosphere surpassed 400 parts per million for the first time in human history. The last time levels were that high was about three to five million years ago, during the Pliocene era.

Because we are already committed to some level of climate change, responding to climate change involves a two-pronged approach:

1. Reducing emissions of and stabilizing the levels of heat-trapping greenhouse gases in the atmosphere ("**mitigation**");
2. Adapting to the climate change already in the pipeline ("**adaptation**").

Mitigation and Adaptation

Mitigation—reducing climate change—involves **reducing the flow of heat-trapping greenhouse gases into the atmosphere**, either by reducing sources of these gases (for example, the burning of fossil fuels for electricity, heat or transport) or enhancing the "sinks" that accumulate and store these gases (such as the oceans, forests and soil). The goal of mitigation is to avoid significant human interference with the climate system, and "stabilize greenhouse gas levels in a timeframe sufficient to allow **ecosystems** to adapt naturally to climate change, ensure that food production is not threatened and to enable economic development to proceed in a sustainable manner" (from the 2014 report on Mitigation of Climate Change from the United Nations Intergovernmental Panel on Climate Change, page 4).

Adaptation—adapting to life in a changing climate—involves adjusting to actual or expected future climate. The goal is to reduce our vulnerability to the harmful effects of climate change (like sea-level encroachment, more intense extreme weather events or food insecurity). It also encompasses making the most of any potential beneficial opportunities associated with climate change (for example, longer growing seasons or increased yields in some regions).

Throughout history, people and societies have adjusted to and coped with changes in climate and extremes with varying degrees of success. Climate change (drought in particular) has been at least partly responsible for the rise and fall of civilizations. Earth's climate has been relatively stable for the past 12,000 years and this stability has been crucial for the development of our modern civilization and life as we know it. Modern life is tailored to the stable

ecosystems unique biological communities or environments

climate we have become accustomed to. As our climate changes, we will have to learn to adapt. The faster the climate changes, the harder it could be.

While climate change is a global issue, it is felt on a local scale. Cities and municipalities are therefore at the frontline of adaptation. In the absence of national or international climate policy direction, cities and local communities around the world have been focusing on solving their own climate problems. They are working to build flood defenses, plan for heatwaves and higher temperatures, install water-**permeable** pavements to better deal with floods and stormwater and improve water storage and use.

According to the 2014 report on Climate Change Impacts, Adaptation and Vulnerability (page 8) from the United Nations Intergovernmental Panel on Climate Change, governments at various levels are also getting better at adaptation. Climate change is starting to be factored into a variety of development plans: how to manage the increasingly extreme disasters we are seeing and their associated risks, how to protect coastlines and deal with sea-level encroachment, how to best manage land and forests, how to deal with and plan for reduced water availability, how to develop resilient crop varieties and how to protect energy and public infrastructure.

....

permeable porous; capable of allowing liquid to pass through

How NASA Is Involved

NASA, with its Eyes on the Earth and wealth of knowledge on the Earth's climate system and its components, is one of the world's experts in climate science. NASA's purview is to provide the robust scientific data needed to understand climate change. For example, data from the agency's Gravity Recovery and Climate Experiment (GRACE) and Ice, Cloud and land Elevation Satellite (ICESat) missions and from radar instruments in space have shown rapid changes in the Earth's great ice sheets. The Jason-3, Jason-2/OSTM Surface Topography Mission (OSTM) and Jason-1 missions have documented an increasing sea level since 1992.

NASA makes detailed climate data available to the global community—the public, policy- and decision-makers and scientific and planning agencies around the world. It is not NASA's role to set climate policy or prescribe particular responses or solutions to climate change. NASA is one of 13 U.S. government agencies that form part of the U.S. Global Change Research Program, which has a legal **mandate** to help the nation and the world understand, assess, predict and respond to global change. These U.S. partner agencies include the Department of Agriculture, the Environmental Protection Agency and the Department of Energy, each of which has a different purview depending on their area of expertise.

----

mandate the legal authority to carry something out

Started in 2010, NASA's Carbon Monitoring System (CMS) is a forward-looking initiative established under direction by the U.S. government. The CMS is improving the monitoring of global carbon stocks (where carbon is stored around the planet) and fluxes (how carbon is cycled from one stock to the next). The ultimate goal is to make breakthroughs in quantifying, understanding and predicting how worldwide carbon sources and sinks are changing, since this could have major ramifications for how our planet will respond to increasing emissions and/or efforts to combat climate change. The work will also help inform near-term policy development and planning.

NASA's related Megacities Carbon Project is focused on the problem of accurately measuring and monitoring greenhouse-gas emissions from the world's biggest cities. About three-quarters of fossil-fuel carbon dioxide emissions come from about 2 percent of the land surface—the cities and the power plants that feed them. At present the focus is on pilot projects in Los Angeles and Paris that sample the air there. The goal is to add other cities around the world and to ultimately deploy a worldwide urban carbon monitoring system that will enable local policymakers to fully account for the many sources and sinks of carbon and how they change over time.

Although NASA's main focus is not on energy-technology research and development, work is being done around the agency and by/with various partners and collaborators to find viable alternative sources of energy to power our needs. These sources of energy include the wind, waves, the Sun and biofuels. ❖

Freedom of Expression
in the United States

courtesy of United States Department of State

The Universal Declaration of Human Rights (UDHR) and the International Covenant on Civil and Political Rights (ICCPR), to which the United States is a party, both state that individuals have a right to freedom of expression; this right includes the freedom to seek, receive, and impart information and ideas of all kinds.

The United States safeguards this right through the First Amendment to the U.S. Constitution, which provides that "Congress shall make no law respecting an establishment of religion, or prohibiting the free exercise thereof; or abridging the freedom of speech, or of the press; or the right of the people peaceably to assemble, and to petition the government for a redress of grievances."

The U.S. Constitution protects even the most offensive and controversial speech from government suppression, and permits regulation of speech only under certain limited and narrow circumstances. The U.S. system is built on the idea that the free and open exchange of ideas encourages understanding, advances truth-seeking, and allows for the rebuttal of falsehoods. The United States believes, and experience has shown, that the best way to counter offensive speech is not with regulation but with more speech.

The Foundation of Free Expression

The U.S. Constitution's protection of freedom of expression embodies the notion that an individual's ability to express himself freely—without fear of government punishment— produces the autonomy and liberty that promote better governance. Allowing citizens to openly discuss topics of public concern results in a more transparent and representative government, more tolerant ideas, and a more stable society.

History has shown that curtailing free expression by banning speech does not advance democracy. The drafters of the U.S. Constitution recognized that when governments forbid citizens from talking about certain topics, it often forces those citizens to discuss such topics secretly. By allowing individuals to express their opinions—no matter how much the government and other citizens may disagree with them—the First Amendment promotes transparency and social stability. This uninhibited public debate also forces ideas into the intellectual marketplace, where they must compete with the ideas freely expressed by other individuals.[1] This competition of ideas means that inferior or offensive ideas give way to better ones.

Narrowly Drawn Exceptions

While the First Amendment provides very broad protections for expression in the United States, freedom of speech is not absolute. Generally, the government has more discretion to impose content-neutral restrictions than content-based restrictions.

Content-Neutral Restrictions

The government can generally place time, place, and manner restrictions on the exercise of freedom of expression, provided that the restrictions are not based on the content of the speech or the viewpoint of the speaker. These restrictions must (1) be content neutral, (2) be narrowly tailored to serve a significant government interest, and (3) leave open other channels of communication.[2]

For example, the government may impose reasonable regulations on the volume of loudspeakers used in a downtown business district, impose reasonable limits on protests in residential neighborhoods in the middle of the night, or require permits for parades and organized protests to ensure that they do not create public safety hazards, provided that such restrictions apply to all speakers without regard to the particular content or viewpoint of the speech.

Content-Based Restrictions

While content-based restrictions are generally impermissible, there are a few narrow exceptions. Special categories of expression that may be restricted under the First Amendment include incitement to **imminent** violence, true threats, defamatory speech, and obscenity.

....

imminent immediate

Incitement to Imminent Violence

An individual's speech may be restricted if (1) it is intended to incite or produce lawless action (2) it is likely to incite such action, and (3) such action is likely to occur imminently. This is a very high standard, which courts have rarely found to have been met. General advocacy of violence, such as writing on a website that violent revolution is the only cure to society's problems, does not constitute incitement to imminent violence.

For example, in 1969, a Ku Klux Klan member delivered a speech in Ohio in which he advocated "revengence" (sic) against Jews and African Americans.[3] The U.S. Supreme Court struck down a statute prohibiting his speech because it criminalized speech that was not "directed at inciting or producing imminent lawless action" and was not "likely to incite or produce such action."[4]

Similarly, if a person burns a U.S. flag at a protest against the U.S. government's immigration policies, and a counterprotester becomes upset and physically attacks someone who appears to be an immigrant, the flag burner's expression likely would be protected by the First Amendment because it was not intended to incite violence.

In contrast, if a speaker belonging to a particular ethnic group calls on an angry mob to imminently and specifically physically attack someone of a different ethnic group to prove his group's superiority, and someone from that mob immediately physically attacks someone from that different ethnic group, the speaker's speech likely would not be protected by the First Amendment because it was intended to incite imminent violence and was likely to incite such violence.

True Threats

Speech may also be restricted based on its content if it falls within the narrow class of "true threats" of violence. A true threat is a statement that a reasonable recipient would take to mean that the speaker, or people working with the speaker, intend to commit physical harm against the recipient. For example, a Philadelphia woman was sentenced to eight months confinement after she left an anonymous threatening note on her colleague's chair.

Defamation

In the United States, defamatory speech is a false statement of fact that damages a person's character, fame, or reputation. It must be a false statement of fact; statements of opinion, however insulting they may be, cannot be defamation under U.S. law.

Under U.S. defamation law, there are different standards for public officials and private individuals. Speakers are afforded greater protection when they comment about a public official, as opposed to a private citizen. In 1964, the U.S. Supreme Court ruled that public officials could prove defamation only if they could demonstrate "actual malice," that is, that the speaker acted with knowledge that the defamatory statement was false or "with reckless disregard of whether it was false or not."[5]

This decision was later extended to cover "public figures," in addition to public officials.[6] For the private concerns of private individuals, though, the standard for proving defamation remains lower.[7] Defamation of private individuals can be established if the statements were false and damaged the person's reputation without showing actual malice. Only individuals, not groups, can be defamed.

Even where courts find defamation, they do not impose criminal punishment. Instead, courts may require the speaker to publish a correction to the defamatory statement and/or to financially compensate the victim.

Obscenity

Obscenity may be restricted under the First Amendment, but there has been a long debate over what constitutes obscenity and how it should be regulated. The U.S. Supreme Court defined obscenity in 1973 as expression that the average person, applying contemporary community standards, would find (1) appeals to prurient interests, (2) depicts or describes sexual conduct in a patently offensive way, and (3) lacks serious literary, artistic, political or scientific value, when taken as a whole.[8]

A court evaluates each element independently and will not classify expression as obscene unless all factors exist. For example, if a book uses coarse language and depicts sexual conduct but, taken as a whole, does not appeal to prurient interests or has literary value, it is not obscene.[9] Given such high standards, it is rare for the courts to find expression obscene.

Hate Speech

Hate speech—generally defined as speech that maligns a person or group based on race, ethnicity, gender, religion, sexual orientation, or disability—receives full First Amendment protection. Speech that is intended to incite imminent violence or credibly threaten individuals, however, can be restricted as outlined above.

While the United States does not restrict hate speech, it understands that the most effective weapon in combating hate speech is not suppression, but tolerant, truthful, and intelligent counter speech.

Banning intolerant or offensive speech can be counterproductive, raising the profile of the offensive speech and causing hateful ideologies to fester in dangerous, sometimes hidden ways. Persuasion—not regulation—is the solution.

The United States' strong constitutional protections for and belief in freedom of expression do not mean that it sits idly by as individuals and groups seek to spread toxic expressions of hatred. Rather, the United States deploys an array of policies to reach out to affected communities, provide conflict resolution services, and enhance dialogue.

Government Versus Private Action

The First Amendment protects citizens from government restrictions on free expression. It is inapplicable to situations in which a private party restricts another's speech. A private employer, for example, may forbid its employees from sharing the company's trade secrets. Still, those employees enjoy First Amendment protections with respect to government action. ❖

1. See *Hustler Magazine, Inc. v. Falwell,* 485 U.S. 46, 50 (citing *Abrams v. United States,* 250 U.S. 616, 630 (1919) (Holmes, J., dissenting)).
2. *Perry Educ. Ass'n v. Perry Educators' Ass'n,* 460 U.S. 37, 45 (1983).
3. *Brandenburg v. Ohio,* 395 U.S. 444, 446 (1969).
4. Id. at 447.
5. *New York Times Co. v. Sullivan,* 376 U.S. 254, 279–80 (1964).
6. *Gertz v. Robert Welch, Inc.,* 418 U.S. 323 (1974).
7. *Dun & Bradstreet, Inc. v. Greenmoss Builders, Inc.,* 472 U.S. 749 (1985) (plurality opinion).
8. *Miller v. California,* 413 U.S. 15 (1973).
9. See *United States v. One Book Called "Ulysses,"* 5 F. Supp. 182 (S.D.N.Y. 1933).

The Power of Poetry

I dwell
in Possibility

by Emily Dickinson

I dwell in Possibility –
A fairer House than **Prose** –
More numerous of Windows –
Superior – for Doors –

Of Chambers as the Cedars –
Impregnable of Eye –
And for an Everlasting Roof
The **Gambrels** of the Sky –

Of Visitors – the fairest –
For Occupation – This –
The spreading wide my narrow Hands
To gather Paradise – ❖

prose ordinary speech or writing, as opposed to poetry
impregnable difficult to attack or destroy
gambrels roofs, like barn roofs, that slope on each side, or the angled frames that
support such roofs

378

Ozymandias

by Percy Bysshe Shelley

I met a traveler from an **antique** land,
Who said—"Two vast and trunkless legs of stone
Stand in the desert....Near them, on the sand,
Half sunk a shattered **visage** lies, whose frown,
And wrinkled lip, and sneer of cold command,
Tell that its sculptor well those passions read
Which yet survive, stamped on these lifeless things,
The hand that mocked them, and the heart that fed;
And on the pedestal, these words appear:
My name is Ozymandias, King of Kings,
Look on my Works, ye Mighty, and despair!
Nothing beside remains. Round the decay
Of that **colossal** Wreck, boundless and bare
The lone and level sands stretch far away." ❖

....

antique of or from ancient times
visage face; appearance of a person
colossal gigantic; enormous

Do Not Go Gentle into That Good Night

by Dylan Thomas

Do not go gentle into that good night,
Old age should burn and **rave** at close of day;
Rage, rage against the dying of the light.

Though wise men at their end know dark is right,
Because their words had forked no lightning they
Do not go gentle into that good night.

Good men, the last wave by, crying how bright
Their frail deeds might have danced in a green bay,
Rage, rage against the dying of the light.

Wild men who caught and sang the sun in flight,
And learn, too late, they grieved it on its way,
Do not go gentle into that good night.

Grave men, near death, who see with blinding sight
Blind eyes could blaze like meteors and be gay,
Rage, rage against the dying of the light.

And you, my father, there on the sad height,
Curse, bless, me now with your fierce tears, I pray.
Do not go gentle into that good night.
Rage, rage against the dying of the light. ❖

---

rave to rage; to speak or act wildly

The Charge of the Light Brigade

by Alfred, Lord Tennyson

1

Half a **league**, half a league,

Half a league onward,

All in the valley of Death

    Rode the six hundred.

"Forward the Light Brigade!

Charge for the guns!" he said.

Into the valley of Death

    Rode the six hundred.

2

"Forward, the Light Brigade!"

Was there a man dismayed?

Not though the soldier knew

    Someone had blundered.

Theirs not to make reply,

Theirs not to reason why,

Theirs but to do and die.

Into the valley of Death

    Rode the six hundred.

Light Brigade British cavalry troops who met with disaster during a battle in the Crimean War in 1854

league a distance of about three miles

3

Cannon to right of them,
Cannon to left of them,
Cannon in front of them
    Volleyed and thundered;
Stormed at with **shot** and **shell**,
Boldly they rode and well,
Into the jaws of Death,
Into the mouth of hell
    Rode the six hundred.

4

Flashed all their **sabers** bare,
Flashed as they turned in air
Sab'ring the gunners there,
Charging an army, while
    All the world wondered.
Plunged in the **battery** smoke
Right through the line they broke;
Cossack and Russian
Reeled from the saber stroke
    Shattered and **sundered**.
Then they rode back, but not,
    Not the six hundred.

volleyed simultaneously fired
shot matter fired from a cannon
shell a bombshell
sabers swords

battery a group of army artillery
Cossack a soldier from a region in southeast Russia
sundered broken apart; torn apart

5

Cannon to right of them,
Cannon to left of them,
Cannon behind them
    Volleyed and thundered;
Stormed at with shot and shell,
While horse and hero fell,
They that had fought so well
Came through the jaws of Death,
Back from the mouth of hell,
All that was left of them,
    Left of six hundred.

6

When can their glory fade?
O the wild charge they made!
    All the world wondered.
Honor the charge they made!
Honor the Light Brigade,
    Noble six hundred! ❖

The Battle of Blenheim

by Robert Southey

It was a summer evening,
   Old Kaspar's work was done,
And he before his cottage door
   Was sitting in the sun,
And by him **sported** on the green
His little grandchild Wilhelmine.

She saw her brother Peterkin
   Roll something large and round,
Which he beside the **rivulet**
   In playing there had found;
He came to ask what he had found,
That was so large, and smooth, and round.

Old Kaspar took it from the boy,
   Who stood expectant by;
And then the old man shook his head,
   And, with a natural sigh,
"'Tis some poor fellow's skull," said he,
"Who fell in the great victory.

Blenheim now a part of modern Germany, the site of a major battle in 1704 during the War of Spanish Succession
sported played
rivulet a small stream

"I find them in the garden,
    For there's many here about;
And often, when I go to plow,
    The **plowshare** turns them out!
For many thousand men," said he,
"Were slain in that great victory."

"Now tell us what 'twas all about,"
    Young Peterkin, he cries;
And little Wilhelmine looks up
    With wonder-waiting eyes;
"Now tell us all about the war,
And what they fought each other for."

plowshare the wedge-shaped steel cutting blade of a plow

"It was the English," Kaspar cried,
    "Who **put the French to rout**;
But what they fought each other for,
    I could not well make out;
But everybody said," **quoth** he,
"That 'twas a famous victory.

"My father lived at Blenheim then,
    Yon little stream hard by;
They burnt his dwelling to the ground,
    And he was forced to fly;
So with his wife and child he fled,
Nor had he where to rest his head.

"With fire and sword the country round
    Was wasted far and wide,
And many a childing mother then,
    And new-born baby died;
But things like that, you know, must be
At every famous victory.

....

put the French to rout forced into a disorderly retreat
quoth said
yon yonder

"They say it was a shocking sight
　　After the field was won;
For many thousand bodies here
　　Lay rotting in the sun;
But things like that, you know, must be
After a famous victory.

"Great praise the **Duke of Marlbro'** won,
　　And our good **Prince Eugene**."
"Why, 'twas a very wicked thing!"
　　Said little Wilhelmine.
"Nay...nay...my little girl," quoth he,
"It was a famous victory.

"And everybody praised the Duke
　　Who this great fight did win."
"But what good came of it at last?"
　　Quoth little Peterkin.
"Why that I cannot tell," said he;
"But 'twas a famous victory." ❖

Duke of Marlbro' John Churchill, Duke of Marlborough, leading general of the combined English and Austrian forces that won the Battle of Blenheim in 1704
Prince Eugene Prince Eugene of Savoy, the Austrian general with whom the Duke of Marlborough joined forces

War Is Kind

by Stephen Crane

Do not weep, maiden, for war is kind.
Because your lover threw wild hands toward the sky
And the affrighted **steed** ran on alone,
Do not weep.
War is kind.

Hoarse, booming drums of the regiment,
Little souls who thirst for fight,
These men were born to drill and die.
The unexplained glory flies above them,
Great is the battle god, great, and his kingdom—
A field where a thousand corpses lie.

Do not weep, babe, for war is kind.
Because your father tumbled in the yellow trenches,
Raged at his breast, gulped and died,
Do not weep.
War is kind.

---

steed horse

Swift blazing flag of the regiment,
Eagle with crest of red and gold,
These men were born to drill and die.
Point for them the virtue of slaughter,
Make plain to them the excellence of killing
And a field where a thousand corpses lie.

Mother whose heart hung humble as a button
On the bright splendid shroud of your son,
Do not weep.
War is kind. ❖

The Raven

by Edgar Allan Poe

Once upon a midnight dreary, while I pondered, weak and weary,
Over many a **quaint** and curious volume of forgotten **lore**—
While I nodded, nearly napping, suddenly there came a tapping,
As of some one gently rapping, rapping at my chamber door.
"'Tis some visitor," I muttered, "tapping at my chamber door—
       Only this and nothing more."

Ah, distinctly I remember it was in the bleak December,
And each separate dying ember wrought its ghost upon the floor.
Eagerly I wished the morrow;—vainly I had sought to borrow
From my books **surcease** of sorrow—sorrow for the lost Lenore—
For the rare and radiant maiden whom the angels name Lenore—
       Nameless here for **evermore**.

And the silken sad uncertain rustling of each purple curtain
Thrilled me—filled me with **fantastic** terrors never felt before;
So that now, to still the beating of my heart, I stood repeating
"'Tis some visitor **entreating** entrance at my chamber door—
Some late visitor entreating entrance at my chamber door;
       This it is and nothing more."

---

quaint unusual
lore learning; body of knowledge
surcease an end

evermore always
fantastic unreal; from one's fancy or imagination
entreating pleading; begging

Presently my soul grew stronger; hesitating then no longer,
"Sir," said I, "or Madam, truly your forgiveness I implore;
But the fact is I was napping, and so gently you came rapping,
And so faintly you came tapping, tapping at my chamber door,
That I scarce was sure I heard you"—here I opened wide the
    door;—

                      Darkness there and nothing more.

Deep into that darkness peering, long I stood there wondering,
    fearing,
Doubting, dreaming dreams no mortal ever dared to dream
    before;
But the silence was unbroken, and the stillness gave no **token**,
And the only word there spoken was the whispered word, "Lenore!"
This I whispered, and an echo murmured back the word, "Lenore!"
                      Merely this and nothing more.

Back into the chamber turning, all my soul within me burning,
Soon again I heard a tapping something louder than before.
"Surely," said I, "surely that is something at my window **lattice**;
Let me see, then, what **thereat** is, and this mystery explore—
Let my heart be still a moment and this mystery explore;—
                      Tis the wind and nothing more!"

....

token a sign or clue
lattice the crossed wood or metal frame over the glass of a window
thereat at that place

Open here I flung the shutter, when, with many a **flirt** and flutter,

In there stepped a stately Raven of the saintly days of **yore**;

Not the least **obeisance** made he; not a minute stopped or stayed he;

But, with **mien** of lord or lady, perched above my chamber door—

Perched upon a bust of **Pallas** just above my chamber door—

                    Perched, and sat, and nothing more.

Then this ebony bird **beguiling** my sad **fancy** into smiling,

By the grave and stern decorum of the **countenance** it wore,

"Though thy crest be shorn and shaven, thou," I said, "art sure no
    craven,

Ghastly grim and ancient Raven wandering from the Nightly
    shore—

Tell me what thy lordly name is on the Night's **Plutonian** shore!"

                    Quoth the Raven, "Nevermore."

---

flirt sudden movement
yore long ago
obeisance a show of respect
mien bearing; attitude; appearance
Pallas a name for Athena, the Greek goddess of wisdom
beguiling deceiving; charming through deceptive means
fancy imagination
countenance expression
craven a coward
Plutonian having to do with the underworld, which the ancient Romans
believed to be ruled by the god Pluto

Much I marveled this ungainly fowl to hear **discourse** so plainly,
Though its answer little meaning—little relevancy bore;
For we cannot help agreeing that no living human being
Ever yet was blessed with seeing bird above his chamber door—
Bird or beast upon the sculptured bust above his chamber door,
        With such name as "Nevermore."

But the Raven, sitting lonely on that **placid** bust, spoke only
That one word, as if his soul in that one word he did outpour.
Nothing further then he uttered—not a feather then he fluttered—
Till I scarcely more than muttered, "Other friends have flown
   before—
On the morrow *he* will leave me, as my Hopes have flown before."
        Then the bird said, "Nevermore."

Startled at the stillness broken by reply so aptly spoken,
"Doubtless," said I, "what it utters is its only stock and store
Caught from some unhappy master whom unmerciful Disaster
Followed fast and followed faster till his songs one burden bore—
Till the **dirges** of his Hope that **melancholy** burden bore
        Of 'Never—nevermore.'"

....

discourse conversation; speech
placid calm; serene
dirges slow, sad songs of grief
melancholy gloomy

But the Raven still beguiling all my sad soul into smiling,
Straight I wheeled a cushioned seat in front of bird and bust and door;
Then, upon the velvet sinking, I betook myself to linking
Fancy unto fancy, thinking what this **ominous** bird of yore—
What this grim, ungainly, ghastly, gaunt, and ominous bird of yore
                             Meant in croaking "Nevermore."

This I sat engaged in guessing, but no syllable expressing
To the fowl whose fiery eyes now burned into my bosom's core;
This and more I sat **divining**, with my head at ease reclining
On the cushion's velvet lining that the lamp-light gloated o'er,
But whose velvet violet lining with the lamp-light gloating o'er,
                             She shall press, ah, nevermore!

....

ominous threatening; foreboding
divining figuring out; guessing

Then, methought, the air grew denser, perfumed from an unseen
    censer
Swung by **Seraphim** whose foot-falls tinkled on the tufted floor.
"Wretch," I cried, "thy God hath lent thee—by these angels he
    hath sent thee
Respite—**respite** and **nepenthe** from thy memories of Lenore;
Quaff, oh, quaff this kind nepenthe and forget this lost Lenore!"
                    Quoth the Raven, "Nevermore."

"Prophet!" said I, "thing of evil!—prophet still, if bird or devil!—
Whether Tempter sent, or whether **tempest** tossed thee here
    ashore,
Desolate yet all **undaunted**, on this desert land enchanted—
On this home by Horror haunted—tell me truly, I implore—
Is there—is there **balm in Gilead**?—tell me—tell me, I implore!"
                    Quoth the Raven, "Nevermore."

---

censer container in which incense is burned, usually during a religious ritual
Seraphim angels
respite period of rest or relief
nepenthe liquid used in ancient times to cause forgetfulness of one's grief
quaff to drink
tempest a storm
undaunted unafraid; not discouraged
balm in Gilead a healing ointment mentioned in the Bible

"Prophet!" said I, "thing of evil!—prophet still, if bird or devil!
By that Heaven that bends above us—by that God we both
    adore—
Tell this soul with sorrow **laden** if, within the distant **Aidenn**,
It shall clasp a sainted maiden whom the angels name Lenore—
Clasp a rare and radiant maiden whom the angels name Lenore."
                        Quoth the Raven, "Nevermore."

"Be that word our sign of parting, bird or fiend!" I shrieked,
    upstarting—
"Get thee back into the tempest and the Night's Plutonian shore!
Leave no black plume as a token of that lie thy soul hath spoken!
Leave my loneliness unbroken!—quit the bust above my door!
Take thy beak from out my heart, and take thy form from off my
    door!"
                        Quoth the Raven, "Nevermore."

And the Raven, never flitting, still is sitting, still is sitting
On the **pallid** bust of Pallas just above my chamber door;
And his eyes have all the **seeming** of a demon's that is dreaming,
And the lamp-light o'er him streaming throws his shadow on
    the floor;
And my soul from out that shadow that lies floating on the floor
                  Shall be lifted—nevermore! ❖

---

laden carrying a burden
Aidenn Eden, or paradise
pallid wan; lacking liveliness
seeming appearance

The Song of Wandering Aengus

by William Butler Yeats

I went out to the **hazel** wood,
Because a fire was in my head,
And cut and peeled a hazel **wand**,
And hooked a berry to a thread;
And when white moths were on the wing,
And moth-like stars were flickering out,
I dropped the berry in a stream
And caught a little silver trout.

Aengus in Irish mythology, the god of love
hazel a kind of birch tree
wand a narrow rod

When I had laid it on the floor
I went to blow the fire aflame,
But something rustled on the floor,
And some one called me by my name:
It had become a glimmering girl
With apple blossom in her hair
Who called me by my name and ran
And faded through the brightening air.

Though I am old with wandering
Through hollow lands and hilly lands,
I will find out where she has gone,
And kiss her lips and take her hands;
And walk among long **dappled** grass,
And pluck till time and times are done
The silver apples of the moon,
The golden apples of the sun. ❖

dappled spotted; marked with contrasting patches

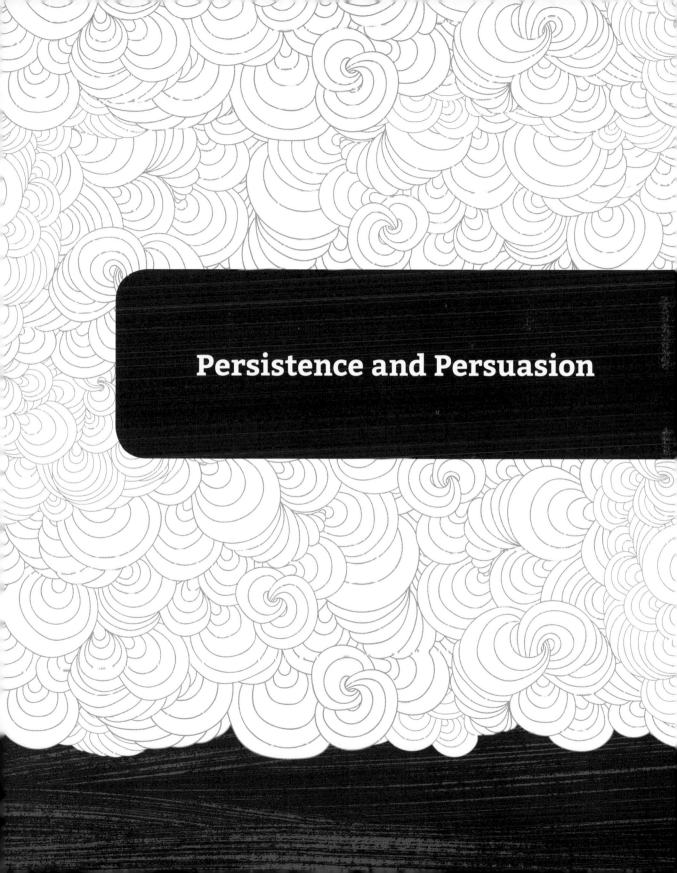

Persistence and Persuasion

opening statements from

John F. Kennedy and Richard M. Nixon First Televised Debate

Chicago, Illinois
September 26, 1960

SENATOR KENNEDY: Mr. Smith, Mr. Nixon. In the election of 1860, Abraham Lincoln said the question was whether this nation could exist half-slave or half-free. In the election of 1960, and with the world around us, the question is whether the world will exist half-slave or half-free, whether it will move in the direction of freedom, in the direction of the road that we are taking, or whether it will move in the direction of slavery. I think it will depend in great measure upon what we do here in the United States, on the kind of society that we build, on the kind of strength that we maintain. We discuss tonight domestic issues, but I would not want that to be any implication to be given that this does not involve directly our struggle with Mr. Khrushchev for survival.

Mr. Khrushchev is in New York, and he maintains the Communist offensive throughout the world because of the productive power of the Soviet Union itself. The Chinese Communists have always had a large population. But

Richard M. Nixon (left) and John F. Kennedy (right) during televised presidential debate, September 26, 1960

they are important and dangerous now because they are mounting a major effort within their own country. The kind of country we have here, the kind of society we have, the kind of strength we build in the United States will be the defense of freedom. If we do well here, if we meet our obligations, if we're moving ahead, then I think freedom will be secure around the world. If we fail, then freedom fails.

Therefore, I think the question before the American people is: Are we doing as much as we can do? Are we as strong as we should be? Are we as strong as we must be if we're going to maintain our independence, and if we're going to maintain and hold out the hand of friendship to those who look to us for assistance, to those who look to us for survival? I should make it very clear that I do not think we're doing enough, that I am not satisfied as an American with the progress that we're making.

This is a great country, but I think it could be a greater country; and this is a powerful country, but I think it could be a more powerful country. I'm not satisfied to have fifty percent of our steel-mill capacity unused. I'm not satisfied when the United States had last year the lowest rate of economic growth of any major industrialized society in the world. Because economic growth means strength and vitality; it means we're able to sustain our defenses; it means we're able to meet our commitments abroad.

I'm not satisfied when we have over nine billion dollars worth of food—some of it rotting—even though there is a hungry world, and even though four million Americans wait every month for a food package from the government, which averages five cents a day per individual. I saw cases in West Virginia, here in the United States, where children took home part of their school lunch in order to feed their families because I don't think we're meeting our obligations toward these Americans.

I'm not satisfied when the Soviet Union is turning out twice as many scientists and engineers as we are. I'm not satisfied when many of our teachers are inadequately paid, or when our children go to school part-time shifts. I think we should have an educational system second to none. I'm not satisfied when I see men like Jimmy Hoffa—in charge of the largest union in the United States—still free. I'm not satisfied when we are failing to develop the natural resources of the United States to the fullest. Here in the United States, which developed the Tennessee Valley and which built the Grand Coulee and the other dams in the Northwest United States at the present rate of **hydropower** production—and that is the hallmark of an industrialized society—the Soviet Union by 1975 will be producing more power than we are. These are all the things, I think, in this country that can make our society strong, or can mean that it stands still.

I'm not satisfied until every American enjoys his full constitutional rights. If a Negro baby is born—and this is true also of Puerto Ricans and Mexicans in some of our cities—he has about one-half as much chance to get through high school as a white baby. He has one-third as much chance to get through college as a white student. He has about a third as much chance to be a professional man, about half as much chance to own a house. He has about four times as much chance that he'll be out of work in his life as the white baby.

---

hydropower electric power generated by the flow of water

I think we can do better. I don't want the talents of any American to go to waste. I know that there are those who want to turn everything over to the government. I don't at all. I want the individuals to meet their responsibilities. And I want the states to meet their responsibilities. But I think there is also a national responsibility. The argument has been used against every piece of social legislation in the last twenty-five years. The people of the United States individually could not have developed the Tennessee Valley; collectively they could have. A cotton farmer in Georgia or a peanut farmer or a dairy farmer in Wisconsin and Minnesota, he cannot protect himself against the forces of supply and demand in the marketplace; but working together in effective governmental programs he can do so. Seventeen million Americans, who live over sixty-five on an average Social Security check of about seventy-eight dollars a month, they're not able to sustain themselves individually, but they can sustain themselves through the social security system. I don't believe in big government, but I believe in effective governmental action. And I think that's the only way that the United States is going to maintain its freedom. It's the only way that we're going to move ahead.

I think we can do a better job. I think we're going to have to do a better job if we are going to meet the responsibilities which time and events have placed upon us. We cannot turn the job over to anyone else. If the United

States fails, then the whole cause of freedom fails. And I think it depends in great measure on what we do here in this country. The reason Franklin Roosevelt was a good neighbor in Latin America was because he was a good neighbor in the United States. Because they felt that the American society was moving again. I want us to recapture that image. I want people in Latin America and Africa and Asia to start to look to America; to see how we're doing things; to wonder what the resident of the United States is doing; and not to look at Khrushchev, or look at the Chinese Communists. That is the obligation upon our generation.

In 1933, Franklin Roosevelt said in his inaugural that this generation of Americans has a **rendezvous** with destiny. I think our generation of Americans has the same rendezvous. The question now is: Can freedom be maintained under the most severe attack it has ever known? I think it can be. And I think in the final analysis it depends upon what we do here. I think it's time America started moving again.

MR. SMITH: And now the opening statement by Vice President Richard M. Nixon.

MR. NIXON: Mr. Smith, Senator Kennedy. The things that Senator Kennedy has said many of us can agree with. There is no question but that we cannot discuss our internal affairs in the United States without recognizing that they

---

rendezvous a meeting

have a tremendous bearing on our international position. There is no question but that this nation cannot stand still; because we are in a deadly competition, a competition not only with the men in the Kremlin, but the men in Peking. We're ahead in this competition, as Senator Kennedy, I think, has implied. But when you're in a race, the only way to stay ahead is to move ahead. And I subscribe completely to the spirit that Senator Kennedy has expressed tonight, the spirit that the United States should move ahead.

Where, then, do we disagree? I think we disagree on the implication of his remarks tonight and on the statements that he has made on many occasions during his campaign to the effect that the United States has been standing still. We heard tonight, for example, the statement made that our growth in national product last year was the lowest of any industrial nation in the world. Now last year, of course, was 1958. That happened to be a recession year. But when we look at the growth of G.N.P. this year, a year of recovery, we find that it's six and nine-tenths percent and one of the highest in the world today. More about that later.

Looking then to this problem of how the United States should move ahead and where the United States is moving, I think it is well that we take the advice of a very famous campaigner: Let's look at the record. Is the United States standing still? Is it true that this Administration, as Senator Kennedy has charged, has been an Administration of retreat, of defeat, of **stagnation**? Is it true that, as far as this country is concerned, in the field of electric power, in all of the fields that he has mentioned, we have not been moving ahead. Well, we have a comparison that we can make. We have the record of the Truman Administration of seven and a half years and the seven and a half years of the Eisenhower Administration. When we compare these two records in the areas that Senator Kennedy has discussed tonight, I think we find that America has been moving ahead.

Let's take schools. We have built more schools in these last seven and a half years than we built in the previous seven and a half, for that matter in the previous twenty years. Let's take hydroelectric power. We have developed more hydroelectric power in these seven and a half years than was developed in any previous administration in history. Let us take hospitals. We find that more have been built in this Administration than in the previous Administration. The same is true of highways.

Let's put it in terms that all of us can understand. We often hear gross national product discussed and in that respect may I say that when we compare the growth in this Administration with that of the previous Administration that then there was a total growth of eleven percent over seven years; in this Administration there has been a total

stagnation a state of inactivity or lack of growth

growth of nineteen percent over seven years. That shows that there's been more growth in this Administration than in its predecessor.

But let's not put it there; let's put it in terms of the average family. What has happened to you? We find that your wages have gone up five times as much in the Eisenhower Administration as they did in the Truman Administration. What about the prices you pay? We find that the prices you pay went up five times as much in the Truman Administration as they did in the Eisenhower Administration. What's the net result of this? This means that the average family income went up fifteen percent in the Eisenhower years as against two percent in the Truman years. Now, this is not standing still.

But, good as this record is, may I emphasize it isn't enough. A record is never something to stand on. It's something to build on. And in building on this record, I believe that we have the secret for progress, we know the way to progress. And I think, first of all, our own record proves that we know the way. Senator Kennedy has suggested that he believes he knows the way. I respect the sincerity which he makes that suggestion. But on the other hand, when we look at the various programs that he offers, they do not seem to be new. They seem to be simply retreads of the programs of the Truman Administration which preceded it. And I would suggest that during the course of the evening he might indicate those areas in which his programs are new, where they will mean more progress than we had then.

What kind of programs are we for?

We are for programs that will expand educational opportunities, that will give to all Americans their equal chance for education, for all of the things which are necessary and dear to the hearts of our people. We are for programs, in addition, which will see that our medical care for the aged is much better handled than it is at the present time. Here again, may I indicate that Senator Kennedy and I are not in disagreement as to the aims. We both want to help the old people. We want to see that they do have adequate medical care. The question is the means. I think that the means that I **advocate** will reach that goal better than the means that he advocates.

I could give better examples, but for, for whatever it is, whether it's in the field of housing, or health, or medical care, or schools, or the development of electric power, we have programs which we believe will move America, move her forward and build on the wonderful record that we have made over these past seven and a half years. Now, when we look at these programs, might I suggest that in evaluating them we often have a tendency to say that the test of a program is how much you're spending.

....

advocate to argue for; to support

I will concede that in all the areas to which I have referred Senator Kennedy would have the federal government spend more than I would have it spend. I costed out the cost of the Democratic platform. It runs a minimum of thirteen and two-tenths billions dollars a year more than we are presently spending to a maximum of eighteen billion dollars a year more than we're presently spending. Now the Republican platform will cost more too. It will cost a minimum of four billion dollars a year more, a maximum of four and nine-tenths billion dollar a year more than we're presently spending.

Now, does this mean that his program is better than ours? Not at all. Because it isn't a question of how much the federal government spends; it isn't a question of which government does the most. It is a question of which administration does the right thing. And in our case, I do believe that our programs will stimulate the creative energies of a hundred and eighty million free Americans. I believe the programs that Senator Kennedy advocates will have a tendency to stifle those creative energies, I believe in other words, that his program would lead to the stagnation of the motive power that we need in this country to get progress.

The final point that I would like to make is this: Senator Kennedy has suggested in his speeches that we lack compassion for the poor, for the old, and for others that are unfortunate. Let us understand throughout this campaign that his motives and mine are sincere. I know what it means to be poor. I know what it means to see people who are unemployed. I know Senator Kennedy feels as deeply about these problems as I do, but our disagreement is not about the goals for America but only about the means to reach those goals.

MR. SMITH: Thank you, Mr. Nixon. That completes the opening statements, and now the candidates will answer questions or comment upon one another's answers to questions, put by correspondents of the networks. The correspondents: [introducing themselves: "I'm Sander Vanocur, NBC News;" "I'm Charles Warren, Mutual News;" "I'm Stuart Novins, CBS News;" "Bob Fleming, ABC News."] The first question to Senator Kennedy from Mr. Fleming. ❖

President Franklin D. Roosevelt's Address to Congress Requesting a Declaration of War

December 8, 1941

Mr. Vice President, and Mr. Speaker, and Members of the Senate and House of Representatives:

Yesterday, December 7, 1941—a date which will live in infamy—the United States of America was suddenly and deliberately attacked by naval and air forces of the Empire of Japan.

The United States was at peace with that Nation and, at the solicitation of Japan, was still in conversation with its Government and its Emperor looking toward the maintenance of peace in the Pacific. Indeed, one hour after Japanese air squadrons had commenced bombing in the American Island of Oahu, the Japanese Ambassador to the United States and his colleague delivered to our Secretary of State a formal reply to a recent American message. And while this reply stated that it seemed useless to continue the existing diplomatic negotiations, it contained no threat or hint of war or of armed attack.

It will be recorded that the distance of Hawaii from Japan makes it obvious that the attack was deliberately planned many days or even weeks ago. During the

President Franklin D. Roosevelt addressing the joint session of Congress, December 8, 1941

intervening time the Japanese Government has deliberately sought to deceive the United States by false statements and expressions of hope for continued peace.

The attack yesterday on the Hawaiian Islands has caused severe damage to American naval and military forces. I regret to tell you that very many American lives have been lost. In addition American ships have been reported torpedoed on the high seas between San Francisco and Honolulu.

Yesterday the Japanese Government also launched an attack against Malaya.

Last night Japanese forces attacked Hong Kong.

Last night Japanese forces attacked Guam.

Last night Japanese forces attacked the Philippine Islands.

Last night the Japanese attacked Wake Island. And this morning the Japanese attacked Midway Island.

Japan has, therefore, undertaken a surprise offensive extending throughout the Pacific area. The facts of yesterday and today speak for themselves. The people of the United States have already formed their opinions and well understand the implications to the very life and safety of our Nation.

As Commander in Chief of the Army and Navy, I have directed that all measures be taken for our defense.

But always will our whole Nation remember the character of the **onslaught** against us.

No matter how long it may take us to overcome this **premeditated** invasion, the American people in their righteous might will win through to absolute victory. I believe that I interpret the will of the Congress and of the people when I assert that we will not only defend ourselves to the uttermost but will make it very certain that this form of treachery shall never again endanger us.

Hostilities exist. There is no blinking at the fact that our people, our territory, and our interests are in grave danger.

....

onslaught an attack
premeditated planned in advance

With confidence in our armed forces—with the unbounding determination of our people—we will gain the inevitable triumph, so help us God.

I ask that the Congress declare that since the unprovoked and dastardly attack by Japan on Sunday, December 7, 1941, a state of war has existed between the United States and the Japanese Empire. ❖

Enduring Truths

Antigone

a tragedy by Sophocles
translated by Dudley Fitts and Robert Fitzgerald

Characters

ANTIGONE

HAIMON

ISMENE

TEIRESIAS

EURYDICE

A SENTRY

CREON

A MESSENGER

CHORUS

SCENE: *Before the palace of Creon, King of Thebes. A central double door, and two lateral doors. A platform extends the length of the façade, and from this platform three steps lead down into the "orchestra," or chorus-ground.*

TIME: *Dawn of the day after the repulse of the **Argive** army from the assault on Thebes.*

....

Argive in general, of or relating to the Greeks, and in particular, to those from the Greek city of Argos

(Antigone and Ismene enter from the central door
of the Palace.)

ANTIGONE: Ismene, dear sister,

You would think that we had already suffered enough

For the curse on Oedipus:

I cannot imagine any grief

That you and I have not gone through. And now—   5

Have they told you of the new decree of our King Creon?

ISMENE: I have heard nothing: I know

That two sisters lost two brothers, a double death

In a single hour; and I know that the Argive army

Fled in the night; but beyond this, nothing.   10

ANTIGONE: I thought so. And that is why I wanted you

To come out here with me. There is something we

    must do.

ISMENE: Why do you speak so strangely?

ANTIGONE: Listen, Ismene:

Creon buried our brother Eteocles   15

With military honors, gave him a soldier's funeral,

And it was right that he should; but Polyneices,

Who fought as bravely and died as miserably—

They say that Creon has sworn

No one shall bury him, no one mourn for him,   20

But his body must lie in the fields, a sweet treasure

For **carrion birds** to find as they search for food.

That is what they say, and our good Creon is coming here

To announce it publicly; and the penalty—

Stoning to death in the public square!   25

There it is,

And now you can prove what you are:

A true sister, or a traitor to your family.

ISMENE: Antigone, you are mad! What could I possibly do?

ANTIGONE: You must decide whether you will help me
    or not.   30

ISMENE: I do not understand you. Help you in what?

ANTIGONE: Ismene, I am going to bury him. Will you come?

ISMENE: Bury him! You have just said the new law forbids it.

ANTIGONE: He is my brother. And he is your brother, too.

ISMENE: But think of the danger! Think what Creon will do!   35

ANTIGONE: Creon is not strong enough to stand in my way.

ISMENE: Ah sister!
    Oedipus died, everyone hating him
    For what his own search brought to light, his eyes
    Ripped out by his own hand; and Jocaste died,   40
    His mother and wife at once: she twisted the cords
    That strangled her life; and our two brothers died,
    Each killed by the other's sword. And we are left:

....

carrion birds birds, such as vultures, that eat the flesh of dead creatures

But oh, Antigone,
Think how much more terrible than these 45
Our own death would be if we should go against Creon
And do what he has forbidden! We are only women,
We cannot fight with men, Antigone!
The law is strong, we must give in to the law
In this thing, and in worse. I beg the dead 50
To forgive me, but I am helpless: I must yield
To those in authority. And I think it is dangerous business
To be always meddling.

ANTIGONE: If that is what you think,
I should not want you, even if you asked to come. 55
You have made your choice, you can be what you want
to be.
But I will bury him; and if I must die,
I say that this crime is holy: I shall lie down
With him in death, and I shall be as dear
To him as he to me. 60
It is the dead,
Not the living, who make the longest demands:
We die for ever . . .
You may do as you like,
Since apparently the laws of the gods mean nothing
to you. 65

ISMENE: They mean a great deal to me; but I have no strength

To break laws that were made for the public good.

ANTIGONE: That must be your excuse, I suppose. But as for me,

I will bury the brother I love.

ISMENE: Antigone,   70

I am so afraid for you!

ANTIGONE: You need not be:

You have yourself to consider, after all.

ISMENE: But no one must hear of this, you must tell no one!

I will keep it a secret, I promise!   75

ANTIGONE: Oh tell it! Tell everyone!

Think how they'll hate you when it all comes out

If they learn that you knew about it all the time!

ISMENE: So fiery! You should be cold with fear.

ANTIGONE: Perhaps. But I am doing only what I must.   80

ISMENE: But can you do it? I say that you cannot.

ANTIGONE: Very well: when my strength gives out, I shall do no more.

ISMENE: Impossible things should not be tried at all.

ANTIGONE: Go away, Ismene: 85

I shall be hating you soon, and the dead will too,

For your words are hateful. Leave me my foolish plan:

I am not afraid of the danger; if it means death,

It will not be the worst of deaths—death without honor.

ISMENE: Go then, if you feel that you must.   90

    You are unwise,

    But a loyal friend indeed to those who love you.

(Exit into the Palace. Antigone goes off, Left.
Enter the Chorus.)

✻— PARODOS —✻

CHORUS: *(STROPHE 1)*

    Now the long blade of the sun, lying

    Level east to west, touches with glory

    Thebes of the Seven Gates. Open, unlidded

    Eye of golden day! O marching light

    Across the **eddy** and rush of **Dirce**'s stream,   5

    Striking the white shields of the enemy

    Thrown headlong backward from the blaze of morning!

CHORAGOS: Polyneices their commander

    Roused them with windy phrases,

    He the wild eagle screaming   10

    Insults above our land,

....

Parodos the first choral song in the play, which the chorus sings as it enters
strophe the part of the song sung by the chorus as it moves from right to left
eddy a current that runs against the main current of a body of water
Dirce the name of a spring near the city of Thebes
Choragos the leader of the chorus

His wings their shields of snow,

His crest their **marshaled helms**.

CHORUS: (ANTISTROPHE 1)

Against our seven gates in a yawning ring

The famished spears came onward in the night;   15

But before his jaws were **sated** with our blood,

Or **pinefire** took the garland of our towers,

He was thrown back; and as he turned, great Thebes—

No tender victim for his noisy power—

Rose like a dragon behind him, shouting war.   20

CHORAGOS: For **God** hates utterly

The bray of bragging tongues;

And when he beheld their smiling,

Their swagger of golden helms,

The frown of his thunder blasted   25

Their first man from our walls.

CHORUS: (STROPHE 2)

We heard his shout of triumph high in the air

Turn to a scream; far out in a flaming arc

He fell with his windy torch, and the earth struck him.

....

marshaled gathered and put in proper order
helms helmets used for protection in battle
antistrophe the part of the song sung by the chorus as it moves from left to right
sated satisfied to excess
pinefire flaming arrows
God other translations of this play refer instead to "Zeus"; the name is used to convey
the idea of a supreme deity

And others storming in fury no less than his 30

Found shock of death in the dusty joy of battle.

CHORAGOS: Seven captains at seven gates

Yielded their clanging arms to the god

That bends the battle-line and breaks it.

These two only, brothers in blood, 35

Face to face in matchless rage,

Mirroring each the other's death,

Clashed in long combat.

CHORUS: *(ANTISTROPHE 1)*

But now in the beautiful morning of victory

Let Thebes of the many chariots sing for joy! 40

With hearts for dancing we'll take leave of war:

Our temples shall be sweet with hymns of praise,

And the long night shall echo with our Chorus:

❋— SCENE I —❋

CHORAGOS: But now at last our new King is coming:

Creon of Thebes, Menoikeus' son.

In this **auspicious** dawn of his reign

What are the new complexities

That shifting Fate has woven for him? 5

What is his counsel? Why has he summoned

The old men to hear him?

auspicious boding well or favorably

*(Enter Creon from the Palace, Center. He addresses the
Chorus from the top step.)*

CREON: Gentlemen: I have the honor to inform you that
    our Ship of State, which recent storms have threatened
    to destroy, has come safely to harbor at last, guided by   10
    the merciful wisdom of Heaven. I have summoned you
    here this morning because I know that I can depend
    upon you: your devotion to King Laios was absolute; you
    never hesitated in your duty to our late ruler Oedipus;
    and when Oedipus died, your loyalty was transferred to   15
    his children. Unfortunately, as you know, his two sons,
    the princes Eteocles and Polyneices, have killed each other
    in battle; and I, as the next in blood, have succeeded to
    the full power of the throne.

    I am aware, of course, that no Ruler can expect complete   20
    loyalty from his subjects until he has been tested in office.
    Nevertheless, I say to you at the very outset that I have
    nothing but contempt for the kind of Governor who is
    afraid, for whatever reason, to follow the course that he
    knows is best for the State; and as for the man who sets   25
    private friendship above the public welfare,—I have no
    use for him, either. I call God to witness that if I saw my
    country headed for ruin, I should not be afraid to speak
    out plainly; and I need hardly remind you that I would
    never have any dealings with an enemy of the people.   30

No one values friendship more highly than I; but we must remember friendship more highly than I; but we must remember that friends made at the risk of wrecking our Ship are not real friends at all.

These are my principles, at any rate, and that is why I have made the following decision concerning the sons of Oedipus: Eteocles, who died as a man should die, fighting for his country, is to be buried with full military honors, with all the ceremony that is usual when the greatest heroes die; but his brother Polyneices, who broke his **exile** to come back with fire and sword against his native city and the shrines of his fathers' gods, whose one idea was to spill the blood of his blood and sell his own people into slavery—Polyneices, I say, is to have no burial: no man is to touch him or say the least prayer for him; he shall lie on the plain, unburied; and the birds and the scavenging dogs can do with him whatever they like.

This is my command, and you can see the wisdom behind it. As long as I am King, no traitor is going to be honored with the loyal man. But whoever shows by word and deed that he is on the side of the State,—he shall have my respect while he is living, and my **reverence** when he is dead.

35

40

45

50

....

exile banishment
reverence honor; profound respect

CHORAGOS: If that is your will, Creon son of Menoikeus,
You have the right to enforce it: we are yours. 55

CREON: That is my will. Take care that you do your part.

CHORAGOS: We are old men: let the younger ones carry
it out.

CREON: I do not mean that: the **sentries** have been
appointed.

CHORAGOS: Then what is it that you would have us do?

CREON: You will give no support to whoever breaks
this law. 60

CHORAGOS: Only a crazy man is in love with death!

CREON: And death it is; yet money talks, and the wisest
Have sometimes been known to count a few coins
too many.

(Enter Sentry from Left.)

SENTRY: I'll not say that I'm out of breath from running,
King, because every time I stopped to think about what 65
I have to tell you, I felt like going back. And all the time
a voice kept saying, "You fool, don't you know you're
walking straight into trouble?"; and then another voice:
"Yes, but if you let somebody else get the news to Creon
first, it will be even worse than that for you!" But good 70
sense won out, at least I hope it was good sense, and

....

sentries guards

here I am with a story that makes no sense at all; but I'll tell it anyhow, because, as they say, what's going to happen's going to happen, and—

CREON: Come to the point. What have you to say?   75

SENTRY: I did not do it. I did not see who did it. You must
  not punish me for what someone else has done.

CREON: A **comprehensive** defense! More effective, perhaps,
  If I knew its purpose. Come: what is it?

SENTRY: A dreadful thing... I don't know how to put it—

CREON: Out with it!

SENTRY: Well, then;   80
  The dead man—
  Polyneices—

*(Pause. The Sentry is overcome, fumbles for words.
Creon waits **impassively**.)*

  out there—
  someone,—
  New dust on the slimy flesh!   85

(Pause. No sign from Creon.)

  Someone has given it burial that way, and
  Gone...

---

comprehensive thorough; including or covering much
impassively without showing any emotion

(Long pause. Creon finally speaks with deadly control.)

CREON: And the man who dared do this?

SENTRY: I swear I

Do not know! You must believe me!   90

Listen:

The ground was dry, not a sign of digging, no,

Not a wheeltrack in the dust, no trace of anyone.

It was when they relieved us this morning: and one
  of them,

The corporal, pointed to it.   95

There it was,

The strangest—

Look:

The body, just mounded over with light dust: you see?

Not buried really, but as if they'd covered it   100

Just enough for the ghost's peace. And no sign

Of dogs or any wild animal that had been there.

And then what a scene there was! Every man of us

Accusing the other: we all proved the other man did it,

We all had proof that we could not have done it.   105

We were ready to take hot iron in our hands,

Walk through fire, swear by all the gods,

It was not I!

I do not know who it was, but it was not I!

*(Creon's rage has been mounting steadily, but the Sentry
is too intent upon his story to notice it.)*

And then, when this came to nothing, someone said 110
A thing that silenced us and made us stare
Down at the ground: you had to be told the news,
And one of us had to do it! We threw the dice,
And the bad luck fell to me. So here I am,
No happier to be here than you are to have me: 115
Nobody likes the man who brings bad news.

CHORAGOS: I have been wondering, King: can it be that
the gods have done this?

CREON (*Furiously*): *Stop*!
Must you **doddering** wrecks 120
Go out of your heads entirely? "The gods!"
Intolerable!
The gods favor this corpse? Why? How had he served
them?
Tried to loot their temples, burn their images,
Yes, and the whole State, and its laws with it! 125
Is it your **senile** opinion that the gods love to honor
bad men?
A **pious** thought!—
No, from the very beginning
There have been those who have whispered together,

....

doddering shaky and feeble due to age
intolerable completely unacceptable; unbearable
senile mentally confused from old age
pious showing religious devotion

Stiff-necked **anarchists**, putting their heads together,   130
Scheming against me in alleys. These are the men,
And they have bribed my own guard to do this thing.

Money! (**Sententiously**)
There's nothing in the world so **demoralizing** as money.
Down go your cities,   135
Homes gone, men gone, honest hearts **corrupted**,
Crookedness of all kinds, and all for money!
(*To Sentry*) But you—!
I swear by God and by the throne of God,
The man who has done this thing shall pay for it!   140
Find that man, bring him here to me, or your death
Will be the least of your problems: I'll string you up
Alive, and there will be certain ways to make you
Discover your employer before you die;
And the process may teach you a lesson you seem
    to have missed: 145
The dearest profit is sometimes all too dear:
That depends on the source. Do you understand me?
A fortune won is often misfortune.

SENTRY: King, may I speak?

CREON: Your very voice distresses me.   150

....

anarchists people who oppose any government or ruling authority
sententiously in the manner of a pompous moralizer
demoralizing corrupting
corrupted made immoral
discover to reveal

SENTRY: Are you sure that it is my voice, and not
    your conscience?

CREON: By God, he wants to analyze me now!

SENTRY: It is not what I say, but what has been done,
    that hurts you.

CREON: You talk too much.

SENTRY: Maybe; but I've done nothing.   155

CREON: Sold your soul for some silver: that's all you've
    done.

SENTRY: How dreadful it is when the right judge judges
    wrong!

CREON: Your figures of speech
    May entertain you now; but unless you bring me the man,
    You will get little profit from them in the end.   160

(Exit Creon in to the Palace.)

SENTRY: "Bring me the man"—!
    I'd like nothing better than bringing him the man!
    But bring him or not, you have seen the last of me here.
    At any rate, I am safe!

(Exit Sentry.)

✳— ODE I —✳

CHORUS: *(STROPHE 1)*

  Numberless are the world's wonders, but none
More wonderful than man; the storm-gray sea
Yields to his prows, the huge crests bear him high;
Earth, holy and inexhaustible, is graven
With shining **furrows** where his plows have gone   5
Year after year, the timeless labor of stallions.

(ANTISTROPHE 1)

The lightboned birds and beasts that cling to cover,
The **lithe** fish lighting their reaches of dim water,
All are taken, tamed in the net of his mind;
The lion on the hill, the wild horse windy-maned,   10
Resign to him; and his blunt yoke has broken
The **sultry** shoulders of the mountain bull.

(STROPHE 2)

Words also, and thought as rapid as air,
He fashions to his good use; statecraft is his,
And his the skill that deflects the arrows of snow,   15
The spears of winter rain: from every wind
He has made himself secure—from all but one:
In the late wind of death he cannot stand.

---

furrows grooves cut in a field by a plow for the planting of seeds
lithe graceful and slender; moving with ease
sultry hot and moist

O clear intelligence, force beyond all measure!
O fate of man, working both good and evil!   20
When the laws are kept, how proudly his city stands!
When the laws are broken, what of his city then?
Never may the anarchic man find rest at my hearth,
Never be it said that my thoughts are his thoughts.

❈— SCENE II —❈

(Reenter Sentry leading Antigone.)

CHORAGOS: What does this mean? Surely this captive woman
    Is the Princess, Antigone: Why should she be taken?

SENTRY: Here is the one who did it! We caught her
    In the very act of burying him.—Where is Creon?

CHORAGOS: Just coming from the house.   5
    (Enter Creon, Center.)
    What has happened?

CREON: Why have you come back so soon?

SENTRY *(Expansively)***:** O King,
    A man should never be too sure of anything:
    I would have sworn   10
    That you'd not see me here again: your anger
    Frightened me so, and the things you threatened me with;
    But how could I tell then
    That I'd be able to solve the case so soon?

No dice throwing this time: I was only too glad to come! 15
Here is this woman. She is the guilty one:
We found her trying to bury him,
Take her, then; question her; judge her as you will.
I am through with the whole thing now, and glad of it.

CREON: But this is Antigone! Why have you brought

    her here? 20

SENTRY: She was burying him, I tell you!

CREON (*Severely*): Is this the truth?

SENTRY: I saw her with my own eyes. Can I say more?

CREON: The details: come, tell me quickly!

SENTRY: It was like this: 25
After those terrible threats of yours, King,
We went back and brushed the dust away from the body.
The flesh was soft by now, and stinking,
So we sat on a hill to **windward** and kept guard.
No napping this time! We kept each other awake. 30
But nothing happened until the white round sun
Whirled in the center of the round sky over us:
Then, suddenly,
A storm of dust roared up from the earth, and the sky
Went out, the plain vanished with all its trees 35
In the stinging dark. We closed our eyes and endured it.

---

windward facing the direction from which the wind is blowing

The whirlwind lasted a long time, but it passed;
And then we looked, and there was Antigone!
I have seen
A mother bird come back to a stripped nest, heard 40
Her crying bitterly a broken note or two
For the young ones stolen. Just so, when this girl
Found the bare corpse, and all her love's work wasted,
She wept, and cried on heaven to damn the hands
That had done this thing. 45
And then she brought more dust
And sprinkled wine three times for her brother's ghost.
We ran and took her at once. She was not afraid,
Not even when we charged her with what she had done.
She denied nothing. 50
And this was a comfort to me,
And some uneasiness: for it is a good thing
To escape from death, but it is no great pleasure
To bring death to a friend.
Yet I always say 55
There is nothing so comfortable as your own safe skin!

CREON (*Slowly, dangerously*): And you, Antigone,
    You with your head hanging, do you confess this thing?

ANTIGONE: I do. I deny nothing.

CREON (*To Sentry*): You may go. 60

(*Exit Sentry.*)

(To Antigone) Tell me, tell me briefly:

Had you heard my proclamation touching this matter?

ANTIGONE: It was public. Could I help hearing it?

CREON: And yet you dared defy the law.

ANTIGONE: I dared.   65

It was not God's proclamation. That final Justice

That rules the world below makes no such laws.

Your **edict**, King, was strong,

But all your strength is weakness itself against

The immortal unrecorded laws of God.   70

They are not merely now: they were, and shall be,

Operative for ever, beyond man utterly.

I knew I must die, even without your decree:

I am only mortal. And if I must die

Now, before it is my time to die,   75

Surely this is no hardship: can anyone

Living, as I live, with evil all about me,

Think Death less than a friend? This death of mine

Is of no importance; but if I had left my brother

Lying in death unburied, I should have suffered.   80

Now I do not.

You smile at me. Ah Creon,

Think me a fool, if you like; but it may well be

That a fool convicts me of folly.

....

edict a command

CHORAGOS: Like father, like daughter: both headstrong,   85
    deaf to reason!
  She has never learned to yield.

CREON: She has much to learn.
  The inflexible heart breaks first, the toughest iron
  Cracks first, and the wildest horses bend their necks   90
  At the pull of the smallest curb.
  Pride? In a slave?
  This girl is guilty of a double **insolence**,
  Breaking the given laws and boasting of it.
  Who is the man here,   95
  She or I, if this crime goes unpunished?
  Sister's child, or more than sister's child,
  Or closer yet in blood—she and her sister
  Win bitter death for this!
  (To Servants) Go, some of you,   100
  Arrest Ismene: I accuse her equally.
  Bring her: you will find her sniffling in the house there.
  Her mind's a traitor: crimes kept in the dark
  Cry for light, and the guardian brain shudders;
  But how much worse than this   105
  Is **brazen** boasting of barefaced anarchy!

ANTIGONE: Creon, what more do you want than my death?

....

insolence instance of being boldly rude, haughty, or insulting
brazen scornfully bold; shameless

CREON: Nothing.

Ｔhat gives me everything.

ANTIGONE: Then I beg you: kill me.

This talking is a great weariness: your words
Are distasteful to me, and I am sure that mine   110
Seem so to you. And yet they should not seem so:
I should have praise and honor for what I have done.
All these men here would praise me
Were their lips not frozen shut with fear of you.
(Bitterly) Ah, the good fortune of kings,   115
Licensed to say and do whatever they please!

CREON: You are alone here in that opinion.

ANTIGONE: No, they are with me. But they keep their
tongues in leash.

CREON: Maybe. But you are guilty, and they are not.

ANTIGONE: There is no guilt in reverence for the dead.   120

CREON: But Eteocles—was he not your brother too?

ANTIGONE: My brother too.

CREON: And you insult his memory.

ANTIGONE (Softly): The dead man would not say that I
insult it.

CREON: He would: for you honor a traitor as much as him.   125

ANTIGONE: His own brother, traitor or not, and equal in
blood.

CREON: He made war on his country. Eteocles defended it.

ANTIGONE: Nevertheless, there are honors due all the dead.

CREON: But not the same for the wicked as for the just.

ANTIGONE: Ah Creon, Creon,   130
> Which of us can say what the gods hold wicked?

CREON: An enemy is an enemy, even dead.

ANTIGONE: It is my nature to join in love, not hate.

CREON (*Finally losing patience*): Go join them,
> then; if you must have your love,
> Find it in hell!   135

CHORAGOS: But see, Ismene comes:

(*Enter Ismene, guarded.*)

> Those tears are sisterly, the cloud
> That shadows her eyes rains down gentle sorrow.

CREON: You too, Ismene,
> Snake in my ordered house, sucking my blood   140
> **Stealthily**—and all the time I never knew
> That these two sisters were aiming at my throne!
> Ismene,
> Do you confess your share in this crime, or deny it?
> Answer me.   145

ISMENE: Yes, if she will let me say so. I am guilty.

....

stealthily sneakily

ANTIGONE (*Coldly*): No, Ismene: You have no right to
 say so.
 You would not help me, and I will not have you help me.

ISMENE: But now I know what you meant; and I am here
 To join you, to take my share of punishment.   150

ANTIGONE: The dead man and the gods who rule the dead
 Know whose act this was. Words are not friends.

ISMENE: Do you refuse me, Antigone? I want to die with you:
 I too have a duty that I must **discharge** to the dead.

ANTIGONE: You shall not lessen my death by sharing it. 155

ISMENE: What do I care for life when you are dead?

ANTIGONE: Ask Creon. You're always hanging on his
 opinions.

ISMENE: You are laughing at me. Why, Antigone?

ANTIGONE: It's a joyless laughter, Ismene.

ISMENE: But can I do nothing?   160

ANTIGONE: Yes. Save yourself. I shall not envy you.
 There are those who will praise you; I shall have
  honor, too.

ISMENE: But we are equally guilty!

ANTIGONE: No more, Ismene:
 You are alive, but I belong to Death.   165

---

discharge to complete a task one is expected or bound by duty to do

CREON (*To the Chorus*): Gentlemen, I beg you to
    observe these girls:
One has just now lost her mind; the other,
It seems, has never had a mind at all.

ISMENE: Grief teaches the steadiest minds to waver, King.

CREON: Yours certainly did, when you **assumed** guilt   170
    with the guilty!

ISMENE: But how could I go on living without her?

CREON: You are.
    She is already dead.

ISMENE: But your own son's bride!

CREON: There are places enough for him to push his plow.   175
    I want no wicked women for my sons!

ISMENE: O dearest Haimon, how your father wrongs you!

CREON: I've had enough of your childish talk of marriage!

CHORAGOS: Do you really intend to steal this girl from
    your son?

CREON: No; Death will do that for me.   180

CHORAGOS: Then she must die?

CREON (*Ironically*): You dazzle me.
    —But enough of this talk!

....

assumed took upon oneself

(*To Guards*) You, there, take them away and guard
    them well:
For they are but women, and even brave men run   185
When they see Death coming.

(*Exit Ismene, Antigone, and Guards.*)

❋— ODE II —❋

CHORUS: (*STROPHE 1*)

Fortunate is the man who has never tasted God's
    vengeance!
Where once the anger of heaven has struck, that house
    is shaken
For ever: damnation rises behind each child
Like a wave cresting out of the black northeast,
When the long darkness under sea roars up   5
And bursts drumming death upon the windwhipped sand.

                                      (*ANTISTROPHE 1*)

I have seen this gathering sorrow from time long past
Loom upon Oedipus' children: generation from generation
Takes the **compulsive** rage of the enemy god.
So lately this last flower of Oedipus' line   10
Drank the sunlight! but now a passionate word
And a handful of dust have closed up all its beauty.

---

compulsive as if driven, compelled, or obsessed

What mortal **arrogance**,

    Transcends the wrath of Zeus?

Sleep cannot lull him, nor the effortless long months   15

Of the timeless gods: but he is young for ever,

And his house is the shining day of high Olympus.

    All that is and shall be,

    And all the past, is his.

(ANTISTROPHE 1)

No pride on earth is free of the curse of heaven.   20

    The straying dreams of men

    May bring them ghosts of joy:

But as they drowse, the waking embers burn them;

Or they walk with fixed eyes, as blind men walk.

But the ancient wisdom speaks for our own time: 25

    Fate works most for woe

    With Folly's fairest show.

Man's little pleasure is the spring of sorrow.

⚜— SCENE III —⚜

CHORAGOS: But here is Haimon, King, the last of all

    your sons.

    Is it grief for Antigone that brings him here,

    And bitterness at being robbed of his bride?

---

arrogance a feeling of superiority; haughtiness; conceited pride
transcends goes beyond; surpasses

(Enter Haimon.)

CREON: We shall soon see, and no need of **diviners**.—Son,
   You have heard my final judgment on that girl: 5
   Have you come here hating me, or have you come
   With **deference** and with love, whatever I do?

HAIMON: I am your son, father. You are my guide.
   You make things clear for me, and I obey you.
   No marriage means more to me than your continuing
      wisdom.   10

CREON: Good. That is the way to behave: **subordinate**
   Everything else, my son, to your father's will.
   This is what a man prays for, that he may get
   Sons attentive and dutiful in his house,
   Each one hating his father's enemies,   15
   Honoring his father's friends. But if his sons
   Fail him, if they turn out **unprofitably**,
   What has he fathered but trouble for himself
   And amusement for the **malicious**?
   So you are right   20
   Not to lose your head over this woman.
   Your pleasure with her would soon grow cold, Haimon.
   Let her find her husband in Hell!

---

diviners soothsayers; persons who predict the future
deference submission; respect
subordinate to make subject to; to treat as less important
unprofitably in a way that brings no gain or benefit
malicious those who are purposefully mean or spiteful

Of all the people in this city, only she
Has had contempt for my law and broken it.   25
Do you want me to show myself weak before the people?
Or to break my sworn word? No, and I will not.
The woman dies.
I suppose she'll plead "family ties." Well, let her.
If I permit my own family to rebel,   30
How shall I earn the world's obedience?
Show me the man who keeps his house in hand,
He's fit for public authority.
I'll have no dealings
With law-breakers, critics of the government: 35
Whoever is chosen to govern should be obeyed—
Must be obeyed, in all things, great and small,
Just and unjust! O Haimon,
The man who knows how to obey, and that man only,
Knows how to give commands when the time comes.   40
You can depend on him, no matter how fast
The spears come: he's a good soldier, he'll stick it out.
Anarchy, anarchy! Show me a greater evil!
This is why cities tumble and the great houses rain
     down,
This is what scatters armies!   45
No, no: good lives are made so by discipline.
We keep the laws then, and the lawmakers,
And no woman shall seduce us. If we must lose,

Let's lose to a man, at least! Is a woman stronger
    than we?

CHORAGOS: Unless time has rusted my wits,   50
    What you say, King, is said with point and dignity.

HAIMON (*Boyishly earnest*): Father:
    Reason is God's crowning gift to man, and you are right
    To warn me against losing mine. I cannot say—
    I hope that I shall never want to say!—that you   55
    Have reasoned badly. Yet there are other men
    Who can reason, too; and their opinions might be helpful.
    You are not in a position to know everything
    That people say or do, or what they feel:
    Your temper terrifies them—everyone   60
    Will tell you only what you like to hear.
    But I, at any rate, can listen; and I have heard them
    Muttering and whispering in the dark about this girl.
    They say no woman has ever, so unreasonably,
    Died so shameful a death for a generous act: 65
    "She covered her brother's body. Is this indecent?
    She kept him from dogs and vultures. Is this a crime?

    Death?—She should have all the honor that we can
        give her!"
    This is the way they talk out there in the City.

You must believe me: 70

Nothing is closer to me than your happiness.

What could be closer? Must not any son

Value his father's fortune as his father does his?

I beg you, do not be unchangeable:

Do not believe that you alone can be right. 75

The man who thinks that,

The man who maintains that only he has the power

To reason correctly, the gift to speak, the soul—

A man like that, when you know him, turns out empty.

It is not reason never to yield to reason! 80

In flood time you can see how some trees bend,

And because they bend, even their twigs are safe,

While stubborn trees are torn up, roots and all.

And the same thing happens in sailing:

Make your sheet fast, never slacken, and over you go, 85

Head over heels and under: and there's your voyage.

Forget you are angry! Let yourself be moved!

I know I am young; but please let me say this:

The ideal condition

Would be, I admit, that men should be right by instinct; 90

But since we are all too likely to go astray,

The reasonable thing is to learn from those who can teach.

CHORAGOS: You will do well to listen to him, King,

If what he says is sensible. And you, Haimon,

Must listen to your father.—Both speak well. 95

CREON: You consider it right for a man of my years and experience
   To go to school to a boy?

HAIMON: It is not right
   If I am wrong. But if I am young, and right,
   What does my age matter?   100

CREON: You think it right to stand up for an anarchist?

HAIMON: Not at all. I pay no respect to criminals.

CREON: Then she is not a criminal?

HAIMON: The City would deny it, to a man.

CREON: And the City proposes to teach me how to rule?   105

HAIMON: Ah. Who is it that's talking like a boy now?

CREON: My voice is the one voice giving orders in this City!

HAIMON: It is no City if it takes orders from one voice.

CREON: The State is the King!

HAIMON: Yes, if the State is a desert.   110

CREON (Pause): This boy, it seems, has sold out to a woman.

HAIMON: If you are a woman: my concern is only for you.

CREON: So? Your "concern"! In a public brawl with your father!

HAIMON: How about you, in a public brawl with justice?

CREON: With justice, when all that I do is within my rights?   115

HAIMON: You have no right to trample on God's right.

CREON *(Completely out of control)*: Fool, adolescent fool! Taken
    in by a woman!

HAIMON: You'll never see me taken in by anything vile.

CREON: Every word you say is for her!

HAIMON *(Quietly, darkly)*: And for you.   120
    And for me. And for the gods under the earth.

CREON: You'll never marry her while she lives.

HAIMON: Then she must die.—But her death will
    cause another.

CREON: Another?
    Have you lost your senses? Is this an open threat?   125

HAIMON: There is no threat in speaking to emptiness.

CREON: I swear you'll regret this superior tone of yours!
    You are the empty one!

HAIMON: If you were not my father,
    I'd say you were **perverse**.   130

CREON: You girlstruck fool, don't play at words with me!

HAIMON: I am sorry. You prefer silence.

CREON: Now, by God—!
    I swear, by all the gods in heaven above us,

---

perverse stubborn and wrongheaded in the face of evidence

You'll watch it, I swear you shall!   135

(To the Servants) Bring her out!

Bring the woman out! Let her die before his eyes!

Here, this instant, with her bridegroom beside her!

HAIMON: Not here, no; she will not die here, King.

And you will never see my face again.   140

Go on raving as long as you've a friend to endure you.

(Exit Haimon.)

CHORAGOS: Gone, gone.

Creon, a young man in a rage is dangerous!

CREON: Let him do, or dream to do, more than a man can.

He shall not save these girls from death.   145

CHORAGOS: These girls?

You have sentenced them both?

CREON: No, you are right.

I will not kill the one whose hands are clean.

CHORAGOS: But Antigone?   150

CREON (Somberly): I will carry her far away

Out there in the wilderness, and lock her

Living in a vault of stone. She shall have food,

As the custom is, to **absolve** the State of her death.

And there let her pray to the gods of hell: They are her

only gods: 155

....

absolve to clear of blame or guilt

Perhaps they will show her an escape from death,

Or she may learn, though late,

That **piety** shown the dead is pity in vain.

(Exit Creon.)

 **ODE III**

CHORUS: *(STROPHE)*

Love, unconquerable

Waster of rich men, keeper

Of warm lights and all-night vigil

In the soft face of a girl:

Sea-wanderer, forest-visitor! 5

Even the pure Immortals cannot escape you,

And mortal man, in his one day's dusk,

Trembles before your glory.

(ANTISTROPHE)

Surely you swerve upon ruin

The just man's **consenting** heart, 10

As here you have made bright anger

Strike between father and son—

And none has conquered but Love!

A girl's glance working the will of heaven;

....

piety dutifulness; devotion
consenting agreeing

Pleasure to her alone who mocks us,   15
Merciless **Aphrodite**.

 **SCENE IV**

CHORAGOS *(As Antigone enters guarded)*: But I can no
        longer stand in awe of this,
Nor, seeing what I see, keep back my tears.
Here is Antigone, passing to that chamber
Where all find sleep at last.

                                                    (STROPHE 1)

ANTIGONE: Look upon me, friends, and pity me   5
    Turning back at the night's edge to say
    Good-by to the sun that shines for me no longer;
    Now sleepy Death
    Summons me down to **Acheron**, that cold shore:
    There is no bridesong there, nor any music.   10

CHORUS: Yet not unpraised, not without a kind of honor,
    You walk at last into the underworld;
    Untouched by sickness, broken by no sword.
    What woman has ever found your way to death?

....

Aphrodite the Greek goddess of love
Acheron the river that the ancient Greeks believed the dead crossed to enter Hades, the
underworld realm of the dead

(ANTISTROPHE 2)

ANTIGONE: How often I have heard the story of **Niobe,**   15

  Tantalos' wretched daughter, how the stone

  Clung fast about her, ivy-close: and they say

  The rain falls endlessly

  And sifting soft snow; her tears are never done.

  I feel the loneliness of her death in mine.   20

CHORUS: But she was born of heaven, and you

  Are woman, woman-born. If her death is yours,

  A mortal woman's, is this not for you

  Glory in our world and in the world beyond?

(ANTISTROPHE 2)

ANTIGONE: You laugh at me. Ah, friends, friends,   25

  Can you not wait until I am dead? O Thebes,

  O men many-charioted, in love with Fortune,

  Dear springs of Dirce, sacred Theban grove,

  Be witnesses for me, denied all pity,

  Unjustly judged! and think a word of love   30

  For her whose path turns

  Under dark earth, where there are no more tears.

CHORUS: You have passed beyond human daring and come

    at last

....

Niobe in Greek mythology, an ancestor of Antigone, a Greek queen and mother whose children died and who herself was turned to stone as a result of her pride

Tantalos (also spelled *Tantalus*) in Greek mythology, a king who, for offending the gods, was punished by being placed in water that drew away when he tried to drink, and near fruit that moved out of his reach when he tried to eat

Into a place of stone where Justice sits.

I cannot tell 35

What shape of your father's guilt appears in this.

(ANTISTROPHE 2)

ANTIGONE: You have touched it at last: that bridal bed

Unspeakable, horror of son and mother mingling:

Their crime, infection of all our family!

O Oedipus, father and brother! 40

Your marriage strikes from the grave to murder mine.

I have been a stranger here in my own land:

All my life

The **blasphemy** of my birth has followed me.

CHORUS: Reverence is a virtue, but strength 45

Lives in established law: that must prevail.

You have made your choice,

Your death is the doing of your conscious hand.

(EPODE)

ANTIGONE: Then let me go, since all your words are bitter,

And the very light of the sun is cold to me. 50

Lead me to my vigil, where I must have

Neither love nor **lamentation**; no song, but silence.

(Creon interrupts impatiently.)

....

blasphemy irreverence and disrespect for the gods
epode literally "after-song," the part of the chorus's song that follows strophe and antistrophe
lamentation expression of sorrow and grief

CREON: If **dirges** and planned lamentations could put off
   death,
   Men would be singing for ever.
   (To the Servants) Take her, go!   55
   You know your orders: take her to the vault
   And leave her alone there. And if she lives or dies,
   That's her affair, not ours: our hands are clean.

ANTIGONE: O tomb, vaulted bride-bed in eternal rock,
   Soon I shall be with my own again   60
   Where **Persephone** welcomes the thin ghosts
      underground:
   And I shall see my father again, and you, mother,
   And dearest Polyneices—dearest indeed
   To me, since it was my hand
   That washed him clean and poured the ritual wine: 65
   And my reward is death before my time!
   And yet, as men's hearts know, I have done no wrong,
   I have not sinned before God. Or if I have,
   I shall know the truth in death. But if the guilt
   Lies upon Creon who judged me, then, I pray,   70
   May his punishment equal my own.

CHORAGOS: O passionate heart,
   Unyielding, tormented still by the same winds!

....

dirges music or songs of mourning performed at a funeral
Persephone the Greek goddess of the underworld

CREON: Her guards shall have good cause to regret
  their delaying.

ANTIGONE: Ah! That voice is like the voice of death!   75

CREON: I can give you no reason to think you are mistaken.

ANTIGONE: Thebes, and you my fathers' gods,
  And rulers of Thebes, you see me now, the last
  Unhappy daughter of a line of kings,
  Your kings, led away to death. You will remember   80
  What things I suffer, and at what men's hands,
  Because I would not **transgress** the laws of heaven.
  (To the Guards, simply) Come: let us wait no longer.

(Exit Antigone, Left, guarded.)

ODE IV

(STROPHE 1)

CHORUS: All **Danae's** beauty was locked away
  In a **brazen** cell where the sunlight could not come:
  A small room, still as any grave, enclosed her.
  Yet she was a princess too,
  And Zeus in a rain of gold poured love upon her.   5
  O child, child,

....

transgress to go beyond the bounds of
Danae in Greek mythology, Danae's father, the king, imprisoned her because of a
prophecy that she would have a son (Perseus) who would cause the death of the king
brazen made of bronze

No power in wealth or war

Or tough sea-blackened ships

Can prevail against untiring Destiny!

(ANTISTROPHE 1)

And **Dryas'** son also, that furious king,   10

Bore the god's prisoning anger for his pride:

Sealed up by **Dionysos** in deaf stone,

His madness died among echoes.

So at the last he learned what dreadful power

His tongue had mocked: 15

For he had **profaned** the revels,

And fired the wrath of the nine

Implacable Sisters that love the sound of the flute.

(STROPHE 2)

And old men tell a half-remembered tale

Of horror done where a dark ledge splits the sea   20

And a double surf beats on the gray shores:

How a king's new woman, sick

With hatred for the queen he had imprisoned,

Ripped out his two sons' eyes with her bloody hands

While grinning **Ares** watched the shuttle plunge   25

Four times: four blind wounds crying for revenge,

Dryas a mad Greek king who punished his son
Dionysos (also spelled *Dionysus*) the Greek god of wine
profaned treated something sacred with great disrespect
implacable impossible to soothe or make peace with
Sisters the nine Muses, the Greek goddesses of the arts and sciences
Ares the Greek god of war

Crying, tears and blood mingled.—Piteously born,
Those sons whose mother was of heavenly birth!
Her father was the god of the North Wind
And she was cradled by gales,   30
She raced with young colts on the glittering hills
And walked **untrammeled** in the open light:
But in her marriage deathless Fate found means
To build a tomb like yours for all her joy.

⁂ SCENE V ⁂

*(Enter blind **Teiresias**, led by a boy. The opening speeches of
Teiresias should be in singsong contrast to the realistic lines
of Creon.)*

TEIRESIAS: This is the way the blind man comes,
    Princes, Princes,
Lock-step, two heads lit by the eyes of one.

CREON: What new thing have you to tell us, old Teiresias?

TEIRESIAS: I have much to tell you: listen to the prophet,
    Creon.

CREON: I am not aware that I have ever failed to listen.   5

TEIRESIAS: Then you have done wisely, King, and ruled well.

....

untrammeled: unrestrained; freely
Teiresias (also spelled *Tiresias*) in Greek mythology, a blind prophet

CREON: I admit my debt to you. But what have you to say?

TEIRESIAS: This, Creon: you stand once more on the edge
     of fate.

CREON: What do you mean? Your words are a kind of dread.

TEIRESIAS: Listen, Creon: 10
    I was sitting in my chair of **augury**, at the place
    Where the birds gather about me. They were all a-chatter,
    As is their habit, when suddenly I heard
    A strange note in their jangling, a scream, a
    Whirring fury; I knew that they were fighting,   15
    Tearing each other, dying
    In a whirlwind of wings clashing. And I was afraid.
    I began the rites of burnt offering at the altar,
    But **Hephaestos** failed me: instead of bright flame,
    There was only the sputtering slime of the fat thigh flesh   20
    Melting: the entrails dissolved in gray smoke,
    The bare bone burst from the **welter**. And no blaze!

    This was a sign from heaven. My boy described it,
    Seeing for me as I see for others.

---

augury the practice of foretelling events by observing the actions of birds
Hephaestos (also spelled *Hephaestus*) the Greek god of fire and the forge
welter a confused mass; jumbled matter

I tell you, Creon, you yourself have brought   25
This new **calamity** upon us. Our hearths and altars
Are stained with the corruption of dogs and carrion birds
That glut themselves on the corpse of Oedipus' son.
The gods are deaf when we pray to them, their fire
Recoils from our offering, their birds of omen   30
Have no cry of comfort, for they are gorged
With the thick blood of the dead.
O my son,
These are no trifles! Think: all men make mistakes,
But a good man yields when he knows his course is
    wrong,   35
And repairs the evil. The only crime is pride.

Give in to the dead man, then: do not fight with
    a corpse—
What glory is it to kill a man who is dead?
Think, I beg you:
It is for your own good that I speak as I do.   40
You should be able to yield for your own good.

CREON: It seems that prophets have made me **their**
    especial province.
All my life long
I have been a kind of **butt** for the dull arrows

---

calamity disaster; catastrophe
their especial province their particular concern; their chief business
butt a target (in archery)

Of doddering fortune tellers!   45
No, Teiresias:
If your birds—if the great eagles of God himself
Should carry him stinking bit by bit to heaven,
I would not yield. I am not afraid of pollution:
No man can **defile** the gods.   50
Do what you will,
Go into business, make money, speculate
In India gold or that synthetic gold from Sardis,
Get rich otherwise than by my consent to bury him.
Teiresias, it is a sorry thing when a wise man   55
Sells his wisdom, lets out his words for hire!

TEIRESIAS: Ah Creon! Is there no man left in the world—

CREON: To do what?—Come, let's have the **aphorism**!

TEIRESIAS: No man who knows that wisdom outweighs
        any wealth?

CREON: As surely as bribes are baser than any baseness.   60

TEIRESIAS: You are sick, Creon! You are deathly sick!

CREON: As you say: it is not my place to challenge a prophet.

TEIRESIAS: Yet you have said my prophecy is for sale.

CREON: The generation of prophets has always loved gold.

TEIRESIAS: The generation of kings has always loved brass.   65

....

defile to make impure
aphorism a proverb; a brief wise saying

CREON: You forget yourself! You are speaking to your King.

TEIRESIAS: I know it. You are a king because of me.

CREON: You have a certain skill; but you have sold out.

TEIRESIAS: King, you will drive *me* to words that—

CREON: Say them, say them!   70
Only remember: I will not pay you for them.

TEIRESIAS: No, you will find them too costly.
CREON: No doubt. Speak:
Whatever you say, you will not change my will.

TEIRESIAS: Then take this, and take it to heart!   75
The time is not far off when you shall pay back
Corpse for corpse, flesh of your own flesh.
You have thrust the child of this world into living night,
You have kept from the gods below the child that is theirs:
The one in a grave before her death, the other,   80
Dead, denied the grave. This is your crime:
And the **Furies** and the dark gods of Hell
Are swift with terrible punishment for you.

Do you want to buy me now, Creon? Not many days,
And your house will be full of men and women weeping,   85
And curses will be hurled at you from far
Cities grieving for sons unburied, left to rot
Before the walls of Thebes.

....

Furies a later Roman name for the Greek goddesses called the Erinyes, three
winged goddesses of vengeance who horribly punished certain crimes

These are my arrows, Creon: they are all for you.
But come, child: lead me home. *(To Boy)*   90

Let him waste his fine anger upon younger men.
Maybe he will learn at last
To control a wiser tongue in a better head.
(Exit Teiresias.)

CHORAGOS: The old man has gone, King, but his words
　　Remain to plague us. I am old, too,   95
　　But I cannot remember that he was ever false.

CREON: That is true . . . . It troubles me.
　　Oh it is hard to give in! but it is worse
　　To risk everything for stubborn pride.

CHORAGOS: Creon: take my advice.   100

CREON: What shall I do?

CHORAGOS: Go quickly: free Antigone from her vault
　　And build a tomb for the body of Polyneices.

CREON: You would have me do this?

CHORAGOS: Creon, yes!   105
　　And it must be done at once: God moves
　　Swiftly to cancel the folly of stubborn men.

CREON: It is hard to deny the heart! But I
　　Will do it: I will not fight with destiny.

CHORAGOS: You must go yourself, you cannot leave it   110
　　　to others.

CREON: I will go.

—Bring axes, servants:

Come with me to the tomb. I buried her, I

Will set her free.

Oh quickly! 115

My mind **misgives**—

The laws of the gods are mighty, and a man must

serve them

To the last day of his life!

(Exit Creon.)

 **PAEAN**

(STROPHE 1)

CHORAGOS: God of many names

CHORUS: O **Iacchos**

son of **Kadmeian Semele**

O born of the Thunder!

Guardian of the West 5

Regent of **Eleusis'** plain

O Prince of **maenad** Thebes

and the Dragon Field by rippling **Ismenos**:

....

misgives feels doubt or apprehension
Iacchos another name for Dionysus
Kadmeian Semele Dionysus' mother, daughter of Kadmus
Eleusis a Greek city sacred to the goddesses Persephone and Demeter
maenad here used as an adjective to mean "raging, frenzied"; from Maenads, the
priestesses of Dionysos, whose rituals were sometimes wild and ecstatic
Ismenos a river in Thebes

(ANTISTROPHE 1)

CHORAGOS: God of many names

CHORUS: The flame of torches   10
    flares on our hills
    the **nymphs** of Iacchos
    dance at the spring of **Castalia**:

    from the vine-close mountain
    come ah come in ivy: 15
    Evohé evohé! sings through the streets of Thebes

(STROPHE 2)

CHORAGOS: God of many names

CHORUS: Iacchos of Thebes
    Pheavenly Child
    of Semele bride of the Thunderer!   20
    The shadow of plague is upon us:
    come with **clement** feet
    oh come from **Parnassos**
    down the long slopes
    across the lamenting water.   25

---

nymphs female nature spirits
Castalia in Greek mythology, a sacred spring
Evohé evohé a cry of Dionysus' worshippers
clement merciful; mild
Parnassos (also spelled *Parnassus*) a mountain in Greece, in ancient times sacred to Dionysus

(ANTISTROPHE 2)

CHORAGOS: Iô Fire! **Chorister** of the throbbing stars!

O purest among the voices of the night!

Thou son of God, blaze for us!

CHORUS: Come with choric rapture of circling Maenads

Who cry *Iô **Iacche***!   30

God of many names!

ÉXODOS

(Enter Messenger, Left.)

MESSENGER: Men of the line of Kadmos, you who live

Near **Amphion's citadel**:

I cannot say

Of any condition of human life "This is fixed,

This is clearly good, or bad." Fate raises up,   5

And Fate casts down the happy and unhappy alike:

No man can foretell his Fate.

Take the case of Creon:

Creon was happy once, as I count happiness:

Victorious in battle, sole governor of the land,   10

Fortunate father of children nobly born.

....

Iô a shout of joy, victory, and celebration

chorister the leader of a choir

Iacche a form of the name *Iacchos*

Éxodos the final scene

Amphion's citadel a fortress in Thebes, believed to have been built by Amphion, husband of Niobe

And now it has all gone from him! Who can say
That a man is still alive when his life's joy fails?
He is a walking dead man. Grant him rich,
Let him live like a king in his great house: 15
If his pleasure is gone, I would not give
So much as the shadow of smoke for all he owns.

CHORAGOS: Your words hint at sorrow: what is your
      news for us?

MESSENGER: They are dead. The living are guilty
      of their death.

CHORAGOS: Who is guilty? Who is dead? Speak!   20

MESSENGER: Haimon.
      Haimon is dead; and the hand that killed him
      Is his own hand.

CHORAGOS: His father's? or his own?

MESSENGER: His own, driven mad by the murder his father   25
      had done.

CHORAGOS: Teiresias, Teiresias, how clearly you saw it all!

MESSENGER: This is my news: you must draw what
      conclusions you can from it.

CHORAGOS: But look: **Eurydice**, our Queen:
      Has she overheard us?

(Enter Eurydice from the Palace, Center.)

....

Eurydice the wife of Creon

EURYDICE: I have heard something, friends: 30
    As I was unlocking the gate of Pallas' shrine,
    For I needed her help today, I heard a voice
    Telling of some new sorrow. And I fainted
    There at the temple with all my maidens about me.
    But speak again: whatever it is, I can bear it: 35
    Grief and I are no strangers.

MESSENGER: Dearest Lady,
    I will tell you plainly all that I have seen.
    I shall not try to comfort you: what is the use,
    Since comfort could lie only in what is not true?   40
    The truth is always best.
    I went with Creon
    To the outer plain where Polyneices was lying,
    No friend to pity him, his body shredded by dogs.
    We made our prayers in that place to **Hecate**   45
    And Pluto, that they would be merciful. And we bathed
    The corpse with holy water, and we brought
    Fresh-broken branches to burn what was left of it,
    And upon the urn we heaped up a towering **barrow**
    Of the earth of his own land.   50
    When we were done, we ran
    To the vault where Antigone lay on her couch of stone.

....

Hecate a Greek goddess associated with the underworld
barrow a large mound of earth over a burial site

One of the servants had gone ahead,
And while he was yet far off he heard a voice
Grieving within the chamber, and he came back   55
And told Creon. And as the King went closer,
The air was full of wailing, the words lost,
And he begged us to make all haste. "Am I a prophet?"
He said, weeping, "And must I walk this road,
The saddest of all that I have gone before?   60
My son's voice calls me on. Oh quickly, quickly!
Look through the crevice there, and tell me
If it is Haimon, or some deception of the gods!"

We obeyed; and in the cavern's farthest corner
We saw her lying: 65
She had made a noose of her fine linen veil
And hanged herself. Haimon lay beside her,
His arms about her waist, lamenting her,
His love lost under ground, crying out
That his father had stolen her away from him.   70

When Creon saw him the tears rushed to his eyes
And he called to him: "What have you done, child?
    Speak to me,
What are you thinking that makes your eyes so strange?
O my son, my son, I come to you on my knees!"
But Haimon spat in his face. He said not a word,   75
Staring—

And suddenly drew his sword
And lunged. Creon shrank back, the blade missed;
   and the boy,
Desperate against himself, drove it half its length
Into his own side, and fell. And as he died   80
He gathered Antigone close in his arms again,
Choking, his blood bright red on her white cheek.
And now he lies dead with the dead, and she is his
At last, his bride in the houses of the dead.

(Exit Eurydice into the Palace.)

CHORAGOS: She has left us without a word. What can
     this mean?   85

MESSENGER: It troubles me, too; yet she knows what is best,
    Her grief is too great for public lamentation,
    And doubtless she has gone to her chamber to weep
    For her dead son, leading her maidens in his dirge.

CHORAGOS: It may be so: but I fear this deep silence.   90

MESSENGER *(Pause)*: I will see what she is doing.
    I will go in.

(Exit Messenger into the Palace.)

(Enter Creon with attendants, bearing Haimon's body.)

CHORAGOS: But here is the King himself: oh look at him,
    Bearing his own damnation in his arms.

CREON: Nothing you say can touch me any more.
    My own blind heart has brought me   95
    From darkness to final darkness. Here you see
    The father murdering, the murdered son—
    And all my civic wisdom!

    Haimon my son, so young, so young to die,
    I was the fool, not you; and you died for me.   100

CHORAGOS: That is the truth; but you were late in
    learning it.

CREON: This truth is hard to bear. Surely a god
    Has crushed me beneath the hugest weight of heaven.
    And driven me headlong a barbaric way
    To trample out the thing I held most dear.   105
    The pains that men will take to come to pain!

(Enter Messenger from the Palace.)

MESSENGER: The burden you carry in your hands is heavy,
    But it is not all: you will find more in your house.

CREON: What burden worse than this shall I find there?

MESSENGER: The Queen is dead.   110

CREON: O port of death, deaf world,
    Is there no pity for me? And you, Angel of evil,
    I was dead, and your words are death again.
    Is it true, boy? Can it be true?
    Is my wife dead? Has death bred death?   115

MESSENGER: You can see for yourself.

(The doors are opened, and the body of Eurydice is disclosed within.)

CREON: Oh pity!
    All true, all true, and more than I can bear!
    O my wife, my son!

MESSENGER: She stood before the altar, and her heart   120
    Welcomed the knife her own hand guided,
    And a great cry burst from her lips for Megareus dead,
    And for Haimon dead, her sons; and her last breath
    Was a curse for their father, the murderer of her sons.
    And she fell, and the dark flowed in through her closing
       eyes.   125

CREON: O God, I am sick with fear.
    Are there no swords here? Has no one a blow for me?

MESSENGER: Her curse is upon you for the deaths of both.

CREON: It is right that it should be. I alone am guilty.
    I know it, and I say it. Lead me in,   130
    Quickly, friends.
    I have neither life nor substance. Lead me in.

CHORAGOS: You are right, if there can be right in
       so much wrong.
    The briefest way is best in a world of sorrow.

CREON: Let it come, 135
Let death come quickly, and be kind to me.
I would not ever see the sun again.

CHORAGOS: All that will come when it will; but we, meanwhile,
Have much to do. Leave the future to itself.

CREON: All my heart was in that prayer! 140

CHORAGOS: Then do not pray any more: the sky is deaf.

CREON: Lead me away. I have been rash and foolish
I have killed my son and my wife.
I look for comfort; my comfort lies here dead.
Whatever my hands have touched has come to nothing. 145
Fate has brought all my pride to a thought of dust.

(As Creon is being led into the house, the Choragos advances and speaks directly to the audience.)

CHORAGOS: There is no happiness where there is no wisdom;
No wisdom but in submission to the gods.
Big words are always punished,
And proud men in old age learn to be wise. ❖

The Game

by Louise Bryant

Characters

LIFE	YOUTH
DEATH	GIRL

At the rise, Death is lying on the ground at left, idly flipping dice.
*Now and then, he glances **sardonically** at Life who is standing*
at the extreme right and counting aloud.

....

sardonically in a bitter or mocking way

LIFE *(Counting abstractly)*: Fifty thousand, fifty-one, sixty-five, ninety—*(She goes on through the next speech.)*

DEATH: Come come, Life, forget your losses. It's no fun playing with a dull partner. I had hoped for a good game tonight, although there is little in it for me—just a couple of suicides.

LIFE *(With a gesture of anxiety)*: My dear Death, I wish you would grant me a favor.

DEATH *(Grumbling)*: A favor. A favor. Now isn't that just like a woman? I never saw one yet who was willing to **abide** by the results of a fair game.

LIFE *(Earnestly)*: But I want these two, whether I win or lose. I really must have them. They are geniuses—and you know how badly I am in need of geniuses right now. Ungrateful spoiled children! They always want to commit suicide over their first disappointments.

DEATH *(Impatiently)*: How many times must I tell you that the game must be played! It's the law—you know it as well as I do.

LIFE *(Shrugging)*: O, the law! Laws are always in your favor, Death!

DEATH: There you are. I always said the universe would be in a wild state of disorder if the women had any say! No, you must play the game.

----

abide to accept without argument or question

LIFE *(Indignantly)*: Whoever said anything about not playing? All I want is your consent to let them meet here before the game begins.

DEATH: I'll bet this isn't so innocent as it sounds. Who are they? I haven't paid much attention to the case.

LIFE: Youth and the Girl. He is a Poet, and she a Dancer.

DEATH: A strong man and a beautiful woman. *(He laughs, ironically.)* Up to the same old tricks, eh? You sly thing, you think if they meet they'll fall in love and cheat me! *(Pause.)* Well, suppose I consent. What will you give?

LIFE *(Quickly)*: I'll give you Kaiser Wilhelm, the Czar of Russia, George of England, and old Francis Joseph— that's two to one!

DEATH: Now that's dishonest. You're always trying to unload a lot of monarchs on me when you know I don't want them. Why, when you play for them you almost go to sleep and I always win. No bargaining in kings, my dear.

LIFE: I'll give you a whole regiment of soldiers.

DEATH *(With scorn)*: Soldiers! What do you care about soldiers? Look at your figures again. You've been losing millions of soldiers in Europe for the past two years— and you're much more excited about these two rattle-pated young idiots. Your idea of a fair trade is to get something for nothing. You love too much. With such **covetness** how can you ever know the thrill of chance?

LIFE *(Pleading)*: O I'll give you anything.

Enter Youth, with hanging melancholy head.

DEATH: Sshh! Too late! Here's one of them.

LIFE *(Turning)*: Youth! *(To Death)* You've tricked me. You were only playing for time.

DEATH: Come, sister. Be game. All's fair in everything but the dice. And just think. If you win this cast the other is half won. They'll meet then ...

YOUTH *(Seeing the two and starting. To Life)*: Who are you?

LIFE *(Anxiously)*: I am Life!

YOUTH *(Bitterly)*: O, I am through with you ... I want none of you! *(Turning his back and addressing Death)* And who are you?

DEATH *(Rising with cheerful complacency)*: I am Death!

YOUTH *(Taken aback)*: Death! How different from my dream of you. I thought you were **sombre**, **austere**; and instead, you're—if I may say so—just a trifle commonplace.

---

covetness desire or wish for something
somber depressing
austere severe; serious

DEATH: I'm not as young as I once was. One's figure, you know—

LIFE *(Delightedly)*: Ah!

DEATH: Look at her. A pleasing exterior, eh? And yet you wouldn't be seeking me if you didn't know better. Alas, my boy, beauty is not even skin deep.

YOUTH: That is true. *(Going to Death)* Ah, Death, I have been seeking you for weeks.

DEATH: Yet I am always present. Where did you seek me?

YOUTH *(Excitedly, with gestures)*: I tried poison, but just as I was about to swallow it they snatched it from me... I tried to shoot myself. They cheated me; the pistol wouldn't go off.

DEATH: Well-meaning idiots!

YOUTH: So I came here to leap into the sea!

DEATH: Very good. Only hurry. Someone might come.

LIFE: Why do you wish to die?

YOUTH *(Hotly)*: As if you didn't know. Did you not give me the power to string beautiful words into songs—did you not give me Love to sing to and take Love away? I cannot sing anymore! And yet you ask me why I want to die! I am not a slave! Slaves live just to eat and be clothed—you have plenty of them!

LIFE *(Sadly)*: Yes, I have plenty of them.

YOUTH: If I cannot have Love to warm me, I cannot create beauty. And if I cannot create beauty, I will not live!

LIFE: Are you sure it was Love? I think it was only Desire I gave you; you did not seem ready for Love.

YOUTH (*Passionately*): Falsehoods. Evasions. What is Love, then? You gave me a girl who sold flowers on the street. She had hair like gold and a body all curves and rose-white like marble. I sang my songs for her, and the whole world listened. Then an ugly beast came and offered her gold…and she laughed at me—and went away.

DEATH (*Laughing indulgently*): That is Love, my boy. You are lucky to find it out so young.

LIFE: Now I know it was desire.

YOUTH (*To Death*): Why will she persist in lying?

DEATH (*Gallantly*): I am a sport and a gentleman and I must admit that Life is as truthful as I am.

LIFE: Listen, Youth, and answer me. Did your sweetheart understand your songs?

YOUTH: Why should she? Women do not have to understand. They must be fragrant and beautiful—like flowers.

LIFE: And is that all?

YOUTH (*Slightly confused*): I do not know many women.

LIFE: I will show you one who understands your songs. She is coming here.

DEATH *(Harshly)*: To leap into the sea, like you!

LIFE: Because she is lonely—waiting for you.

YOUTH: For me! But I do not know her!

LIFE: But she knows you—through your songs…

DEATH *(Scornfully)*: And you have been seeking me for weeks! Are you to be fooled again by this tricky **charlatan**? You who have had enough of Life? There is no place for cowards among the lofty dead!

YOUTH: O Death, forgive me! Life, farewell!

He stretches out his arms and turns towards the cliff.

LIFE *(Crying out)*: Hold! We must play first.

Youth stands as he is, with outstretched arms as they play.

DEATH *(Jovially)*: So now it is you who are asking me to play! Come, Life do me a favor. Give me this one and the girl shall be yours!

LIFE *(Excitedly)*: No. The game must be played. It is the law!

Death laughs. They go to center stage and throw the dice. Death frowns and grumbles.

....

charlatan one who pretends to have more skill or knowledge that he or she has
jovially with joyous humor

LIFE (*Rising with a happy smile*): I have won!

YOUTH (*Dropping his arms and turning slowly. Sadly*): Then I am to live—in spite of myself. Death, I have lost you. Life, I hate you. Without Love you are crueler than Death.

LIFE: Soon the Girl will be here. Then you will think me beautiful.

DEATH: That's the comedy of it. You probably will, you know.

YOUTH (*With a gesture of revulsion*): Promises. Promises. Love comes but one—

He breaks off and stares as the Girl rushes in. She almost runs into Life, then suddenly recoils.

GIRL: Who are you?

LIFE: I am Life.

GIRL: O, Life dear, I must leave you! I cannot bear you any longer. You are so white and so cold!

LIFE: What have you to complain of? Have I not given you Fame, and Worship and Wealth?

GIRL: What are all these…without Love?

DEATH (*With a smile*): What—you without Love? How about those who stand at the stage door every evening—and send you flowers and jewels? One of them shot himself because you stamped on his flowers. Believe me, my dear, that is all the Love there is—

GIRL: Love? No. That was Desire!

DEATH: Bah! Desire when they seek you—Love when you seek them.

GIRL: No, No. Love understands. They didn't. They wanted to buy me in order to destroy me. That is why I stamped on their flowers.

DEATH (*Humorously*): Ah, the young. Incurably **sentimental**.

YOUTH (*Impetuously*): Good. I'm glad you did.

GIRL (*Startled*): Why, who are you?

YOUTH: I am Youth.

GIRL (*Drawing back*): Youth, the Poet? You? O I know all your songs by heart. I have kissed every line. Always, when I dance, I try to dance them. (*Looking around fearfully*) But why are you here?

DEATH (*Grimly*): He came to throw himself into the sea!

GIRL (*Alarmed. Clutching him by the arm*): Oh, no. You must not. What would the poor world do without your beautiful songs?

LIFE: Do not be afraid, my dear, I have won.

....

sentimental emotional, especially about love, pity, or nostalgia
impetuously suddenly or rashly

YOUTH (*Sighing*): Alas!

GIRL: Why did you want to die?

DEATH (*Slyly*): His sweetheart left him.

GIRL (*Drawing back coldly*): His sweetheart! So he loves
someone! I don't believe you. How could any woman he
loved…when he sings so sweetly—

LIFE: His songs meant nothing to her.

GIRL: Nothing! (*Going to Youth*) O then she was not worth
your love. She was like the men who wait for me at the
stage-door; she wanted to destroy you.

DEATH: Such is Life, my dear young lady, Love is the
destroyer always.

YOUTH (*Bitterly*): You are right. It is all a myth—Life, Love,
Happiness. I must idealize someone, something—and
then the bubble bursts and I am alone. No. If she could
not understand, no one could understand.

GIRL (*Eagerly*): O how wrong you are! I understand. Don't
you believe me? I have danced all you have sung. Do
you remember "The Bird Calls"?

*She dances. Youth watches with astonishment and growing
delight.*

YOUTH: How beautiful! You do understand—you do!
Wings flash and soar when you dance! You skim the sea

....
slyly cunningly or mischievously

gloriously, lifting your quivering feathery breast against the sunny wind. Dance again for me. Dance my "Cloud Flight"!

GIRL: The loveliest of all! (*Remembering sadly*) But I can never dance for you anymore. I came here to die!

DEATH: And you'd forgotten it already! O you're all alike, you suicides. Life's shallowest little **deceit** fools you again—though you have seen through her and know her for what she is.

GIRL (*Hesitating*): But I have found Youth.

YOUTH (*Swiftly*): Yes, and Youth has found Love—real Love at last. Love that burns like fire and flowers like the trees. You shall not die. (*To Death*) And I will fight you for her! Love is stronger than Death!

DEATH: Than Life, you mean. Think of the great lovers of the world—Paola and Francesca, Romeo and Juliet, Tristan and Isolde. I, I claimed them all. Who are you to set yourself up against such august precedents? (*To the Girl*) You think he loves you. It is not you he loves, but your dancing of his songs. He is a Poet—therefore he loves only himself. And his sweetheart, for lack of whom he was going to die. See! He has already forgotten her! (*Slowly*) As you will one day be forgotten.

---

deceit an act of lying or misleading

LIFE *(To Girl)*: Why ask too much of me? I can only give happiness for a moment—but it is real happiness— Love, Creation, Unity with the tremendous rhythm of the universe. I can't promise it will endure. I won't say you will not some day be forgotten. What if it is himself he loves in you? That, too, is Love.

GIRL: To be supremely happy for a moment—an hour— that is worth living for!

DEATH: Life offers you many things—I but one. She pours out the sunshine before you to make you glad; she sends the winter to chill your heart. She gives you Love and Desire—and takes them away. She brings you warm quietness—and kills it with hunger and anxiety. Life offers you many things—I but one. Come closer, tired heart, and hold out your weary hands. See! What a pearl I offer—to kings and beggars alike. Come—I will give you peace!

GIRL *(Spurning him)*: Peace? Do you think I want peace—I, a dancer, a child of the whirling winds? Do you think I would be blind to the sunlight, deaf to Youth's music—to my sweet applause, dumb to laughter? All this joy that is in me—scattered in darkness? Dust in my hair—in my eyes—on my dancing feet? *(Hesitating)* And yet—and yet Life is so cruel!

YOUTH *(Going to her)*: My dearest. We will never leave one another.

LIFE: She is mine!

DEATH (*Sardonically*): Haven't you forgotten something? The game!

LIFE: It is half-won. She too has found love.

DEATH: Ah! But in willing to die she laid her life on the knees of the Fates. So we must play for her. It is the law.

LIFE: O I am not afraid to play. This time I have you, Death.

DEATH: Have me! Ho, Ho. Nay, Life. I am cleverer than you. On this game hangs the doom of both!

LIFE (*Astonished*): Of both? (*Furiously*) You lie, Death! I have already won Youth, he cannot die.

DEATH (*Laughing*): Ho. Ho. Youth cannot die, you say. True. But the Girl dies if I win; isn't that so? (*Life nods.*) Well, and if she dies, what then? He loves her, yet he cannot follow. Nay, he shall live—forever mute, forever regretting his lost love, until you yourself will beg me to take him!

LIFE (*Falling on her knees*): O Death, I beg of you—

DEATH: Ho. Ho. Life on her knees to Death. No, sister. I couldn't help you if I would. It is the law. Let us play.

LIFE (*Resigned*): It is the law.

They go to the center of stage and play.

LIFE *(Joyously)*: O I have won again!

DEATH *(Blackly, hurling the dice to the ground)*: Yes, curse the luck! But some day we'll play for those two again—and then it will be my turn.

YOUTH: Yes. But we will have lived. Until then, Death, you are Powerless. I fear you not, and I will guard her from you.

DEATH *(Shrugging)*: Geniuses! Geniuses!

GIRL *(To Youth)*: How brave—how strong—how beautiful is my lover!

They go offstage with their arms about each other.

DEATH: Well, it was a good game after all. You see, that's the difference between you and me; you play to win, and I play for the fun of the thing. *(He laughs.)* But tell me, Life; why is it you make such a fuss over dreamers and care so little for soldiers?

LIFE: O, soldiers don't matter one way or the other to me; but some day the dreamers will chain you to the earth, and I will have the game all my way.

DEATH: That remains to be seen. But how about kings?

LIFE: Kings are my enemies. Do you remember how careless I was during the French Revolution? I've always had it on my conscience, and I think I'd feel better if I told you; whenever I threw a good combination, I— juggled the dice!

DEATH *(Nodding)*: I'm not surprised. Heavens, aren't women unscrupulous! And yet they call me unfair... Well, I suppose I've got to keep an eye on you.

LIFE: I warn you I will stop at nothing. By the way, what's the game tomorrow night?

DEATH: A Plague. And in that game, I regret to say you haven't a chance in the world.

LIFE: Don't forget I have Science to help me.

DEATH: Science, Bah! A fool's toy! I sweep them all together in my net—the men of learning and the ones they try to cure.

LIFE: But remember that the sun, the blessed healing sun still rises every morning.

DEATH *(Irritated)*: Oh, don't remind me of the sun!

He goes.

LIFE *(Beginning to count her losses again)*: Two hundred thousand, seventy-five, three hundred, and ten. *(Looking up)* I must never let him know how much I mind losing soldiers. They are the flower of youth— there are dreamers among them...

Curtain ❖

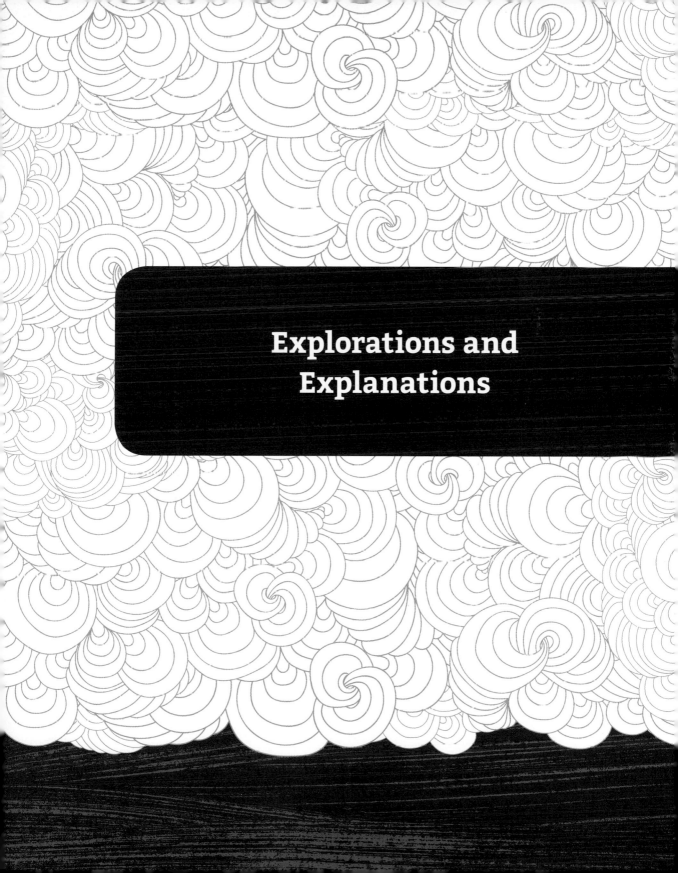

Explorations and Explanations

Spring and Fall
to a young child

by Gerard Manley Hopkins

Márgarét, áre you gríeving
Over Goldengrove **unleaving**?
Leáves, líke the things of man, you
With your fresh thoughts care for, can you?
Áh! ás the heart grows older
It will come to such sights colder
By and by, nor spare a sigh
Though worlds of **wanwood leafmeal** lie;
And yet you *will* weep and know why.
Now no matter, child, the name:
Sórrow's spríngs áre the same.
Nor mouth had, no nor mind, expressed
What heart heard of, **ghost** guessed:
It ís the **blight** man was born for,
It is Margaret you mourn for. ❖

....

unleaving losing leaves
wanwood *probably* wan (pale, sickly, feeble) + wood (forest)
leafmeal *probably* leaf + piecemeal (in pieces); thus, with leaves fallen in pieces
ghost spirit; soul
blight a disease that injures or kills plants; something that crushes one's hopes or plans; something that harms or destroys

in Just

by e.e. cummings

in Just–
spring   when the world is mud-
luscious the little
lame balloonman

whistles   far and   wee

and eddieandbill come
running from marbles and
piracies and it's
spring

when the world is puddle-wonderful

the queer
old balloonman whistles
far   and   wee
and bettyandisbel come dancing

from hop-scotch and jump-rope and

....

luscious delicious; appealing strongly to the senses

it's
spring
and
   the

     goat-footed

balloonMan   whistles
far
and
wee ❖

July

by Susan Hartley Swett

When the scarlet cardinal tells
    Her dream to the dragonfly,
And the lazy breeze makes a nest in the trees,
    And murmurs a lullaby,
        It is July.

When the tangled cobweb pulls
    The cornflower's cap **awry**,
And the lilies tall lean over the wall
    To bow to the butterfly,
        It is July.

When the heat like a mist veil floats,
    And poppies flame in the rye,
And the silver note in the **streamlet**'s throat
    Has softened almost to a sigh,
        It is July.

awry out of place; askew
streamlet a small stream

502

When the hours are so still that time
Forgets them, and lets them lie
'Neath petals pink till the night stars wink
At sunset in the sky,
It is July.

When each **fingerpost** by the way
Says that Slumbertown is **nigh**;
When the grass is tall, and the roses fall,
And nobody wonders why,
It is July. ❖

fingerpost a guidepost with a sign shaped like a pointing finger
nigh near

To Autumn

by John Keats

1

Season of mists and mellow fruitfulness,
    Close **bosom-friend** of the maturing sun;
Conspiring with him how to load and bless
    With fruit the vines that round the **thatch-eves** run;
To bend with apples the moss'd cottage-trees,
    And fill all fruit with ripeness to the core;
      To swell the gourd, and plump the hazel shells
    With a sweet kernel; to set budding more,
And still more, later flowers for the bees,
Until they think warm days will never cease,
    For summer has **o'er-brimm'd** their clammy cells.

2

Who hath not seen thee **oft amid** thy **store**?
    Sometimes whoever seeks abroad may find
Thee sitting careless on a **granary** floor,
    Thy hair soft-lifted by the **winnowing** wind;

---

bosom-friend a dear, cherished friend

conspiring planning or plotting together

thatch-eves the overhanging edges (eaves) of a roof covered with straw, reeds, or similar material (thatch)

o'erbrimm'd filled to overflowing

oft often

amid surrounded by; in the middle of

store abundance; a great quantity

granary building where grain is stored

winnowing from *winnow* = to blow away the chaff (seed coverings) from the grain

Or on a half-reap'd furrow sound asleep,
    Drows'd with the fume of poppies, while thy hook
        Spares the next swath and all its twined flowers:
And sometimes like a gleaner thou dost keep
    Steady thy laden head across a brook;
        Or by a cyder-press, with patient look,
Thou watchest the last oozings hours by hours.

3

Where are the songs of spring? Ay, where are they?
    Think not of them, thou hast thy music too,—
While barred clouds bloom the soft-dying day,
    And touch the stubble-plains with rosy hue;
Then in a wailful choir the small gnats mourn
    Among the river sallows, borne aloft
        Or sinking as the light wind lives or dies;
And full-grown lambs loud bleat from hilly bourn;
    Hedge-crickets sing; and now with treble soft
    The red-breast whistles from a garden-croft;
        And gathering swallows twitter in the skies. ❖

----

drows'd made sleepy

fume vapor

hook a scythe (a long-curved blade at the end of a handle, used for cutting grain)

swath a row or strip; the path cut by a scythe

gleaner one who gathers grain left behind by reapers

stubble-plains fields covered by short stalks of grain left behind after harvesting

sallows willow trees

bourn region (from an old meaning of bourn as "boundary")

croft a small field enclosed by a fence or wall

It sifts from Leaden Sieves

by Emily Dickinson

It sifts from **Leaden** Sieves —
It powders all the Wood.
It fills with **Alabaster** Wool
The Wrinkles of the Road —

It makes an Even Face
Of Mountain, and of Plain —
Unbroken Forehead from the East
Unto the East again —

It reaches to the Fence —
It wraps it Rail by Rail
Till it is lost in Fleeces —
It deals **Celestial** Vail

To Stump, and Stack — and Stem —
A Summer's empty Room —
Acres of Joints, where Harvests were,
Recordless, but for them —

It Ruffles Wrists of Posts
As Ankles of a Queen —
Then stills its **Artisans** — like Ghosts —
Denying they have been — ❖

leaden like lead; dull and heavy; dark gray in color
alabaster a kind of fine white stone often carved into vases or ornaments
celestial relating to the sky or the heavens
artisans skilled craftsmen

The Snow-Storm

by Ralph Waldo Emerson

Announced by all the trumpets of the sky,
Arrives the snow, and, driving o'er the fields,
Seems nowhere to **alight**: the whited air
Hides hills and woods, the river, and the heaven,
And veils the farm-house at the garden's end.
The sled and traveler stopped, the **courier's** feet
Delayed, all friends shut out, the housemates sit
Around the radiant fireplace, enclosed
In a **tumultuous** privacy of storm.

alight to land; to come to rest
courier a messenger
tumultuous noisy and confused; disorderly

Come see the north wind's **masonry**.

Out of an unseen **quarry** evermore

Furnished with tile, the fierce **artificer**

Curves his white **bastions** with projected roof

Round every **windward** stake, or tree, or door.

Speeding, the **myriad**-handed, his wild work

So fanciful, so savage, **nought** cares he

For number or proportion. Mockingly,

On coop or kennel he hangs **Parian** wreaths;

A swan-like form **invests** the hidden thorn;

Fills up the farmer's lane from wall to wall,

Maugre the farmer sighs; and at the gate,

A **tapering turret** overtops the work.

And when his hours are numbered, and the world

Is all his own, retiring, as he were not,

Leaves, when the sun appears, astonished Art

To **mimic** in slow structures, stone by stone,

Built in an age, the mad wind's night-work,

The **frolic** architecture of the snow. ❖

....

masonry stone or brickwork

quarry a pit from which stone is cut or dug

artificer a skilled craftsman; an artist

bastions protective walls that project outward

windward facing the direction from which the wind is blowing

myriad a great many; a vast number

nought (also spelled *naught*) nothing

Parian looking like white marble (from Páros, the Greek island known for its fine marble)

invests adorns; covers

maugre in spite of; regardless of

tapering becoming thinner or narrower at one end

turret a small tower or tower-like structure

mimic to copy; to imitate

frolic playful; merry

A House of My Own

introduction to The House on Mango Street
by Sandra Cisneros

The young woman in this photograph is me when I was writing *The House on Mango Street*.* She's in her office, a room that had probably been a child's bedroom when families lived in this apartment. It has no door and is only slightly wider than the walk-in pantry. But it has great light and sits above the hallway door downstairs, so she can hear her neighbors come and go. She's posed as if she's just looked up from her work for a moment, but in real life she never writes in this office. She writes in the kitchen, the only room with a heater.

It's Chicago, 1980, in the down-at-the-heels Bucktown neighborhood before it's discovered by folks with money. The young woman lives at 1814 N. Paulina Street second floor front. Nelson Algren once wandered these streets. Saul Bellow's turf was over on Division Street, walking distance away. It's a neighborhood that reeks of beer and urine, of sausage and beans.

The young woman fills her "office" with things she drags home from the flea market at Maxwell Street. Antique typewriters, alphabet blocks, asparagus ferns,

* When this essay was first published, it was accompanied by a picture of Cisneros in her 20s. In the photograph, she was seated next to a typewriter, facing the camera.

bookshelves, ceramic figurines from Occupied Japan, wicker baskets, birdcages, hand-painted photos. Things she likes to look at. It's important to have this space to look and think. When she lived at home, the things she looked at scolded her and made her feel sad and depressed. They said, "Wash me." They said, "Lazy." They said, "You ought." But the things in her office are magical and invite her to play. They fill her with light. It's the room where she can be quiet and still and listen to the voices inside herself. She likes being alone in the daytime.

As a girl, she dreamed about having a silent home, just to herself, the way other women dreamed of their weddings. Instead of collecting lace and linen for her trousseau, the young woman buys old things from the thrift stores on grimy Milwaukee Avenue for her future house-of-her-own—faded quilts, cracked vases, chipped saucers, lamps in need of love.

The young woman returned to Chicago after graduate school and moved back into her father's house, 1754 N. Keeler, back into her girl's room with its twin bed and floral wallpaper. She was twenty-three and a half. Now she summoned her courage and told her father she wanted to live alone again, like she did when she was away at school. He looked at her with that eye of the rooster before it attacks, but she wasn't alarmed. She'd seen that look before and knew he was harmless. She was his favorite, and it was only a matter of waiting.

The daughter claimed she'd been taught that a writer needs quiet, privacy, and long stretches of **solitude** to think. The father decided too much college and too many gringo friends had ruined her. In a way he was right. In a way she was right. When she thinks to herself in her father's language, she knows sons and daughters don't leave their parents' house until they marry. When she thinks in English, she knows she should've been on her own since eighteen.

For a time father and daughter reached a truce. She agreed to move into the basement of a building where the oldest of her six brothers and his wife lived, 4832 W. Homer. But after a few months, when the big brother upstairs turned out to be Big Brother, she got on her bicycle and rode through the neighborhood of her high school days until she spotted an apartment with fresh-painted walls and masking tape on the windows. Then she knocked on the storefront downstairs. That's how she convinced the landlord she was his new tenant.

Her father can't understand why she wants to live in a hundred-year-old building with big windows that let in the cold. She knows her apartment is clean, but the hallway is scuffed and scary, though she and the woman upstairs take turns mopping it regularly. The hall needs paint, and there's nothing they can do about that. When the father

....

solitude time spent alone

visits, he climbs up the stairs muttering with disgust. Inside, he looks at her books arranged in milk crates, at the futon on the floor in a bedroom with no door, and whispers, "Hippie," in the same way he looks at boys hanging out in his neighborhood and says, "Drogas." When he sees the space heater in the kitchen, the father shakes his head and sighs, "Why did I work so hard to buy a house with a furnace so she could go backwards and live like this?"

When she's alone, she savors her apartment of high ceilings and windows that let in the sky, the new carpeting and walls white as typing paper, the walk-in pantry with empty shelves, her bedroom without a door, her office with its typewriter, and the big front-room windows with their view of a street, rooftops, trees, and the dizzy traffic of the Kennedy Expressway.

Between her building and the brick wall of the next is a tidy, sunken garden. The only people who ever enter the garden are a family who speak like guitars, a family with a Southern accent. At dusk they appear with a pet monkey in a cage and sit on a green bench and talk and laugh. She spies on them from behind her bedroom curtains and wonders where they got the monkey.

Her father calls every week to say, "*Mija*, when are you coming home?" What does her mother say about all this? She puts her hands on her hips and boasts, "She gets it from me." When the father is in the room, the mother just shrugs and says, "What can I do?" The mother doesn't object. She knows what it is to live a life filled with regrets, and she doesn't want her daughter to live that life too. She always supported the daughter's projects, so long as she went to school. The mother who painted the walls of their Chicago homes the color of flowers; who planted tomatoes and roses in her garden; sang arias; practiced solos on her son's drum set; boogied along with the *Soul Train* dancers; glued travel posters on her kitchen wall with Karo syrup; herded her kids weekly to the library, to public concerts, to museums; wore a button on her lapel that said "Feed the People Not the Pentagon"; who never went beyond the ninth grade. *That* mother. She nudges her daughter and says, "Good lucky you studied."

The father wants his daughter to be a weather girl on television, or to marry and have babies. She doesn't want to be a TV weather girl. Nor does she want to marry and have babies. Not yet. Maybe later, but there are so many other things she must do in her lifetime first. Travel. Learn how to dance the tango. Publish a book. Live in other cities. Win a National Endowment for the Arts award. See the Northern Lights. Jump out of a cake.

She stares at the ceilings and walls of her apartment the way she once stared at the ceilings and walls of the apartments she grew up in, inventing pictures in the cracks in the plaster, inventing stories to go with these pictures. At night, under the circle of light from a cheap metal lamp clamped to the kitchen table, she sits with paper and a pen and pretends she's not afraid. She's trying to live like a writer.

Where she gets these ideas about living like a writer, she has no clue. She hasn't read Virginia Woolf yet. She doesn't know about Rosario Castellanos or Sor Juana Inés de la Cruz. Gloria Anzaldúa and Cherríe Moraga are cutting their own paths through the world somewhere, but she doesn't know about them. She doesn't know anything. She's making things up as she goes.

When the photo, of the young woman who was me was snapped, I still called myself a poet, though I'd been writing stories since grammar school. I'd gravitated back to fiction while in the Iowa poetry workshop. Poetry, as it was taught at Iowa, was a house of cards, a tower of ideas, but I can't communicate an idea except through a story.

The woman I am in the photo was working on a series of **vignettes**, little by little, along with her poetry. I already had a title—*The House on Mango Street*. Fifty pages had been written, but I still didn't think of it as a novel. It was just a jar of buttons, like the mismatched embroidered pillowcases and monogrammed napkins I tugged from the bins at the Goodwill. I wrote these things and thought of them as "little stories," though I sensed they were connected to each other. I hadn't heard of story

....

vignettes brief descriptions of an event or episode

cycles yet. I hadn't read Ermilo Abreu Gómez's *Canek*, Elena Poniatowska's *Lilus Kikus*, Gwendolyn Brooks' *Maud Martha*, Nellie Campobello's *My Mother's Hands*. That would come later, when I had more time and solitude to read.

The woman I once was wrote the first three stories of *House* in one weekend at Iowa. But because I wasn't in the fiction workshop, they wouldn't count toward my MFA thesis. I didn't argue; my thesis advisor reminded me too much of my father. I worked on these little stories on the side for comfort when I wasn't writing poetry for credit. I shared them with colleagues like poet Joy Harjo, who was also having a hard time in the poetry workshops, and fiction writer Dennis Mathis, a small-town Illinois native, but whose paperback library was from the world.

Little-little stories were in literary vogue at the time, in the '70s. Dennis told me about the Japanese Nobel Prize winner Kawabata's minimal "palm of the hand" stories. We fried omelets for dinner and read García Márquez and Heinrich Böll stories aloud. We both preferred experimental writers—all men back then except for Grace Paley—rebels like ourselves. Dennis would become a lifelong editor, ally, and voice on the phone when either one of us lost heart.

The young woman in the photo is modeling her book-in-progress after *Dream Tigers* by Jorge Luis Borges—a writer she'd read since high school, story fragments that ring like Hans Christian Andersen, or Ovid, or entries from the encyclopedia. She wants to write stories that ignore borders between genres, between written and spoken, between highbrow literature and children's nursery rhymes, between New York and the imaginary village of Macondo, between the U.S., and Mexico. It's true, she wants the writers she admires to respect her work, but she also wants people who don't usually read books to enjoy these stories too. She *doesn't* want to write a book that a reader won't understand and would feel ashamed for not understanding.

She thinks stories are about beauty. Beauty that is there to be admired by anyone, like a herd of clouds grazing overhead. She thinks people who are busy working for a living deserve beautiful little stories, because they don't have much time and are often tired. She has in mind a book that can be opened at any page and will still make sense to the reader who doesn't know what came before or comes after.

She experiments, creating a text that is as **succinct** and flexible as poetry, snapping sentences into fragments so that the reader pauses, making each sentence serve her and not the other way round, abandoning quotation marks to streamline the typography and make the page as simple and readable as possible. So that the sentences are pliant as branches and can be read in more ways than one.

Sometimes the woman I once was goes out on weekends to meet with other writers. Sometimes I invite these friends to come to my apartment to workshop each other's work.

....

succinct concise

We come from Black, white, Latino communities. We are men and we are women. What we have in common is our sense that art should serve our communities. Together we publish an anthology—*Emergency Tacos*—because we finish our collaborations in the early hours before dawn and gather at the same twenty-four-hour *taquería* on Belmont Avenue, like a multicultural version of Hopper's *Nighthawks* painting. The *Emergency Tacos* writers organize monthly arts events at my brother Keek's apartment—Galena Quique. We do this with no capital except our valuable time. We do this because the world we live in is a house on fire and the people we love are burning.

The young woman in the photograph gets up in the morning to go to the job that pays the rent on her Paulina Street apartment. She teaches at a school in Pilsen, her mother's old neighborhood on Chicago's south side, a Mexican neighborhood where the rent is cheap and too many families live crowded together. Landlords and the city take no responsibility for the rats, trash that isn't collected often enough, porches that collapse, apartments without fire escapes, until a tragedy happens and several people die. Then they hold investigations for a little while, but the problems go on until the next death, the next investigation, the next bout of forgetting.

The young woman works with students who have dropped out of high school but have decided to try again for their diplomas. She learns from her students that they have more difficult lives than her storyteller's imagination can invent. Her life has been comfortable and privileged compared to theirs. She never had to worry about feeding her babies before she went to class. She never had a father or boyfriend who beat her at night and left her bruised in the morning. She didn't have to plan an alternative route to avoid gangs in the school hallway. Her parents didn't plead with her to drop out of school so she could help them earn money.

How can art make a difference in the world? This was never asked at Iowa. Should she be teaching these students to write poetry when they need to know how to defend themselves from someone beating them up? Can a memoir by Malcolm X or a novel by García Márquez save them from the daily blows? And what about those who have such learning problems they can't even manage a book by Dr. Seuss, but can weave a spoken story so wondrous, she wants to take notes. Should she give up writing and study something useful like medicine? How can she teach her students to take control of their own destiny? She loves these students. What should she be doing to save their lives?

The young woman's teaching job leads to the next, and now she finds herself a counselor/recruiter at her alma mater, Loyola University on the north side, in Rogers Park. I have health benefits. I don't bring work home anymore. My work day ends at five p.m. Now I have evenings free to do my own work. I feel like a real writer.

At the university I work for a program that no longer exists, the Educational Opportunity Program, that assists "disadvantaged" students. It's in keeping with my philosophy, and I can still help the students from my previous job. But when my most brilliant student is accepted, enrolls, and drops out in her first semester, I collapse on my desk from grief, from exhaustion, and feel like dropping out myself.

I write about my students because I don't know what else to do with their stories. Writing them down allows me to sleep.

On the weekends, if l can sidestep guilt and avoid my father's demands to come home for Sunday dinner, I'm free to stay home and write. I feel like a bad daughter ignoring my father, but I feel worse when I don't write. Either way, I never feel completely happy.

One Saturday the woman at the typewriter accepts an invitation to a literary **soiree**. But when she arrives, she feels she's made a terrible mistake. All the writers are old men. She has been invited by Leon Forrest, a Black novelist who was trying to be kind and invite more women, more people-of-color, but so far, she's the only woman, and he and she the only coloreds.

She's there because she's the author of a new book of poetry—*Bad Boys* from Mango Press, the literary efforts of

....

soiree party

Gary Soto and Lorna Dee Cervantes. Her book is four pages long and was bound together on a kitchen table with a stapler and a spoon. Many of the other guests, she soon realizes, have written real books, hardbacks from big New York houses, printed in editions of hundreds of thousands on actual presses. Is she really a writer or is she only pretending to be a writer?

The guest of honor is a famous writer who went to the Iowa Workshop several years before she got there. His latest book has just been sold to Hollywood. He speaks and carries himself as if he's the Emperor of Everything.

At the end of the evening, she finds herself searching for a ride home. She came on the bus, and the Emperor offers to give her a lift home. But she's not going home, she's got her heart set on a movie that's showing only tonight. She's afraid of going to the movies alone, and that's why she's decided to go. Because she's afraid.

The famous writer drives a sports car. The seats smell of leather, and the dashboard is lit like an airplane cockpit. Her own car doesn't always start and has a hole in the floor near the accelerator that lets in rain and snow, so she has to wear boots when she drives. The famous writer talks and talks, but she can't hear what he is saying, because her own thoughts are drowning him out like a wind. She doesn't say anything, doesn't have to. She is just young and pretty enough to feed the famous writer's ego by nodding enthusiastically at everything he says until he drops her off in front of the cinema. She hopes the famous writer notices she is going to see *Gentlemen Prefer Blondes* alone. To tell the truth, she feels miserable walking up to the box office by herself, but she forces herself to buy the ticket and go in because she loves this movie.

The theater is packed. It feels to the young woman as if everybody is there with somebody, except her. Finally, the scene where Marilyn sings "Diamonds Are a Girl's Best Friend." The colors are cartoon-wonderful, the set deliriously campy, the lyrics clever, the whole number is pure old-style glamour. Marilyn is sensational. After her song is over, the audience breaks into applause as if this were a live performance, though sad Marilyn has been dead years and years.

The woman who is me goes home proud of having gone to the movies alone. *See? It wasn't that difficult.* But as she bolts the door of her apartment, she bursts into tears. "I don't have diamonds," she sobs, not knowing what she means, except she knows even then it's not about diamonds. Every few weeks, she has a messy crying **jag** like this that leaves her feeling shipwrecked and awful. It's such a regular occurrence she thinks these storms of depression are as normal as rain.

----

jag fit

What is the woman in the photograph afraid of? She's afraid of walking from her parked car to her apartment in the dark. She's afraid of the scuffling sounds in the walls. She's afraid she'll fall in love and get stuck living in Chicago. She's afraid of ghosts, deep water, rodents, night, things that move too fast—cars, airplanes, her life. She's afraid she'll have to move back home again if she isn't brave enough to live alone.

Throughout all this, I am writing stories to go with that title, *The House on Mango Street*. Sometimes I write about people I remember, sometimes I write about people I've just met, often I mix the two together. My students from Pilsen who sat before me when I was teaching, with girls who sat beside me in another classroom a decade before. I pick up parts of Bucktown, like the monkey garden next door, and plop it down in the Humboldt Park block where I lived during my middle and high school years—1525 N. Campbell Street.

Often all I have is a title with no story—"The Family of Little Feet,"—and I have to make the title kick me in the behind to get me going. Or, sometimes all I've got is a first sentence—"You can never have too much sky." One of my Pilsen students said I had said this, and she never forgot it. Good thing she remembered and quoted it back to me. "They came with the wind that blows in August…" This line came to me in a dream. Sometimes the best ideas come in dreams. Sometimes the worst ideas come from there, too!

Whether the idea came from a sentence I heard buzzing around somewhere and saved in a jar, or from a title I picked up and pocketed, the stories always insist on telling me where they want to end. They often surprise me by stopping when I had every intention of galloping along a little further. They're stubborn. They know best when there's no more to be said. The last sentence must ring like the final notes at the end of a mariachi song—*tan-tán*—to tell you when the song is done.

The people I wrote about were real, for the most part, from here and there, now and then, but sometimes three real people would be braided together into one made-up person. Usually when I thought I was creating someone from my imagination, it turned out I was remembering someone I'd forgotten or someone standing so close I couldn't see her at all.

I cut apart and stitched together events to tailor the story, gave it shape so it had a beginning, middle, and end, because real life stories rarely come to us complete. Emotions, though, can't be invented, can't be borrowed. All the emotions my characters feel, good or bad, are mine.

I meet Norma Alarcón. She is to become one of my earliest publishers and my lifetime friend. The first time she walks through the rooms of the apartment on North Paulina, she notices the quiet rooms, the collection of typewriters, the books and Japanese figurines, the windows with the view of freeway and sky. She walks as if on tiptoe, peering into every room, even the pantry and closet as if looking for something. "You live here…" she asks, "alone?"

"Yes."

"So…" She pauses. "How did you do it?"

Norma, I did it by doing the things I was afraid of doing so that I would no longer be afraid. Moving away to go to graduate school. Traveling abroad alone. Earning my own money and living by myself. Posing as an author when I was afraid, just as I posed in that photo you used on the first cover of *Third Woman*.

And, finally, when I was ready, after I had apprenticed with professional writers over several years, partnering with the right agent. My father, who sighed and wished for me to marry, was, at the end of his life, much more gratified I had my agent Susan Bergholz providing for me rather than a husband. *¿Ha llamado Susan?* he asked me daily, because if Susan called it meant good news. Diamonds may do for a girl, but an agent is a woman writer's best friend.

I couldn't trust my own voice, Norma. People saw a little girl when they looked at me and heard a little girl's voice when I spoke. Because I was unsure of my own adult voice and often censored myself, I made up another voice, Esperanza's, to be my voice and ask the things I needed answers to myself—"Which way?" I didn't know exactly, but I knew which routes I didn't want to take—Sally, Rafaela, Ruthie—women whose lives were white crosses on the roadside.

At Iowa we never talked about serving others with our writing. It was all about serving ourselves. But there were no other examples to follow until you introduced me to Mexican writers Sor Juana Inés de la Cruz, Elena Poniatowska, Elena Garro, Rosario Castellanos. The young woman in the photograph was looking for another way to be—"*otro modo de ser,*" as Castellanos put it.

Until you brought us all together as U.S. Latina writers—Cherríe Moraga, Gloria Anzaldúa, Marjorie Agosín, Carla Trujillo, Diana Solís, Sandra María Esteves, Diane Gómez, Salima Rivera, Margarita López, Beatriz Badikian, Carmen Abrego, Denise Chávez, Helena Viramontes—until then, Normita, we had no idea what we were doing was extraordinary.

I no longer make Chicago my home, but Chicago still makes its home in me. I have Chicago stories I have yet to write. So long as those stories kick inside me, Chicago will still be home.

Eventually I took a job in San Antonio. Left. Came back. And left again. I kept coming back lured by cheap rent. Affordable housing is essential to an artist. I could, in time, even buy my own first house, a hundred-year-old home once periwinkle, but now painted a Mexican pink.

Two years ago my office went up in my backyard, a building created from my Mexican memories. I am writing this today from this very office, Mexican marigold on the outside, morning-glory violet on the inside. Wind chimes ring from the terrace. Trains moan in the distance all the time, ours is a neighborhood of trains. The same San Antonio River tourists know from the Riverwalk wends its way behind my house to the Missions and beyond until it empties into the Gulf of Mexico. From my terrace you can see the river where it bends into an S.

White cranes float across the sky like a scene painted on a lacquered screen. The river shares the land with ducks, raccoons, possums, skunks, buzzards, butterflies, hawks, turtles, snakes, owls, even though we're walking distance to downtown. And within the confines of my town garden there are plenty of other creatures too—yappy dogs, kamikaze cats, one lovesick parrot with a crush on me.

This is my house.

Bliss.

October 24th, 2007. You come down from Chicago for a visit, Mama. You don't want to come. I make you come. You don't like to leave your house anymore, your back hurts you say, but I insist. I built this office beside the river for you as much as for me, and I want you to see it.

Once, years ago, you telephoned and said in an urgent voice, "When are you going to build your office? I I just saw Isabel Allende on PBS and she has a HUGE desk and a BIG office." You were upset because I was writing on the kitchen table again like in the old days.

And now here we are, on the rooftop of a **saffron** building with a river view, a space all my own just to write. We climb up to the room I work in, above the library, and out to the balcony facing the river.

You have to rest. There are industrial buildings on the opposite bank—abandoned granaries and silos—but they're so rain-rusted and sun-bleached, they have their own charm, like public sculptures. When you've recovered your breath, we continue.

I'm especially proud of the spiral staircase to the rooftop. I'd always dreamed of having one, just like the houses in Mexico. Even the word for them in Spanish is wonderful—*un caracol*—a snail. Our footsteps clang on each metal step, the dogs following so close we have to scold them.

"Your office is bigger than in the pictures you sent," you say delighted. I imagine you're comparing it to Isabel Allende's.

"Where did you get the drapes in the library? I bet they cost a pretty penny. Too bad your brothers couldn't

saffron orange-yellow

upholster your chairs for you and save you some money. Boy, this place is niiiiice!" you say, your voice sliding up the scales like a river grackle.

I plop yoga mats on the rooftop, and we sit cross-legged to watch the sun descend. We drink your favorite, Italian sparkling wine, to celebrate your arrival, to celebrate my office.

The sky absorbs the night quickly-quickly, dissolving into the color of a plum. I lie on my back and watch clouds scurry past in a hurry to get home. Stars come out shyly, one by one. You lie down next to me and drape one leg over mine like when we sleep together at your home. We always sleep together when I'm there. At first because there isn't any other bed. But later, after Papa dies, just because you want me near. It's the only time you let yourself be affectionate.

"What if we invite everybody down here for Christmas next year?" I ask, "What do you think?"

"We'll see," you say lost in your own thoughts.

The moon climbs the front yard mesquite tree, leaps over the terrace ledge and astonishes us. It's a full moon a huge nimbus like the prints of Yoshitoshi. From here on, I won't be able to see a full moon again without thinking of you, this moment. But right now, I don't know this.

You close your eyes. You look like you're sleeping. The plane ride must've tired you. "Good lucky you studied," you say without opening your eyes. You mean my office, my life.

I say to you, "Good lucky."

For my mother, Elvira Cordero Cisneros
July 11th, 1929–November 1st, 2007

May 26th, 2008
Casa Xóchitl, San Antonio de Béxar, Texas

The Thirsty Tree
Confronting Invasive Salt Cedar
in the American Southwest

by Melissa L. Sevigny

I think that I shall never see
A poem lovely as a tree.
A tree whose hungry mouth is prest
Against the sweet earth's flowing breast …
> — Joyce Kilmer

Tamarisk was a convenient scapegoat for the complex
problems encountered by government water managers,
be they true believers in the monster or otherwise.
> — Matthew Chew, "The Monstering of Tamarisk"

Thirst for New Water

Like all stories about the American Southwest, this one
begins with water. The open, rugged landscape had
everything else—mountains laced with copper ore, vast
stands of timber, fertile soil, and warm weather. But rivers,
running rampant through red-rimmed canyons and rocky
gullies, held only a fraction of the water demanded by the
influx of 19th-century settlers. Scorching months could pass

without an inch of rain, and then a single storm would tear the topsoil to pieces. Water never came in the right amounts, or at the right time.

By the early 20th century, desert cities like Las Vegas, Phoenix, and Los Angeles had become sprawling webs of lights, surrounded by acres of agricultural fields. Development drove the Southwest region. It required ever-increasing amounts of water in a landscape that had little to spare.

Dams offered one solution, halting rivers in their tracks and preventing valuable water resources from disappearing into the sea. The grand sweep of Hoover Dam, completed in 1935, held enough space behind its bulk to store two years' worth of the Colorado River's flow. **Aquifers** provided another source of water. Deep wells drew up rainwater stored between soil pores sometime in the Pleistocene era, when mammoths still roamed the savanna-like plains of the Southwest.

But dams held only what river and rainfall provided, and depleted aquifers soon began cutting ominous fissures into the ground. The old adage says that when wells run dry, we know the worth of water. History suggests we merely look elsewhere. Midway through the 20th century, the fight to find more water settled on an unlikely candidate—a tree.

....

aquifers underground reserves of water

The gold leaves of salt cedar in the autumn along a western river

In the two centuries since salt cedar took root in America, it has been welcomed, **vilified**, battled, and exhaustively researched. Targeted as a needless waste of water, this tenacious, non-native species is a somber reflection of our drive to supply the thirst of western states. Attempts to control salt cedar call into question our understanding of what we label invasive, unwanted, and destructive, and what has come to belong to the transforming desert.

vilified harshly criticized

The Unbeneficial Tree

Salt cedar trees grow rapantly in the Middle East, Asia, and parts of Africa, accustomed to harsh landscapes with little rain. They first appeared on the East Coast of America in the early 1800s, carried over the sea and sold to plant nurseries as ornamental shrubs. The brushy trees flourished in saline soils, their grey-green leaves rough-textured with salt. Scientists call the species *Tamarix*, but most people know it by the nickname "salt cedar" or tamarisk.

At first, Americans welcomed the new addition to their gardens. The exotic tree, with its slender branches and miniscule rows of leaves, was beautiful. When it bloomed— an event that could take place from spring to autumn, sometimes even in winter—the tree burst forth into masses of feathery pink blossoms. Flowers gave way to hard, brown seedpods that broke open to reveal a cottony fluff, packed with seeds.

Merely ornamental in the gardens of the lush East, salt cedar had a different role to play in the settlement of the Southwest. As farmers and homesteaders wrestled wild rivers into submission with dams and drilled deep wells to reach intractable aquifers, native trees began to die out. The long gallery forests of cottonwoods and willows that once graced desert streams disappeared. Silt crumbled into the water, filling reservoirs and eroding the fragile banks of streams. Cutting winds blew the topsoil away from cultivated fields.

By the early 1900s, farmers in Arizona, southern California, and other western states had begun planting salt cedar to act as windbreaks, stabilize the soil, and provide much-needed shade over the evaporating surfaces of streams. The hardy desert shrub took a liking to its new ecosystem. Downy seeds scattered in the dry desert breeze. Soon, slender salt cedar shrubs sprouted on their own accord along river bottoms.

But trees require water—and nothing that claims water in the Southwest remains unchallenged for long. In Arizona, a new hostility toward salt cedar arose in

Spring flowers on a salt cedar

concert with urgent water demands. The Phelps Dodge Corporation, for instance, made plans in the 1930s to expand a copper mine in Morenci, a tiny company town in the southeastern part of the state where layers of lavender and pink ringed the ore-rich hills. Phelps Dodge had legal rights to Eagle Creek, a thin tributary of the Upper Gila River. But the creek didn't have enough water for the company's grand plans.

Finding water in Arizona—let alone claiming it in court—proved to be a **formidable** task. Western water law required Phelps Dodge to meet two requirements. First, it had to put the water to a "beneficial use." As the mining operation expanded beneath the ominous shadow of World War II, the company found it easy to fulfill this requirement. After all, the war effort required copper, and Phelps Dodge could supply it.

The second rule of western water law, called "prior appropriation," states that the earliest claim on a water source has the highest priority. The rivers and aquifers of Safford Valley, downstream of the copper mine, had long since been divvied up among developments, farmers and corporations. War effort notwithstanding, Phelps Dodge would have to wait last in a long line to get a portion of the existing water. They needed "new" water, untouched by other claims.

....

formidable daunting or difficult

Around the same time, the United States Geological Survey (USGS) began to inventory the water available in the Upper Gila River Basin. By definition, water consumed by plants didn't count as a "beneficial use." Surveyors eyed the long strips of riparian forests, lining the banks of the rivers, with transits and calculators in hand. Completed in 1941, the study estimated that killing the riparian vegetation in Safford Valley would free up 70,000 acre-feet of water annually —roughly a quarter of all the legally claimed irrigation rights in Safford Valley at the time.

As the concept of killing trees for "water salvage" gained momentum, a botanical hierarchy emerged in the minds of scientists and resource managers. The USGS invented a new term—"phreatophytes"—literally, well plants, or a species that regularly feeds on groundwater rather than depending on rainfall and rivers. The phrase was oddly mechanical for the teeming, vibrant ecosystems along river bottoms, but it suited resource managers. Trees became classified as machines, sucking up water with their roots the way a farmer laboriously pumps the handle of a well.

The Phelps Dodge Company wrote a list of 19 phreatophyte species in Safford Valley, including native trees like cottonwoods, and asked the USGS to continue its investigation. In 1950, the USGS published the agency's conclusions. For the first time, salt cedar appeared as the lead villain, set apart from other phreatophytes as an invasive plant that didn't belong on western streams.

The USGS reported that salt cedar had high rates of evapotranspiration—the trees were literally breathing precious water resources into vapor through their leaves. It seemed that westerners had created their own worst enemy. Logically, removing the trees would free up water for truly beneficial uses—like copper mines and exploding suburban growth.

For Arizona, salt cedar became the home front of a new kind of war. Researchers attacked the dense jumble of trees along the Upper Gila River with flamethrowers. Clouds of ash and smoke choked the river valley. But salt cedar fought back. Green shoots arose in the rich black cinders, spouting anew from the deep-reaching root system. When fire failed to kill the trees, the researchers returned with bulldozers. One of the authors of the USGS report, hydrologist Thomas Robinson, later wrote that "new growth appeared from each severed root, so that two plants grew where one had grown before." Like the mythical hydra, salt cedar always sprang new heads.

A Monster in the Making

"This is an account of scientists creating a monster," Matthew K. Chew writes in "The Monstering of Tamarisk," appearing in *Journal of the History of Biology*. A biologist at Arizona State University, Chew studies the way people create categories to recast plants into malevolent roles. His work describes how, two centuries after Mary Shelley published her Gothic horror novel, the story replayed itself in the botany of the American Southwest. Scientific studies proclaimed salt cedar trees to be voracious, hazardous, aggressive, useless, and alien. Above all, they labeled it thirsty, in a landscape that could not afford to satisfy another thirst.

The theory of water salvage pivoted on one solid, irreproachable fact: Salt cedar did not belong in the Southwest. In 1959, the University of Arizona published a **seminal** report, optimistically titled "Recovering Rainfall: More Water for Irrigation." The author, George W. Barr, proposed replacing high-water use plants like trees with low-water use grasses along western rivers. Invasive salt cedar seemed the perfect target.

On the heels of that study, federal agencies like the U.S. Bureau of Reclamation, the U.S. Forest Service, and the Agricultural Research Service embarked on what river scientist William Graf calls "an evangelistic crusade against botanical water pirates." Only crude methods existed to measure phreatophyte water use, and millions of dollars poured from the Senate floor into research that resulted in little trustworthy data.

Nevertheless, by the 1960s few people questioned the perceived worthlessness of the salt cedar tree. Its strong taproot greedily **siphoned** up groundwater, claiming the

---

seminal crucial or extremely influential
siphoned sucked

region's most important natural resource. Edward Abbey, champion of the desert wilderness, wrote in *The Journey Home*, "Tamarisk is not native to the American West. It comes from North Africa, and as is often the way with exotics, has spread like a plague in its new environment, clogging the desert watercourses and driving out the willow, the cottonwood, the hackberry, the box elder." Plague, monster—epithets like these became commonplace in biological studies examining the salt cedar tree.

A Surge of Fresh Water

In 1999, a research ecologist from the University of Arizona named Edward Glenn took a plane flight over the Ciénega de Santa Clara in northern Mexico. From overhead, he could see the blazing sunlight striking the surface of the wetland. Locals called this place simply *la laguna*—the lake—a rare oasis of water in the desert. Upstream, Arizona farmers along the banks of the Lower Colorado River had been discharging salty wastewater into a drainage ditch. Around this whisper of water, a lush wetland of cattails and mirror-still pools sprang to life.

The wetland wouldn't last forever. The U.S. government planned to reopen the Yuma Desalting Plant, reclaiming the wastewater for human use. In the meantime, researchers like Glenn studied the ecosystem as an example of a remarkable resurgence of life in a trammeled desert region. At the end of the aerial survey, Glenn asked the pilot to fly back to Yuma by going up the channel of the Lower Colorado River, rather than taking the direct route across scorching acres of agricultural fields. He wanted to take a closer look at the river.

In his book *A River No More*, Philip L. Fradkin described the Lower Colorado, where it flows over the border into Mexico and loses itself in the Gulf of California, as "utterly devoid of any vitality…a tepid ditch for urban crowds." Glenn couldn't shake the troubling image. Many scientists lamented that the once-mighty river had been choked into silence by invasive salt cedar trees. As the pilot winged westward, toward the silver glint of the river, Glenn gazed anxiously out the narrow window.

Below, a winding corridor of green wove through the brown desert scrub, cradling the blue shimmer of the river. Migratory birds flickered from tree to tree, their wings catching glints of sunlight. Poking up through the green-grey canopy of salt cedar, Glenn recognized flourishing stands of cottonwoods and willows. The lushness of the riverbanks caught him by surprise. Everyone knew native trees couldn't compete with salt cedar's deep roots and tolerance for salt.

Later, Glenn learned that the mystery had a simple answer. Recent rainstorms, more than usual, had forced managers of the Lower Colorado River to release water stored behind dams. The surge of water swept downstream, clearing away leaves, sediments and salts from the rank, choking riverbank. Native seeds, lying in wait for that ancient signal—a pulse of fresh water—germinated and came up right through the salt cedar.

The incident set Glenn to wondering. What if salt cedar didn't deserve its reputation after all? What if western rivers clogged with salt cedar trees simply lacked the natural ebb and flow that allowed native species to survive? Below him, the vibrant riparian ecosystem of the Lower Colorado winked in the sun. Glenn did what any good scientist would do. He applied for a research grant.

How Much Water?

After his epiphany over the banks of the Lower Colorado, Glenn discovered a growing community of scientists who questioned the common wisdom about salt cedar trees. As early as 1980, Benjamin Everitt from the Utah Division of Water Resourceshad issued a plea for balanced research. "Profound changes in riparian vegetation involving the spread of salt cedar have coincided with equally profound changes in channel geometry and streamflow," he warned. "The cause and effect relationships involved are sometimes not at all obvious."

Beginning in the late 1990s, freshwater ecologist Juliet Stromberg pioneered new research about the complex interactions between salt cedar and western rivers. With a love of botany inherited from long hours playing in her mother's garden as a child, she determinedly forged a fresh look at salt cedar trees. In a 2009 article in *Restoration Ecology*, she describes a classic case of chicken-or-the-egg. Which came first: eager stands of salt cedar crowding out native species, or the decline of native species followed by the colonization of salt cedar?

Most policy documents labeled salt cedar as the instigator, a marauding plant whose long taproot and salt tolerance allowed it to outcompete natives. The National Park Service listed salt cedar on its "Least Wanted" website, warning that salt cedar replaces native plants, monopolizes water supplies, and increases the danger of fire and floods. But some scientists began to realize the story was more complex. Conditions on rivers had changed over the last two centuries. Groundwater pumping, overgrazing, and the construction of dams altered the natural pulse of a river's seasonal cycle. Was it possible that salt cedar, well-equipped to deal with salt and drought, simply moved into niches where native trees could no longer take root?

This new look at salt cedar threw into doubt long-standing claims about the tree's voracious water use. Scientific methods had greatly improved since the first surge of phreatophyte research, when the best tool available to measure water use involved large cement pots. Yet Glenn worried that an instinctive prejudice against invasive species had blinded scientists to unbiased inquiries. Armed with a NASA grant, Glenn recruited the help of Pamela Nagler, then a graduate student at the

University of Arizona, to examine the questionable claims of salt cedar's thirsty appetite.

Along the Lower Colorado River—the most altered river in the Southwest, its length gauntleted by dams and reservoirs—salt cedar accounted for 90 percent of the riparian vegetation. Flux towers, spindly metal poles poking out above the canopy of trees, measured the gases exhaled into the atmosphere. Originally intended for climate change research, Glenn and Nagler appropriated the technology to track the amount of moisture that the trees breathed back into the air.

The Middle Rio Grande in New Mexico, where salt cedar evenly matched native species in numbers, made another ideal case study. The San Pedro River offered a third example. Flowing northward over the Arizona-Sonora border, the San Pedro **retained** the sweet charm of a wild river—stretches of still blue waters, chattering gravel runs, and tunnels of native trees cradling migrating songbirds in their branches. Some call the San Pedro the last undammed river in the West. Like other unaltered rivers in Mexico, the San Pedro nurtures only a few scattered stands of salt cedar trees. Cottonwoods and willows line the banks in a winding ribbon of green, broken by patches of dense mesquite bosques, abuzz with insects.

....
retained kept

In each river system, the researchers twisted thin strands of wire around tree trunks. The wire could detect a measurable loss of heat whenever water moved through the plant and evaporated from the leaves, adding to the data collected by flux towers. Images from satellites, trailing invisibly across the blue desert sky, provided further corroboration. The result: all three riparian ecosystems transpired an average of just one meter a year of water into the atmosphere, regardless of whether the trees were salt cedar, cottonwood, or willow.

The thirst of the salt cedar tree, on which many eradication efforts had been based, was a myth. Glenn and Nagler's research lasted through a decade, several funding organizations and Nagler's Ph.D. dissertation. Other investigators conducted their own studies, bolstering the conclusion that removing riparian vegetation from riverbeds would salvage little water for humans. Instead, bare soil eroded away without roots to hold it back, or new invasive species simply moved in.

"A mythology has been created about tamarisk," Stromberg announced in the 2009 *Restoration Ecology* article, coauthored with Chew, Nagler, and Glenn. The invasive tree had been blamed for thirst, competitiveness, and the destruction of rare river ecosystems. A closer look revealed, as the authors wrote, that scientists had participated in "a rationalized scapegoating of Tamarix as an agent of change because of its ability to thrive in anthropogenic habitats." Ecologists began to understand that salt cedar had established itself so well in the Southwest because dams and diversions created an environment uniquely suited for them—in other words, because of our own thirst for water.

The Power of a Seed

Slowly, this new perspective began to appear in scientific journals, policy reviews, and newspapers. Yet eradication efforts continued. Some organizations, committed to hacking out salt cedar, refused to admit that little water could be salvaged from their efforts. Others eagerly reviewed the latest scientific studies and accepted salt cedar's modest water use but maintained that good reasons remained for removing the invasive trees.

First and foremost, salt cedar didn't belong. Along vast stretches of western rivers, collared by dams, salt cedar had become the dominant tree. Many environmentalists envisioned returning these streams to their former untrammeled glory, replanting the cottonwoods and calling back the native songbirds. Dense stands of salt cedar provide poor habitat for wildlife and tend to blaze up in devastating fires. Additionally, the tree's extensive root system can channelize streams, increasing the danger of floods. Ultimately, environmentalists argued, a tree dislocated from Asia had no place in the fragile Southwest.

Cottonwood trees

A passionate non-profit organization called The Tamarisk Coalition led the way in Colorado. Tim Carlson, an environmental engineer and one of the Coalition's founders, dedicated his career to restoring native ecosystems along Colorado's streams. The work began with organizing teams of volunteers to chainsaw, bulldoze, or chemically spray salt cedar trees. Soon the Coalition was hosting conferences, writing policy documents, and inventorying the health of watersheds across the Southwest. Federal agencies looked to the Coalition for technical assistance, recognizing Carlson's commitment to understanding and interpreting the latest scientific data.

"Our goal is riparian health, not killing tamarisk," Carlson said. To that end, he insisted that every project have a carefully designed revegetation plan. Some eradication efforts, lacking foresight or funding, left tracts of bare soil exposed in their wake, increasing erosion and leaving room for new invasive species like Russian olive or buffelgrass to take root. Carlson's volunteers coaxed native trees to flourish when they removed salt cedar, planting bendy willow saplings and broadcasting grass seed over freshly mulched soil.

In addition to improving habitat, environmentalists cited soil salinity as a good reason for eliminating salt cedar trees. True to its name, salt cedar draws up salt from the soil through its complex web of roots, storing it in leaves. When the leaves flutter downward, they carpet the ground in a saline layer of debris. Some naturalists took this as further evidence that salt cedar is a destructive, alien plant crowding out sensitive native species. The Nature Conservancy's website stated that salt cedar "oozes salt from its leaves," making it difficult for other plants to grow nearby. The authors of a 1997 book, *Assessment and Management of Plant Invasions*, claimed that "salinization of flood-plain habitats may be the most important single way that the invasion of salt cedar fundamentally alters ecosystems."

Other scientists wondered if salt cedar merely colonizes streams that are already too salty for native species to

Native trees such as cottonwood will outcompete invasive salt cedar, it was discovered at the Bosque del Apache National Wildlife Refuge (shown here), when regular spring river flows of fresh water, resembling historic snowmelt patterns, are allowed to occur.

tolerate. Along the Colorado River, for example, water that once ran swiftly downstream, thick with mud, now languishes behind dams. The increased evaporation from the surfaces of reservoirs concentrates the amount of salts in the water. Summertime floods no longer rinse the riverbanks, so salts accumulate in a pale crust. In contrast, natural floods still exist on the San Pedro, where saline soils—and salt cedar trees—are rare.

If humans created the niche that salt cedar loves so well, then could careful management undo the damage? In 1996, a dense stand of salt cedar trees caught fire on a stretch of the Rio Grande in southern New Mexico. The inferno spread to several thousand acres of native cottonwood trees. When Phil Norton, manager of the Bosque del Apache National Wildlife Refuge, walked through the ashes that spring, he noticed that the new seeds germinating in the scorched earth sprouted salt cedar trees. Something had to be done to rescue the native ecosystem.

High Country News reports that Norton had been battling salt cedar on his 13-mile stretch of the river for a decade. Every winter, he watched flurries of snow geese and sandhill cranes alight in the trees, and it was his idea to celebrate their arrival with a local festival. Salt cedar threatened the refuge that he had promised to protect. Norton sprayed herbicides and hired bulldozers, to little effect. His attempts to beat back the spreading salt cedar trees were becoming expensive. Seeds couldn't be controlled. They scattered on the wind, new batches arriving with every gust.

The power of a seed—that's where he found his inspiration.

In May, just before the cottonwood trees dressed themselves in white, Norton flooded a stretch of the river to create a rich, fertile mudflat. He had a unique tool on hand—a senior water right to the river—that allowed him to open the floodgates on an upstream dam. The resulting surge of water mimicked the pulse of cold snowmelt that occurs on undammed rivers in the springtime. Over the next few weeks, Norton watched the mudflat dry out in the sun, dreading to see it sprout with salt cedar trees.

But when the first tentative green shoots appeared, they belonged to cottonwood trees. The experiment was a success: Norton had timed the flood to coincide precisely with the first flight of the cottonwood seeds, and they had taken root before salt cedar could colonize the area. The invasive tree was no monster after all, only a symptom of river systems that had been robbed of their seasonal rhythms.

Beetles Munch into Battle

In the late 1990s, the story of the war against salt cedar took an odd turn. In its native habitat, naturalists reasoned, salt cedar is controlled by several species of leaf-eating beetles that feed on nothing else. Why not import boxes of beetles to the beleaguered streams of the Southwest, an exotic predator to feed on an exotic pest?

Culver "Jack" DeLoach, an entomologist with the U.S. Department of Agriculture, spearheaded the biocontrol effort. DeLoach spent a decade traveling Europe and Asia looking for a worthy adversary for salt cedar trees. Returning to his lab in Texas with a handful of candidates, he conducted rigorous tests to ensure the beetles ate nothing but salt cedar leaves. At last, he settled on a species called *Diorahadba elongata*, a plain brown beetle about the size of a pencil eraser.

In 1995, DeLoach received permission to release his beetles in several Southwestern states. Then a fax appeared in his lab: The U.S. Fish and Wildlife Service had just listed the southwestern willow flycatcher, a tiny brown songbird, as endangered. All biocontrol efforts ground to a halt. DeLoach would have to spend another two years tediously documenting that eliminating salt cedar trees with beetles wouldn't threaten the survival of the songbird.

Ironically, the U.S. Fish and Wildlife Service listed salt cedar invasion as one reason for the decline in willow flycatcher populations. Dense stands of salt cedar usually provide poor habitat for native creatures. But lacking actual willows to nest in, flycatchers along the Colorado River settled on salt cedar branches as the only available real estate. Now protected by the toothy Endangered Species Act, nothing that threatened the bird's fragile existence would be allowed.

Entomologists didn't give up on their beetles. Over the next several years, research labs across the Southwest examined the miniscule insects, searching for a way to satisfy the concerns of the Endangered Species Act. Dan Bean, director of the Colorado Department of Agriculture Palisade Insectory, discovered that a certain strain of *Diorahadba* from northwestern China required at least 14½ hours of daylight to reproduce. That confined them to the region north of the 38th parallel—southern Colorado

Diorahadba elongata, also called the Mediterranean tamarisk beetle or salt cedar leaf beetle, has been imported to help fight the salt cedar invasion.

and Utah—skirting the willow flycatcher's habitat in Arizona entirely.

The argument satisfied the Endangered Species Act committee. In 2001, after a three-year experimental phase with beetles in cages, the U.S. Department of Agriculture released the beetle in California, Nevada, Utah, Colorado, and Wyoming. Two years later, they extended the experiment to Montana, Oregon, and New Mexico. As an added precaution, the USDA promised they would not release beetles within 200 miles of willow flycatcher habitat, an area encircling the Colorado River Basin in Arizona, southern Utah, and southern Colorado.

The beetles worked slowly. For a year or two after their release, little changed. Then tracts of trees along riverbanks began to turn brown. In the winter, when the beetles snuggled down beneath leaf litter, some salt cedar recovered. But most trees couldn't withstand several years of repeated attacks. Beetle larvae robbed them of their photosynthetic power by removing their leaves. The experiment was working.

Jack DeLoach, Dan Bean, and their entomologist colleagues understood that the *Diorahadba* beetle was no silver bullet. Hoards of the tiny creatures could limit the spread of salt cedar, but not eliminate it entirely. And killing salt cedar alone wouldn't return health to a river. Humans would have to follow in the beetles' wake, removing stands of dead trees and replanting cottonwood saplings and willow sprigs. Nevertheless, the results seemed promising. Ecologist Tom Dudley, quoted in the *Christian Science Monitor*, greeted the beetles as "little green liberators," waging war against the botanical pariah of the Southwest.

Then local agencies and private individuals began to collect beetles for release on nonfederal lands. In 2004, a county weed supervisor introduced a slightly different strain of beetle—one from Kazakhstan, not China— into southwestern Utah, near Moab. With a rapidity that startled Utah residents, the beetles swarmed up the Colorado River corridor. In the hot summer months, they ate through 25 miles of the Dolores River and crossed the state line into Colorado.

No one had tested the photoperiodic requirement of the Kazakhstan beetles. But in his lab in Colorado, Dan Bean discovered that the China beetles could now reproduce with just 14 hours and 10 minutes of daylight, in what he called "probably the fastest case known" of evolution. The invisible barrier of the 38th parallel no longer existed. In 2006, the City of St. George, Utah, released beetles along the Virgin River, well below the promised boundary line. The insects thrived. Two years later, they entered Arizona and began munching on trees that cradled willow flycatcher nests.

In 2009, the Center for Biological Diversity and the Maricopa Audubon Society filed a lawsuit against the U.S. Department of Agriculture for violating their promise to keep beetles away from flycatcher habitat. The USDA quickly settled the lawsuit by agreeing to rethink the biocontrol program in cooperation with the U.S. Fish and Wildlife Service. In 2010, the USDA formally banned the release or interstate transport of the *Diorahadba* beetle in 13 western states, under the threat of stiff penalties imposed by the Endangered Species Act.

In the meantime, the beetles already released continued their southward march. "If they move down the Colorado, into central Arizona, then we're going to have the extinction of the flycatcher," said Dr. Robin Silver of the Center for Biological Diversity. Willow flycatchers, he warns, are incredibly faithful to their birthplace. If the trees disappear, the songbirds will go with them. Hanging in this delicate balance, the remaining willow flycatchers continue building their nests in whatever trees they can find.

Old Ideas and New Research

Dreams of water salvage never quite disappeared from salt cedar control efforts. In 2006, Congress passed the Salt Cedar and Russian Olive Control Demonstration Act, which authorized $15 million a year to remove invasive species from western rivers. Among other things, the act required the Secretary of the Interior to "monitor and document any water savings from the control of salt cedar and Russian olive trees, including impacts to both groundwater and surface water."

Water savings—that goal meant everything to the politicians and resource managers of the Southwest. To "save" water meant not to conserve it, but to rescue it from rivers and aquifers and make it available to humans. Demand for water continued to increase, while climate change studies troubled predictions for the future. Higher temperatures would mean more evaporation from reservoirs and canals. On the Colorado River, a series of agreements ensured that water shortages would be dealt with quickly and ruthlessly.

The Central Arizona Project operates a 336-mile long canal that supplies Colorado River water to fast-growing cities like Phoenix and Tucson. The project holds a junior water right on the river, meaning its supply is cut off first in a time of shortage. Recognizing this risk, CAP managers set out in search of "new" water. Desalination, cloud seeding, a new dam a canal to Mexico—among all the newfangled options discussed in the 2009 annual report, "vegetation management" stands out as an echo of old ideas about invasive species, embedded deep in Southwestern culture.

The southwestern willow flycatcher has become rare across its natural range as riparian habitats are lost.

"Non-native plants such as the tamarisk (salt-cedar) and Russian olive are pervasive along the lower Colorado River," the CAP report states. "These thirsty plants grow quickly and cover a larger area than native vegetation such as cottonwood and willow. It is estimated that as much as two million acre-feet of water could be saved by removing the non-native invaders and replacing them with native plants."

Two million acre-feet—enough water to supply the entire state of Arizona for three months. But this is "paper water," disconnected from the realities of ecosystems. The old idea of "plant as machine," a monster of our own making, imagines salt cedar roots drinking from a deep bucket of water, easily reallocated to human use. The reality is much more complex. Stark numbers ignore the intricate workings of tree, rain, soil, river—not a machine whose parts can be scrapped for other uses, but a delicate dance of interrelationships.

In response to the 2006 congressional act, the United States Geological Survey spent four years reviewing scientific literature about salt cedar and compiling a comprehensive document with the agency's conclusions. Coauthored by dozens of scientists from the USGS, the U.S. Bureau of Reclamation, the U.S. Forest Service, and universities, including researchers Edward Glenn and Pamela Nagler, the *Science Assessment* firmly overturns the notion of water salvage. "To date, research and demonstration projects have not shown that is it feasible to salvage (or save) significant amounts of water for consumptive use by removing salt cedar," the report states.

The authors list one possible exception. Native trees in river corridors, like cottonwoods and willows, can grow in stands just as dense, and drink just as much water, as the "thirsty" salt cedar trees. But higher up in the floodplain, smaller plants like desert broom, whitethorn acacia, and creosote subsist almost entirely on rainfall. Salt cedar can march into this drier zone by tapping into the water table with its long roots. Theoretically, clearing away salt cedar from these higher terraces could "save" groundwater. The report's authors caution that this approach has never been effectively demonstrated. Recent studies by scientists at the University of Utah suggest that salt cedar trees on the upper terraces of the Colorado River consume only small amounts of water.

Even if a salvageable amount could be calculated, claiming the water in court remains a serious obstacle. A 2004 Colorado law review, dramatically entitled "Death Penalty to Water Thieves," describes how a farmer named Harvey Phelps attempted to claim 181 acre-feet of water by clearing away salt cedar from a section of the Arkansas River. The Colorado Supreme Court reluctantly ruled against him, stating that the water was not "new" but simply reallocated from the existing supplies, and thus subject to the priority right system. Fearing the **pandemonium** that would ensue if they allowed farmers to salvage water from trees, the judges wrote that "thirsty men cannot step into the shoes of a water thief."

While the notion of water salvage is difficult to relinquish, scientists and resource managers are beginning to recognize the significance of hydrological and legal barriers. The Science Assessment signifies how far science has come since the USGS first torched salt cedar trees in

----

pandemonium chaos

Safford Valley for the sake of a copper mine. The document acknowledges the complexities of living ecosystems, and gently suggests changes to policies that simplify salt cedar as the scapegoat. It cites recent work by Juliet Stromberg and others showing that if underlying ecological processes support salt cedar habitat, even the most effective removal and restoration plan is likely to fail.

Neatly summing up two centuries of mistakes, the report cautions: "In many cases, tremendous effort, resources, and time have been applied to achieve an intended goal (for example, water salvage) with little yield on the investment, poor ability to quantify yields, or lack thereof, and little new knowledge to inform future efforts."

A Question of Values

Today, salt cedar might cover as much as 900,000 acres of the western United States, although no detailed surveys have been conducted. As the climate warms, the trees are likely to march northward and upward, invading cooler regions and higher elevations. Drought, dams, and depleted groundwater create ready-made niches no longer suitable for native plants, further encouraging salt cedar spread. The imported beetles, meanwhile, are adjusting their life cycles to swarm southward. In time, the two species—eater and eaten—will adapt to a new **equilibrium**.

....

equilibrium balance

The image we've created for salt cedar trees—thirsty, voracious, and overcrowding—is a mirror we can hold up to our own interaction with the Southwestern landscape. We might learn something from invasive trees and imported beetles about coexistence. Ecosystems don't collapse when a new, stronger species arrives on the scene. Landscapes have proven flexible and resilient, adopting new species with surprisingly little impact on their overall health. In most cases, the addition of a new species doesn't mean the subtraction of an old one. Unlike clear-cutting or the destruction of a river, invasions alone don't devastate a region.

This holistic perspective on ecosystem health stands at odds with traditional resource management in the Southwest. Sweeping policy decisions are often made based on a single target resource—water, timber, copper or an endangered species. Scientists are calling for a different kind of management, one that recognizes the needs of entire ecosystems, with all their complicated and marvelous interconnections. That means changing our notions of value, stripping away the stereotypes and labels we've crafted, and seeing what's really there.

There's no returning the Southwest to the idyllic environment that existed before salt cedar, or Anglo-American settlers, arrived. But there may be a way to restore some portion of that wildness, by recognizing wildness as a valuable asset in human history. Water slipping through a riverbank or evaporating from the broad surfaces of leaves isn't a wasted resource. It's exactly what ecosystems need to continue their quiet, everyday services, purifying the air, strengthening the soil, and providing the water we drink. A healthy ecosystem, given the chance, will heal itself from damaging invasions, or accept new species as belonging within its web of interactions.

To preserve that health, we need to recognize our own voracity, and relinquish some water from the demands of human consumption for the sake of the environment that sustains us. This is a new vision for the Southwest—a springtime pulse of cold snowmelt, branches cradling the twiggy nests of songbirds, and trees casting their seeds windward to settle in the rich black silt of the riverbanks. ❖

Melissa L. Sevigny (formerly Melissa L. Lamberton) is a poet and writer from Tucson, Arizona. She has a degree in environmental science from the University of Arizona and an MFA in Creative Writing and Environment from Iowa State University. Her first book, Mythical River, *was published in 2016 by the University of Iowa Press.*

Read additional work by Melissa appearing in Terrain.org: "On the Trail of Mountain Lions" and "The Bighorn's Dilemma."

References

Chew, Matthew K. "The Monstering of Tamarisk: How Scientists made a Plant into a Problem." *Journal of the History of Biology*. (2009) 231–266.

Larmer, Paul. "Tackling Tamarisk." *High Country News*. 25 May 1998.

Nijhuis, Michelle. "Beetle Warfare." *High Country News*. 26 Nov 2007.

Shafroth, P.B., C.A. Brown, and D.M. Merritt (eds.). *Salt cedar and Russian Olive Control Demonstration Act Science Assessment: U.S. Geological Survey Scientific Investigations Report 2009-5247*. (2010) 143 p.

Stromberg, Juliet C., Matthew K. Chew, Pamela L. Nagler, and Edward P. Glenn. "Changing Perceptions of Change: The Role of Scientists in Tamarix and River Management." *Restoration Ecology* 17.2. (March 2009) 177–186.

excerpt from

Pilgrim at Tinker Creek

by Annie Dillard

Annie Dillard was born in 1945 in Pittsburgh,
Pennsylvania. She began writing poetry in high school.
In college, she wrote a long essay on Thoreau's Walden.
Like Thoreau, Dillard is a close observer of the natural
world, and a deep thinker about the meanings of all
she observes.

After a severe illness in 1971, Dillard lived for a year
by Tinker Creek in the Blue Ridge Mountains of Virginia.
Surrounded by the woods, she walked, watched, and
pondered. She recorded her thoughts and observations in
a journal that became the basis for a book, Pilgrim at
Tinker Creek. The book was awarded the Pulitzer Prize
for nonfiction in 1975.

"In nature," Dillard has said, "I find grace tangled in
a rapture with violence;…I find mystery, newness, and
a kind of exuberant, spendthrift energy." The following
excerpt from Pilgrim at Tinker Creek gives a sense of how
Dillard perceives the natural world—with clarity and awe.

A couple of summers ago I was walking along the edge of the island to see what I could see in the water, and mainly to scare frogs. Frogs have an **inelegant** way of taking off from invisible positions on the bank just ahead of your feet, in **dire** panic, emitting a froggy, "Yike!" and splashing into the water. Incredibly, this amused me, and, incredibly, it amuses me still.

As I walked along the grassy edge of the island, I got better and better at seeing frogs both in and out of the water. I learned to recognize, slowing down, the difference in texture of the light reflected from mudbank, water, grass, or frog. Frogs were flying all around me. At the end of the island I noticed a small green frog. He was exactly half in and half out of water, looking like a schematic diagram of an amphibian, and he didn't jump.

He didn't jump; I crept closer. At last I knelt on the island's winterkilled grass, lost, dumbstruck, staring at the frog in the creek just four feet away. He was a very small frog with wide, dull eyes. And just as I looked at him, he slowly crumpled and began to sag. The spirit vanished from his eyes as if **snuffed**. His skin emptied and dropped; his very skull seemed to collapse and settle like a kicked tent. He was shrinking before my eyes like a

....

inelegant graceless; lacking refinement
dire desperate; terrible
snuffed put out (as one might snuff a candle)

deflating football. I watched the **taut**, glistening skin on his shoulders **ruck**, and rumple, and fall. Soon, part of his skin, formless as a pricked balloon, lay in floating folds like bright scum on top of the water; it was a monstrous and terrifying thing. I **gaped** bewildered, **appalled**. An oval shadow hung in the water behind the drained frog; then the shadow glided away. The frog skin bag started to sink.

I had read about the giant water bug, but never seen one. "Giant water bug" is really the name of the creature, which is an enormous, heavy-bodied brown beetle. It eats insects, tadpoles, fish, and frogs. Its grasping forelegs are mighty and hooked inward. It seizes a victim with these legs, hugs it tight, and paralyzes it with **enzymes** injected during a vicious bite. That one bite is the only bite it ever takes. Through the puncture shoot the poisons that dissolve the victim's muscles and bones and organs—all but the skin—and through it the giant water bug sucks out the victim's body reduced to a juice. This event is quite common in warm fresh water. The frog I saw was being sucked by a giant water bug. I had been kneeling on the island grass; when the unrecognizable flap of frog skin settled on the creek bottom, swaying, I stood up

....

taut pulled tight
ruck to become creased or wrinkled
gaped stared with one's mouth open
appalled filled with fear, dread, dismay
enzymes any of various proteins produced by living organisms

and brushed the knees of my pants. I couldn't catch my breath ....

About five years ago I saw a mockingbird make a straight vertical **descent** from the roof-gutter of a four-story building. It was an act as careless and spontaneous as the curl of a stem or the **kindling** of a star.

The mockingbird took a single step into the air and dropped. His wings were still folded against his sides as though he were singing from a limb and not falling, accelerating **thirty-two feet per second per second**, through empty air. Just a breath before he would have been dashed to the ground, he unfurled his wings with exact, deliberate care, revealing the broad bars of white, spread his elegant, white-banded tail, and so floated onto the grass. I had just rounded a corner when his **insouciant** step caught my eye; there was no one else in sight. The fact of his free fall was like the old philosophical **conundrum** about the tree that falls in the forest. The answer must be, I think, that beauty and grace are performed whether or not we will or sense them. The least we can do is try to be there.

....

descent a downward movement
kindling catching fire; bursting into flame
thirty-two feet per second per second the rate at which a falling body accelerates toward the ground
insouciant casual; nonchalant; without concern
conundrum a riddle; a difficult question or problem

Another time I saw another wonder: sharks off the Atlantic coast of Florida. There is a way a wave rises above the ocean horizon, a triangular wedge against the sky. If you stand where the ocean breaks on a shallow beach, you see the raised water in a wave is **translucent**, shot with lights. One late afternoon at low tide a hundred big sharks passed the beach near the mouth of the tidal river in a feeding frenzy. As each green wave rose from the churning water, it illuminated within itself the six- or eight-foot-long bodies of twisting sharks. The sharks disappeared as each wave rolled toward me; then a new wave would swell above the horizon, containing in it, like scorpions in **amber**, sharks that **roiled** and heaved. The sight held awesome wonders: power and beauty, grace tangled in a **rapture** with violence. ❖

----

translucent allowing light to pass through
amber a hard yellowish-orange fossilized resin (in which insects are sometimes trapped and preserved)
roiled moved violently
rapture a state of extreme emotion; ecstasy

How Old Man Winter Was Driven Back

an Iroquois myth

Far away in the North Sky lives Old Man Winter. Every year he leaves his wigwam in the sky and comes to earth.

At the foot of a mountain, he builds a lodge of ice and snow, which no human being, animal, or bird can enter. There he lives for a time.

North Wind is the only friend of Old Man Winter. When he passes near Old Man Winter's lodge, he gives a loud shriek, and with his **blustering** breath he blows open the door and enters.

Near a fire which glows, but does not warm, North Wind finds a seat. There he and Old Man Winter sit and smoke, and lay their plans for the next snowstorm.

When the council is ended, North Wind departs, to drive up the snow and hail from the corners of the earth.

Old Man Winter also leaves his lodge. He stalks over the mountains and valleys of the Red Children. The land becomes white with his breath. The rivers are stilled, and all the voices of the wood are hushed as he passes. A deep sleep falls upon every living thing.

....

blustering strongly blowing

No sound is heard in the forest but the rapping on the trees. Old Man Winter carries a great hammer, and he strikes the trees a blow as he passes. The colder it grows, the louder and more frequently he raps. The trees snap, and the Indian lodges crack with his blows.

One day, as Old Man Winter was stalking through a forest, he came upon a hunter's lodge. For days the snow had been falling. No track of deer or rabbit was to be seen, and the hunter and his little boy sat within, weak from hunger. They were also very cold, for the fire in the lodge burned low.

Old Man Winter laughed and shook his hammer in glee, as he drew near. Once, twice, three times, he rapped. The little boy within heard him, and rapped three times in reply,—just as Old Man Winter had done.

At this, the hunter spoke. He told the boy that he must not mock a nature spirit, lest some harm should come to him. He might be captured and made to serve that spirit.

Now when Old Man Winter heard the mocking raps of the little boy within the lodge, he was very angry. He breathed fiercely upon the little lodge. It shrank and shivered at his touch like a living thing. He struck it several sharp blows with his hammer, and passed on.

The fire inside the lodge burned lower and lower. The hunter and his little son drew closer and watched the last flame flicker and die out.

As they sat by the ashes, numb with the cold, all of a sudden a new warmth filled the lodge. The South Wind gently opened the door, and a young chieftain, with a face like the sun, entered. He saw the dying hunter and the boy, and he warmed them back to life. When they were stronger, he helped them to rekindle the fire. Then he told them to take a few dried blackberries that they had in the lodge, and boil them in water.

He said they must eat a portion of the blackberries, and throw the rest at Old Man Winter when he returned. This would frighten him away, for he was terribly afraid of blackberries.

Blackberries mean sunshine and summer heat. Old Man Winter cannot stay where they are. He never visits the earth at blackberry time.

The hunter and the little boy said they would do as they had been told. Soon the young chieftain left the lodge, with the South Wind.

Not many days later, Old Man Winter returned, and again came rapping at their lodge. But this time the hunter and the little boy were ready. They threw the blackberries at him, as they had been told, and he ran in fear to his ice lodge.

The South Wind and the young chieftain with a face like the sun were near. They followed close upon the Old Man's track. When he was again inside the ice lodge, the South Wind rapped gently at the door.

"Begone!" said the Old Man. "No one but North Wind is welcome to my lodge."

Then the South Wind breathed soft and warm upon the door of the ice lodge, and it melted at their feet. The young chieftain passed in and sat down by the strange fire that had no heat. The South Wind stayed without, and sang, soft and low.

The Old Man was very angry. He raged about the lodge and ordered the young chieftain with sunshine in his face and warmth in his breath to depart.

"I am great and powerful," said the Old Man. "When I touch the sky, the snow falls. When I speak, hunters hide in their lodges; animals crawl into their holes; and birds fly in fear.

"When my hand touches the earth, it grows cold and hard, and all life dies. Begone! or I will make an ice man or a snow man of you."

But the young chieftain moved not. He only sat and smiled at the bluster of the Old Man.

Slowly he filled a pipe, and handed it to the Old Man, saying, "Here, smoke with me. It will give you strength to go to your lodge in the North Sky. It is time for you to depart. You are old, and tired, and worn. You and North Wind have had your day. The days that are to come belong to South Wind and to me.

"I, too, am powerful, and I am young! I do not fear you. When I touch the earth, it grows soft and warm. Every

HOW OLD MAN WINTER WAS DRIVEN BACK

living thing stirs in its sleep,—birds and bees, flowers and trees, animals and men. When I speak, the sleeping sun awakes. See! Already he begins to send down his arrows. Hasten! that they may not find you, on the trail to the North Sky."

The Old Man trembled. His legs and arms grew weak. Icicles fell from his beard. Great tears rolled down his cheeks.

"Who are you?" he whispered, as he was melting at the young chieftain's feet.

"I am *Go hay*—the Spring," answered the young chieftain. "All the earth is glad, when I come to drive you back to your lodge in the North Sky, for I bring sunshine, and love, and joy."

But the Old Man did not hear. He was far on the North Sky trail, and Spring and South Wind were masters of earth. ❖

How the World Was Made

a Cherokee creation myth

The earth is a great floating island in a sea of water. At each of the four corners there is a cord hanging down from the sky. The sky is of solid rock. When the world grows old and worn out, the cords will break, and then the earth will sink down into the ocean. Everything will be water again. All the people will be dead. The Indians are much afraid of this.

In the long time ago, when everything was all water, all the animals lived up above in Galun'lati, beyond the stone arch that made the sky. But it was very much crowded. All the animals wanted more room. The animals began to wonder what was below the water and at last Beaver's grandchild, little Water Beetle, offered to go and find out. Water Beetle darted in every direction over the surface of the water, but it could find no place to rest. There was no land at all. Then Water Beetle dived to the bottom of the water and brought up some soft mud. This began to grow and to spread out on every side until it became the island which we call the earth. Afterwards this earth was fastened to the sky with four cords, but no one remembers who did this.

At first the earth was flat and soft and wet. The animals were anxious to get down, and they sent out different birds to see if it was yet dry, but there was no place to alight; so

the birds came back to Galun'lati. Then at last it seemed to be time again, so they sent out Buzzard; they told him to go and make ready for them. This was the Great Buzzard, the father of all the buzzards we see now. He flew all over the earth, low down near the ground, and it was still soft. When he reached the Cherokee country, he was very tired; his wings began to flap and strike the ground. Wherever they struck the earth there was a valley; whenever the wings turned upwards again, there was a mountain. When the animals above saw this, they were afraid that the whole world would be mountains, so they called him back, but the Cherokee country remains full of mountains to this day. [This was the original home, in North Carolina.]

When the earth was dry and the animals came down, it was still dark. Therefore they got the sun and set it in a track to go every day across the island from east to west, just overhead. It was too hot this way. Red Crawfish had his shell scorched a bright red, so that his meat was spoiled. Therefore the Cherokees do not eat it.

Then the medicine men raised the sun a **handsbreadth** in the air, but it was still too hot. They raised it another time; and then another time; at last they had raised it seven handsbreadths so that it was just under the sky arch. Then it was right and they left it so. That is why the medicine men called the high place "the seventh height." Every day the sun goes along under this arch on the under side; it returns at night on the upper side of the arch to its starting place.

There is another world under this earth. It is like this one in every way. The animals, the plants, and the people are the same, but the seasons are different. The streams that come down from the mountains are the trails by which we reach this underworld. The springs at their head are the doorways by which we enter it. But in order to enter the other world, one must fast and then go to the water, and have one of the underground people for a guide. We know that the seasons in the underground world are different, because the water in the spring is always warmer

handsbreadth a measurement based on the width of a hand

in winter than the air in this world; and in summer the water is cooler.

We do not know who made the first plants and animals. But when they were first made, they were told to watch and keep awake for seven nights. This is the way young men do now when they fast and pray to their medicine. They tried to do this. The first night, nearly all the animals stayed awake. The next night several of them dropped asleep. The third night still more went to sleep. At last, on the seventh night, only the owl, the panther, and one or two more were still awake. Therefore, to these were given the power to see in the dark, to go about as if it were day, and to kill and eat the birds and animals which must sleep during the night.

Even some of the trees went to sleep. Only the cedar, the pine, the spruce, the holly, and the laurel were awake all seven nights. Therefore they are always green. They are also sacred trees. But to the other trees it was said, "Because you did not stay awake, therefore you shall lose your hair every winter."

After the plants and the animals, men began to come to the earth. At first there was only one man and one woman. He hit her with a fish. In seven days a little child came down to the earth. So people came to the earth. They came so rapidly that for a time it seemed as though the earth could not hold them all. ❖

Ormuzd and Arimanes

a Persian myth

Ormuzd, the king of light, and Arimanes, the prince of darkness, both **emanated** from the Eternal One, and consequently were brothers. Arimanes, who was the second emanation, became jealous of Ormuzd, the first born. Because of this, the Eternal One **condemned** Arimanes to remain three thousand years in the realm of shadows, where no ray of light could reach.

During the time of this exile, Ormuzd made the **firmament**, the heavenly orbs, and celestial spirits, without Arimanes's knowledge. When the period of his banishment expired, he came forth from the shadowy realms of his exile into the light; and, dazzled by its beauty, his old feeling of envy returned to such a degree that he resolved to compete with Ormuzd in everything.

He found that Ormuzd had created six Amshaspands,— Immortal Holy Ones,—guardians of the six planets, and attendants on himself, who presided over the seven. Arimanes now created seven spirits, called Archdevs, in opposition to the Amshaspands; and attached them to the seven planets. His goal was to paralyze the Amshaspands'

---

emanated flowed out from a source
condemned sentenced to punishment
firmament the heavenly orbs: sky, moon, and sun

Symbol of Ormuzd

efforts of good and instead to substitute evil. When he found
that Ormuzd had created twenty-eight gentle and kindly
spirits, called Izeds, who govern the sun, moon, and stars;
showered **beneficent** gifts upon the earth; worked to protect
it from evil influences, and serve as messengers between
men and the superior spirits, Arimanes was furious.

He made twenty-eight spirits, called Devs, to defeat the
influence of the Izeds by spreading all manner of disorder
and distress. And for the leader, he created a serpent with
two feet, named Aschmogh. But his work was not yet
completed; for Ormuzd, in the plenitude of his power,
had created another order of spirits , called Fervers,   who
were infinitely more numerous, for they were the ideas
which Ormuzd conceived before he began the creation of

beneficent helpful

the world. Hence they were the models of everything that existed; they **animated** all things in the universe; and were the guardians of stars, men, animals, plants, and all other created things. Every mortal had one of these spirits by his side through life to protect him from evil. Even Ormuzd himself was supposed to have his attendant Ferver.

Arimanes set about making a multitude of genii, who opposed the benevolent operations of the Fervers; so that everything had an attendant bad spirit as well as good one. Perceiving the industry of his brother Arimanes, Ormuzd began creating again; he made an egg containing kind spirits. But Armanes made a counterpart, containing an equal number of spirits of hatred. Then, to add to his disastrous work, he broke the eggs together and good and evil became mixed in the new creation. After this, Ormuzd created the earth and its **inhabitants**. This was done is six successive periods, then, on the seventh, there was a festival among the good spirits.

Ormuzd created a guardian spirit to watch over every human being. Arimanes made an evil spirit to tempt them through life. These wicked ones slipped into thoughts and said, "It is Arimanes who has given the sun, the moon, and all good things." And when they listened to his whisperings, Arimanes cried out loud from his realm of shadows; "O men! Worship me!"

animated gave life to
inhabitants those who lived there

To harass and destroy the good animals of the earth, Arimanes made wolves and tigers and serpents and venomous insects. By eating a certain kind of fruit, he transformed himself into a serpent, and went gliding about on the earth to tempt human beings. His Devs entered the bodies of men, and caused diseases of the mind and body. They entered into human minds, and **incited** them to lies, revenge, and savagery. Into every part of the world they introduced **discord** and death. When Ormuzd tried to lead men against Arimanes,

The king killing Ariman (the Ariman animal)

they deserted him and joined the enemy. This allowed Arimanes to gain the **ascendency** for three thousand years.

After Arimanes' rule, his power will be destroyed. Ormuzd will rule again, bringing goodness to the world. There will be an end to evil and death. ❖

....

incited urged on; stirred up
discord disagreement; war
ascendency govern or control

Proserpine

The story of Persephone—of Proserpine—is a story of spring. When the sun is warming the bare brown earth, and the pale primroses look up through the snowy blackthorns at a kind, blue sky, almost can we hear the soft wind murmur a name as it gently sways the daffodils and breathes through the honey sweetness of the gold-powdered catkins on the grey willows by the river—"Persephone! Persephone!"

Now once there was a time when there was no spring, neither summer nor autumn, nor chilly winter with its black frosts and cruel gales and brief, dark days. Always was there sunshine and warmth, ever were there flowers and corn and fruit, and nowhere did the flowers grow with more dazzling colors and more fragrant perfume than in the fair garden of Sicily.

To Demeter, the Earth Mother, was born a daughter more fair than any flower that grew, and ever more dear to her became her child, the lovely Proserpine. By the blue sea, in the Sicilian meadows, Proserpine and the fair **nymphs** who were her companions spent their happy days. Too short were the days for all their joy, and Demeter made the earth yet fairer than it was that she might bring more gladness to her daughter Proserpine. Each day the

....

nymphs beautiful maidens who inhabit seas, rivers, woods, trees, and meadows

blossoms that the nymphs twined into **garlands** grew more perfect in form and in hue, but from the anemones of royal purple and crimson, and the riotous red of geraniums, Proserpine turned one morning with a cry of gladness, for there stood before her beside a little stream, on one erect, slim stem, a wonderful narcissus, with a hundred blossoms. Her eager hand was stretched out to pluck it, when a sudden black cloud overshadowed the land, and the nymphs, with shrieks of fear, fled swiftly away. And as the cloud descended, there was heard a terrible sound, as of the rushing of many waters or the roll of the heavy wheels of the chariot of one who comes to **slay**. Then was the earth cleft open, and from it there arose the four coal-black horses of Pluto, neighing aloud in their eagerness, while the dark-browed god urged them on, standing erect in his car of gold.

In cold, strong arms Pluto seized her—in that mighty grasp that will not be denied, and Proserpine wept childish tears as she shivered at his icy touch, and sobbed because she had dropped the flowers she had picked, and had never picked the flower she most desired. While still she saw the fair light of day, the little oddly-shaped rocky hills, the vineyards and olive groves and flowery meadows of Sicily, she did not lose hope. Surely the King of Terrors could not

....

garlands wreaths of flowers worn as decoration
slay to kill

steal one so young, so happy, and so fair. She had only tasted the joy of living, and **fain** she would drink deeper in the coming years. Her mother must surely save her—her mother who had never yet failed her—her mother, and the gods.

But **ruthless** as the mower whose scythe cuts down the seeded grass and the half-opened flower and lays them in swathes on the meadow, Pluto drove on. His iron-colored reins were loose on the black manes of his horses, and he urged them forward by name till the froth flew from their mouths like the foam that the furious surf of the sea drives before it in a storm. Across the bay and along the bank of the river Anapus they galloped, until, at the river head, they came to the pool of Cyane. He smote the water with his trident, and downward into the blackness of darkness his horses passed, and Proserpine knew no more the pleasant light of day.

So, to the great Earth Mother came the pangs that have drawn tears of blood from many a mortal mother's heart for a child borne off to the **Shades**.

Over land and sea, from where Dawn, the rosy-fingered, rises in the East, to where Apollo cools the fiery wheels of his chariot in the waters of far western seas, the goddess sought her daughter. With a black robe over her head and

fain gladly; willingly
ruthless without pity
Shades the dead

carrying a flaming torch in either hand, for nine dreary days she sought her loved one. And yet, for nine more weary days and nine sleepless nights the goddess, racked by human sorrow, sat in hopeless misery. The hot sun beat upon her by day. By night the silver rays from Diana's car smote her more gently, and the dew drenched her hair and her black garments and mingled with the saltiness of her bitter tears. At the grey dawning of the tenth day, her elder daughter, Hecate, stood beside her. Queen of ghosts and shades was she, and to her all dark places of the earth were known.

"Let us go to the Sun God," said Hecate. "Surely he hath seen the god who stole away the little Proserpine. Soon his chariot will drive across the heavens. Come, let us ask him to guide us to the place where she is hidden."

Thus did they come to the chariot of the glorious Apollo, and standing by the heads of his horses like two grey clouds that bar the passage of the sun, they begged him to tell them the name of him who had stolen fair Proserpine.

"No less a thief was he," said Apollo, "than Pluto, King of Darkness and robber of Life itself. Mourn not, Demeter. Thy daughter is safe in his keeping. The little nymph who played in the meadows is now Queen of the Shades. Nor does Pluto love her vainly. She is now in love with Death."

No comfort did the words of the Sun God bring to the longing soul of Demeter. And her wounded heart grew bitter. Because she suffered, others must suffer as well.

Because she mourned, all the world must mourn. The fragrant flowers spoke to her only of Persephone, the purple grapes reminded her of a vintage when the white fingers of her child had plucked the fruit. The waving golden grain told her that Persephone was as an ear of wheat that is reaped before its time.

Then upon the earth did there come dearth and drought and **barrenness**.

Gods and men alike suffered from the sorrow of Demeter. To her, in pity for the barren earth, Zeus sent an **embassy**, but in vain it came. Merciless was the great Earth Mother, who had been robbed of what she held most dear.

"Give me back my child!" she said. "Gladly I watch the sufferings of men, for no sorrow is as my sorrow. Give me back my child, and the earth shall grow **fertile** once more."

Unwillingly Zeus granted the request of Demeter.

"She shall come back," he said at last, "and with thee dwell on earth forever. Yet only on one condition do I grant thy fond request. Persephone must eat no food through all the time of her **sojourn** in the realm of Pluto, else must thy beseeching be all in vain."

Then did Demeter gladly leave Olympus and hasten down to the darkness of the shadowy land that once again

....

barrenness not producing anything; fruitless
embassy a group to try to convince Demeter to stop the drought
fertile producing a large amount of crops and plants
sojourn temporary stay or journey

she might hold, in her strong mother's arms, her who had once been her little clinging child.

But in the dark kingdom of Pluto a strange thing had happened. No longer had the pale-faced god, with dark locks, and eyes like the sunless pools of a mountain stream, any terrors for Proserpine. He was strong, and cruel had she thought him, yet now she knew that the touch of his strong, cold hands was a touch of infinite tenderness. When, knowing the decree of the ruler of Olympus, Pluto gave to his stolen bride a **pomegranate**, red in heart as the heart of a man, she had taken it from his hand, and, because he willed it, had eaten of the sweet seeds. Then, in truth, it was too late for Demeter to save her child. She "had eaten of Love's seed" and "changed into another."

Dark, dark was the kingdom of Pluto. Its rivers never mirrored a sunbeam, and ever moaned low as an earthly river moans before a coming flood, and the feet that trod the gloomy **Cocytus** valley were the feet of those who never again would tread on the soft grass and flowers of an earthly meadow. Yet when Demeter had braved all the shadows of Hades, only in part was her end accomplished. In part only was Proserpine now her child, for while half her heart was in the sunshine, rejoicing in the beauties of earth, the other half was with the god who had taken her

---

pomegranate a red fruit
Cocytus also Kokytos; meaning "the river of wailing"; a river in the underworld in Greek mythology

down to the Land of Darkness and there had won her for his own.

Back to the flowery island of Sicily her mother brought her, and the peach trees and the almonds blossomed showily as she passed. The olives decked themselves with their soft grey leaves, the corn sprang up, green and lush and strong. The lemon and orange groves grew golden with luscious fruit, and all the land was carpeted with flowers. For six months of the year she stayed, and gods and men rejoiced at the bringing back of Proserpine. For six months she left her green and pleasant land for the dark kingdom of him whom she loved, and through those months the trees were bare, and the earth chill and brown, and under the earth the flowers hid themselves in fear and awaited the return of the fair daughter of Demeter.

And evermore has she come and gone, and seedtime and harvest have never failed, and the cold, sleeping world has awaked and rejoiced, and heralded with the song of birds, and the bursting of green buds and the blooming of flowers, the **resurrection** from the dead—the coming of spring. ❖

---

resurrection rising from the dead

Orpheus and Eurydice

a Greek myth

When gods and shepherds piped and the stars sang, that was the day of musicians! But the triumph of Phoebus Apollo himself was not so wonderful as the triumph of a mortal man who lived on earth, though some say that he came of divine lineage. This was Orpheus, that best of harpers, who went with the Grecian heroes of the great ship Argo in search of the Golden Fleece.

After his return from the quest, he won Eurydice for his wife, and they were as happy as people can be who love each other and every one else. The very wild beasts loved them, and the trees clustered about their home as if they were watered with music. But even the gods themselves were not always free from sorrow, and one day misfortune came upon that harper Orpheus whom all men loved to honor.

Eurydice, his lovely wife, as she was wandering with the nymphs, unwittingly trod upon a serpent in the grass. Surely, if Orpheus had been with her, playing upon his lyre, no creature could have harmed her. But Orpheus came too late. She died of the sting, and was lost to him in the Underworld.

For days he wandered from his home, singing the story of his loss and his despair to the helpless passers-by. His

grief moved the very stones in the wilderness, and roused a dumb distress in the hearts of savage beasts. Even the gods on Mount Olympus gave ear, but they held no power over the darkness of Hades.

Wherever Orpheus wandered with his lyre, no one had the will to forbid him entrance; and at length he found unguarded that very cave that leads to the Underworld where Pluto rules the spirits of the dead. He went down without fear. The fire in his living heart found him a way through the gloom of that place. He crossed the Styx, the black river that the gods name as their most sacred oath. Charon, the harsh old ferryman who takes the Shades across, forgot to ask of him the coin that every soul must pay. For Orpheus sang. There in the Underworld the song of Apollo would not have moved the poor ghosts so much. It would have amazed them, like a star far off that no one understands. But here was a human singer, and he sang of things that grow in every human heart, youth and love and death, the sweetness of the Earth, and the bitterness of losing aught that is dear to us.

Now the dead, when they go to the Underworld, drink of the pool of Lethe; and forgetfulness of all that has passed comes upon them like a sleep, and they lose their longing for the world, they lose their memory of pain, and live content with that cool twilight. But not the pool of Lethe itself could withstand the song of Orpheus; and in the hearts of the Shades all the old dreams awoke wondering. They remembered once more the life of men on Earth, the glory of the sun and moon, the sweetness of new grass, the warmth of their homes, all the old joy and grief that they had known. And they wept.

Even the Furies were moved to pity. Those, too, who were suffering punishment for evil deeds ceased to be tormented for themselves, and grieved only for the innocent Orpheus who had lost Eurydice. Sisyphus, that **fraudulent** king (who is doomed to roll a monstrous boulder uphill forever), stopped to listen. The daughters of Danaus left off their

....

fraudulent false

task of drawing water in a sieve. Tantalus forgot hunger and thirst, though before his eyes hung magical fruits that were wont to vanish out of his grasp, and just beyond reach bubbled the water that was a torment to his ears; he did not hear it while Orpheus sang.

So, among a crowd of eager ghosts, Orpheus came, singing with all his heart, before the king and queen of Hades. And the queen Proserpina wept as she listened and grew homesick, remembering the fields of Enna and the growing of the wheat, and her own beautiful mother, Demeter. Then Pluto gave way.

They called Eurydice and she came, like a young guest unused to the darkness of the Underworld. She was to return with Orpheus, but on one condition. If he turned to look at her once before they reached the upper air, he must lose her again and go back to the world alone.

Rapt with joy, the happy Orpheus **hastened** on the way, thinking only of Eurydice, who was following him. Past Lethe, across the Styx they went, he and his lovely wife, still silent as a Shade. But the place was full of gloom, the silence weighed upon him, he had not seen her for so long; her footsteps made no sound; and he could hardly believe the miracle, for Pluto seldom relents. When the first gleam of upper daylight broke through the cleft to the dismal world, he forgot all, save that he must know if she

----

hastened hurried

still followed. He turned to see her face, and the promise was broken!

She smiled at him forgivingly, but it was too late. He stretched out his arms to take her, but she faded from them, as the bright snow, that none may keep, melts in our very hands. A murmur of farewell came to his ears,—no more. She was gone.

He would have followed, but Charon, now on guard, drove him back. Seven days he lingered there between the worlds of life and death, but after the broken promise, Hades would not listen to his song. Back to the Earth he wandered, though it was sweet to him no longer. He died young, singing to the last, and round about the place where his body rested, nightingales nested in the trees. His lyre was set among the stars; and he himself went down to join Eurydice, unforbidden.

Those two had no need of Lethe, for their life on earth had been wholly fair, and now that they are together they no longer own a sorrow. ❖

Valhalla:
Hall of the Chosen Slain

On the highest hill of Asgard, upon a great chair, sat
All-Father Odin, watching from thence all that was
happening on and above and under the earth.

The Father of Asas and of men had long grey locks
and thick curling beard, and he wore a great blue coat
flecked with grey like unto the sky when the fleecy clouds
scud across it.

In his hand he carried a spear, so sacred that, if anyone
swore an oath upon its point, that oath could never be
broken.

On his head he wore, when sitting upon his watch-
tower throne, a helmet shaped like an eagle; but when he
wandered, as he loved to do, about the earth, he wore a
large broad-brimmed hat drawn low over his forehead.

Perched on his broad shoulders sat two inky-black
ravens, Hugin and Munin, whom every morning he sent to
wing their flight about the world that they might see what
was going on.

Every evening when they returned, they whispered all
that they had seen and heard in his ears.

....
scud to move quickly due to being blown by the wind

At Odin's feet crouched two great wolves, whom he fed from the meat set before him; for he himself cared not to eat flesh-food, and preferred rather to drink the sacred mead provided by the goat who fed upon the leaves of the Tree of Life.

Sometimes Odin left his watch-tower throne for the great Council Hall where the twelve Asas sat and took counsel together; but his favourite seat of all was in his own palace of Valhalla, or the Hall of the Chosen Slain. This palace stood in the midst of a wonderful grove of trees, whose leaves were all of red gold, rustling and shimmering in the breeze. Five and forty doors opened into it, each wide enough to allow eight hundred warriors to enter abreast, and over the chief entrance was a boar's head and a great eagle, whose keen gaze looked forth over all the world. The walls of the palace were built of spears of polished steel, so bright that they lighted the whole building; and the roof was made of golden shields.

From end to end of the great hall stood long tables and benches loaded with armour, ready prepared for the fortunate guests. And this was the manner of their selection. Whenever a great battle was about to be fought on the earth, Odin sent forth the nine Valkyrs, or Battle Maidens, his especial attendants, to watch the progress of the fight and to choose from the fallen warriors half of their number. These the Battle Maidens carried on their swift steeds over the Rainbow Bridge into the great hall of

Valhalla, where they were welcomed by the sons of Odin and taken to the All-Father's throne to receive his greeting. But if one had shown himself especially heroic in the fight, Odin would descend from his throne and advance to the door to bid him welcome.

And now, seated at the long tables, loaded with great beakers of mead and dishes of boar flesh, the warriors feasted merrily, tended by the fair Battle Maidens.

When they had eaten all they could, the warriors would call for their weapons, ride out into the great courtyard, and there wage desperate fights, in the course of which many a man would be sorely wounded. But this mattered little, for at the sound of the dinner horn all wounds were healed.

These warriors were Odin's special joy and delight, and he was never weary of watching them at feast or in the combat. Sometimes, indeed, when some battle on earth was **impending**, he would appear, riding upon his eight-footed grey horse, and with white shield on arm would fling his glittering spear into the ranks of the warriors as signal for the fight to begin, and would rush into the fray with his war-cry, "Odin has you all!" ❖

---

impending about to begin

Sayadio in Spirit-land

a myth of the Wyandot tribe of the Iroquois

Sayadio, a young Indian, mourned greatly for a beautiful sister who had died young. So deeply did he grieve for her that at length he resolved to seek her in the Land of Spirits. Long he sought the maiden, and many adventures did he meet with. Years passed in the search, which he was about to abandon as wholly in vain, when he encountered an old man, who gave him some good advice. This **venerable** person also bestowed upon him a magic **calabash** in which he might catch and retain the spirit of his sister should he succeed in finding her. He afterward discovered that this old man was the keeper of that part of the Spirit-land which he sought.

Delighted to have achieved so much, Sayadio pursued his way, and in due time reached the Land of Souls. But to his dismay he perceived that the spirits, instead of advancing to meet him as he had expected, fled from him in terror. Greatly **dejected**, he approached Tarenyawago, the spirit master of ceremonies, who took pity upon him and informed him that the dead had gathered together for a great dance festival, just such as the Indians themselves celebrate at certain seasons of the year.

....

venerable commanding respect because of impressive dignity
calabash the dried shell of a gourd used as a container
dejected depressed

Soon the dancing **commenced**, and Sayadio saw the spirits floating round in a mazy measure like wreaths of mist. Among them he perceived his sister, and sprang forward to embrace her, but she eluded his grasp and dissolved into air.

Much cast down, the youth once more appealed to the sympathetic master of ceremonies, who gave him a magic rattle of great power, by the sound of which he might bring her back. Again the spirit-music sounded for the dance, and the dead folk thronged into the circle. Once more Sayadio saw his sister, and observed that she was so wholly entranced with the music that she took no notice of his presence. Quick as thought the young Indian dipped up the ghost with his calabash as one nets a fish, and secured the cover, in spite of all the efforts of the captured soul to regain its liberty.

Retracing his steps earthward, he had no difficulty in making his way back to his native village, where he summoned his friends to come and behold his sister's **resuscitation**. The girl's **corpse** was brought from its resting-place to be reanimated with its spirit, and all was prepared for the ceremony, when a witless Indian maiden felt she had to peep into the calabash in her curiosity to see how a **disembodied** spirit looked.

commenced began
resuscitation the act of from death
corpse a dead body
disembodied outside the body

Instantly, as a bird rises when its cage bars are opened and flies forth to freedom, the spirit of Sayadio's sister flew from the calabash before the startled youth could dash forward and shut down the cover. For a while Sayadio could not realize his loss, but at length his straining eyes revealed to him that the spirit of his sister was not within sight. In a flash he saw the ruin of his hopes, and with a broken heart he sank senseless to the earth. ❖

Pan:
God of the Wild

a Greek myth

Hermes, the swift-footed young god, wedded Dryope, the beautiful daughter of a shepherd in Arcadia, and to them was born, under the greenwood tree, the infant, Pan. When Dryope first looked on her child, she was smitten with horror, and fled away from him. The deserted baby roared **lustily**, and when his father, Hermes, examined him he found a rosy-cheeked thing with **prick** ears and tiny horns that grew amongst his thick curls, and with the dappled furry chest of a **faun**, while instead of dimpled baby legs he had the strong, hairy hind legs of a goat.

He was a fearless creature, and merry withal, and when Hermes had wrapped him up in a **hare** skin, he sped to Olympus and showed his fellow-gods the son that had been born to him and the beautiful nymph of the forest. Baby though he was, Pan made the Olympians laugh. He had only made a woman, his own mother, cry; all others rejoiced at the new creature that had come to increase their merriment. And **Bacchus**, who loved him most of all, and

....

lustily hearty; strongly
prick a sharp point
faun a man with the ears, horns, tail, and hind legs of a goat
hare a rabbit
Bacchus god of wine

felt that here was a babe after his own heart, bestowed on him the name by which he was forever known—Pan, meaning *All*.

Thus Pan grew up, the earthly equal of the Olympians, and, as he grew, he took to himself the lordship of woods and of solitary places. He was king of huntsmen and of fishermen, lord of flocks and herds and of all the wild creatures of the forest. All living, **soulless** things owned him their master; even the wild bees claimed him as their overlord. He was ever merry, and when a riot of music and of laughter slew the stillness of the shadowy woods, it was Pan who led the dancing **throng** of white-limbed nymphs and gamboling satyrs, for whom he made melody from the pipes for whose creation a maid had perished.

Round his horns and thick curls he presently came to wear a crown of sharp pine-leaves, remembrance of another fair nymph whose destruction he had brought about.

Pitys listened to the music of Pan, and followed him even as the children followed the Pied Piper of later story. And ever his playing **lured** her further on and into more dangerous and desolate places, until at length she stood on the edge of a high cliff whose pitiless front rushed sheer down to cruel rocks far below. There Pan's music ceased, and Pitys knew all the joy and the sorrow of the world as

---

soulless not human
throng large crowd
lured enticed or attracted away

the god held out his arms to embrace her. But neither Pan nor Pitys had remembrance of Boreas, the merciless north wind, whose love the nymph had flouted.

Ere Pan could touch her, a blast, fierce and strong as death, had seized the nymph's fragile body, and as a wind of March tears from the tree the first white blossom that has dared to brave the ruthless gales, and casts it, torn and dying, to the earth, so did Boreas grip the slender Pitys and dash her life out on the rocks far down below. From her body sprang the pine tree, slender, erect, clinging for dear life to the sides of **precipices**, and by the **prickly wreath** he always wore, Pan showed that he held her in fond remembrance.

Joy, and youth, and force, and spring, was Pan to all the creatures whose overlord he was. Pan meant the richness of the sap in the trees, the lushness of grass and of the green stems of the blue hyacinths and the golden daffodils; the throbbing of growth in the woodland and in the meadows; the trilling of birds that seek for their mates and find them; the coo of the doves on their nests of young; the arrogant virility of bulls and of stags whose lowing and belling wake the silence of the hills; the lightness of heart that made the nymphs dance and sing, the fauns leap high, and shout

---

ere before
precipices cliffs with very steep sides
prickly wreath a wreath made of fir that Pan wore in honor of Pitys

aloud for very joy of living. All of these things was Pan to those of his own kingdom.

Yet to the human men and women who had also listened to his playing, Pan did not mean only joyousness. He was to them a force that many times became a terror because of its sheer irresistibleness.

While the sun shone and the herdsmen could see the nodding white cotton-grass, the asphodel, and the golden kingcups that hid the black death-traps of the pitiless marshes, they had no fear of Pan. Nor in the daytime, when in the woods the sunbeams played amongst the trees and the birds sang of Spring and of love, and the **syrinx** sent an echo from far away that made the little silver birches give a whispering laugh of gladness and the pines cease to sigh, did man or maid have any fear.

Yet when darkness fell on the land, terror would come with it, and, deep in their hearts, they would know that the terror was Pan. Blindly, madly, they would flee from something that they could not see, something they could barely hear, and many times rush to their own destruction. And there would be no sweet sound of music then, only mocking laughter. Panic was the name given to this fear— the name by which it still is known. And, to this day, panic yet comes, and not only by night, but only in very lonely places. ❖

....

syrinx a mountain nymph who was transformed into a reed from which Pan made a panpipe

A Musical Instrument

by Elizabeth Barrett Browning
abridged

"What was he doing, the great god Pan,
Down in the reeds by the river?
Spreading ruin and scattering **ban**,
Splashing and paddling with hoofs of a goat,
And breaking the golden lilies afloat
With the dragon-fly on the river.

He tore out a reed, the great god Pan,
From the deep cool bed of the river:
The **limpid** water **turbidly** ran,
And the broken lilies a-dying lay,
And the dragon-fly had fled away,
Ere he brought it out of the river.

'This is the way,' laughed the great god Pan
(Laughed while he sat by the river),
'The only way, since gods began
To make sweet music, they could succeed.'
Then, dropping his mouth to a hole in the reed,
He blew in power by the river.

....

ban a curse
limpid clear; unclouded
turbidly in a disturbed way

Sweet, sweet, sweet, O Pan!
Piercing sweet by the river!
Blinding sweet, O great god Pan!
The sun on the hill forgot to die,
And the lilies revived, and the dragon-fly
Came back to dream on the river.

Yet half a beast is the great god Pan,
To laugh as he sits by the river,
Making a poet out of a man:
The true gods sigh for the cost and pain,
For the reed which grows nevermore again
As a reed with the reeds in the river." ❖

Index of Authors and Titles

Acknowledgments

From BARRIO BOY by Ernesto Galarza. Copyright © 1971 by University of Notre Dame Press, Notre Dame, Indiana 46556. Used by permission of the publisher.

Excerpt from I KNOW WHY THE CAGED BIRD SINGS by Maya Angelou, copyright © 1969 and renewed by Maya Angelou. Used by permission of Random House, Inc.

"We Real Cool" by Gwendolyn Brooks. Reprinted by permission of Brooks Permissions.

"The Negro Speaks of Rivers" by Langston Hughes from THE COLLECTED POEMS OF LANGSTON HUGHES by Langston Hughes, copyright © 1994 by The Estate of Langston Hughes. Used by permission of Alfred A. Knopf, a division of Random House, Inc.

"I HAVE A DREAM." Reprinted by arrangement with the Estate of Martin Luther King Jr., c/o Writers House as agent for the proprietor New York, NY. Copyright 1963 Martin Luther King Jr., copyright renewed 1991 Coretta Scott King.

"If Anne Frank Only Knew…Diary Used to Teach U.S. Fear and Hate in North Korea" by Rebecca Leung. 60 MINUTES © 2004 CBS. All rights reserved.

"Rules of the Game" from THE JOY LUCK CLUB by Amy Tan. Copyright © 1989 by Amy Tan. Used by permission of G.P. Putnam's Sons, an imprint of Penguin Publishing Group, a division of Penguin Random House, LLC. All rights reserved.

"Gumption" from SHORT STORIES by Langston Hughes. Copyright © 1996 by Ramona Bass and Arnold Rampersad. Reprinted by permission of Hill and Wang, a division of Farrar Strauss and Giroux, LLC.

"The Secret Life of Walter Mitty" Copyright © 1933, 1961 by James Thurber. Reprinted by arrangement with Rosemary Thurber and The Barbara Hogenson Agency, Inc. All rights reserved.

"The Lottery" from THE LOTTERY AND OTHER STORIES by Shirley Jackson. Copyright © 1948, 1949 by Shirley Jackson. Copyright renewed 1976, 1977 by Laurence Hyman, Barry Hyman, Mrs. Sara Webster and Mrs. Joanne Schnurer. Reprinted by permission of Farrar, Strauss and Giroux, LLC.

"Do Not Go Gentle into That Good Night" by Dylan Thomas, from THE POEMS OF DYLAN THOMAS, copyright © 1952 by Dylan Thomas. Reprinted by permission of New Directions Publishing Corp. and David Higham Associates Limited.

Image Credits

Cover and Interior Pattern Tents and star trails in Canada. © Stocktrek/Getty Images. Circular decorative design. © OlichO/Shutterstock.

10 Sarah Emma Edmonds on horseback. © Bettmann/Getty Images. **15** Portrait of Sarah Emma Edmonds. © Kean Collection/Archive Photos/Getty Images. **19** Pilot house on a Mississippi riverboat. © North Wind Picture Archives/Alamy. **23** Steamers. Library of Congress Prints and Photographs Division Washington, LC-DIG-pga-01055. **29** Lincoln School, Sacramento, Ca., Library of Congress Prints and Photographs Division. **33** School desks from an old classroom. © Willowpix/iStock. **39** Interior of a general store. Library of Congress Prints and Photographs Division Washington, LC-USZ62-51557. **56** Frederick Douglass. © Artokoloro Quint Lox Limited/Alamy; Floral background. © irAArt/Shutterstock. **166** Summer storm. © fotiksonya/iStock. **168** Tree growing from a dead stump. © jack-sooksan/iStock. **170** Pool table. © PLotulitStocker/Shutterstock. **171** The Pyramids at Gizah by Edward Lear. © Ann Ronan Pictures/Print Collector/Getty Images. **172** Daffodils growing against a stone wall. © KenWiedemann/iStock. **178** Martin Luther King Jr. © Francis Miller/Time Life Pictures/Getty Images. **185** Inauguration of President George W. Bush. © Joe Raedle/Newsmakers/Getty Images. **193** The diary of Anne Frank. © Fine Art Images/Heritage Images/Getty Images. **197** North Korean students. © Ed Jones/AFP/Getty Images. **201** Jewish children arriving from Germany in London. © Keystone-France/Gamma-Keystone/Getty Images. **205** Kindertransport documents. © Heritage Image Partnership Ltd/Alamy Stock Photo. **207** Children at Dovercourt Camp walking to dinner. © Hulton Deutsch/Getty Images. **212** Children sleeping in their bunks. © Gerti Deutsch/Picture Post/Hulton Archive/Getty Images. **215** Bombings at Pearl Harbor. National Archives and Records Administration. **217** The USS *West Virginia* burns after the attack on Pearl Harbor. National Archives and Records Administration. **218** The explosion of the USS *Shaw* DD-373. National Archives and Records Administration. **221** Japanese American internees. Library of Congress Prints and Photographs Division Washington, LC-USZ62-44093. **223** A man resting in his bunk at Manzanar. National Archives and Records Administration. **225** Baseball game at Manzanar War Relocation Center. Library of Congress Prints and Photographs Division Washington, LC-DIG-ppprs-0020. **242** Young girl playing chess. © Ratchapoom Anupongpan/iStock. **270** Winter landscape. © Dennis Gross/iStock. **279** Husky. © Anastasiia Cherniavskaia/iStock. **299** B-17 Flying Fortress. © pixeldigits/iStock. **311** *Market at Trouville*. © Christie's Images/Bridgeman Images. **327** Illustration from the Tell-Tale Heart. © Chronicle/Alamy Stock Photo. **349** Wooden doors. © mykhailo pavlenko/Shutterstock. **358** Global disaster. © BenGoode/iStock. **366** © Shannon Workman/Dreamstime.com. **376–377** Open window.

© Simotion/iStock. **378–379** The remains of a giant statue. © Tom Hanley/
Alamy. **380** The Milky Way. © heibaihui/iStock. **382, 385** *Battle of Balaklava.*
© Photo 12. **387** *Battle of Blenheim.* © DEA PICTURE LIBRARY/Getty Images.
391 U.S. cavalrymen. © Archival Image/Alamy. **392** Illustration of a raven.
© GeorgePeters/iStock. **397** Vintage door. © eelphoto1/iStock; Crow. © CSA
Images/iStock; Statue of Athene. © clu/iStock. **400** Sunrise in the woods. © Mark
Carthy/Shutterstock. **405** John F. Kennedy and Richard Nixon. © World History
Archive/Alamy; 1960s television. © trekandshoot/iStock. **417** President Franklin
Roosevelt. © Bettmann/Getty Images. **422** *Antigone the Brave.* © Picturenow/
Getty Images; Golden wall background. © tallinn-irina/iStock. **481** Dice and
clouds. © Andrii Muzyka/Shutterstock. **498** Tree showing two seasons. © Lilkar/
Dreamstime.com. **500–501** Balloons against a cloudy sky. © jakkapan21/iStock.
502–503 Butterflies and lily flowers. © Svetlana_Smirnova/iStock. **504** Fall
forest. © Jeremy Walker/Getty Images. **507** Snow-covered fence. © LeManna/
Shutterstock. **508** House in the snow. © Aquapixel/Dreamstime. **533** Salt cedars
growing next to a pond. © Rolf Nussbaumer/Getty Images. **535** Salt cedar plant.
© Aquamarine4/Dreamstime. **547** Fremont cottonwood trees. © Design Pics/
David Ponton/Getty Images. **549** Bosque del Apache National Wildlife Refuge.
© Aimin Tang/Getty Images. **553** Tamarisk beetle. © Dean Hanson/Journal/
Albuquerque Journal/ZUMA Wire/Alamy. **557** Southwestern willow flycatcher.
© Natural History Collection/Alamy. **564** Frog swimming in a lake. © Andre
Heid/Getty Images. **574** Old Man Winter being driven away. Project Gutenberg.
575 Insects flying in a spring field. Project Gutenberg. **577** Map. © Vera Petruk/
Shutterstock. **581** Ahuramazda, the God of Wisdom. © imageBROKER/Alamy.
583 Ariman killed by the king. © Quagga Media/Alamy. **585** Illustration of
a woman in a white gown standing outdoors. © ilbusca/iStock. **593** *Orpheus
and Eurydice.* By courtesy of Julian Hartnoll/Bridgeman Images. **599** The Norse
God Odin. © Topham Partners LLP/Alamy. **603** Sayadio mouning for the loss
of his sister. © The Print Collector/Alamy. **607** An enchanted maiden and Pan.
© Chronicle/Alamy Stock Photo. **611** Fauns playing pan pipes. © duncan1890/
iStock.